Introduction to

NEUTRON PHYSICS

VAN NOSTRAND NUCLEAR SCIENCE SERIES

JAMES G. BECKERLEY
Editor

_____

FRANK R. WARD   D. W. LILLIE

DAVID H. GURINSKY

_____

CURTISS, L. F.—*Introduction to Neutron Physics*

Additional titles will be listed and announced as published

Introduction to
NEUTRON PHYSICS

---

by

L. F. CURTISS

*Chairman of the Committee on Nuclear Sciences
of the National Academy—Research Council;
Consultant to the Director of
the National Bureau of Standards*

D. VAN NOSTRAND COMPANY, INC.
PRINCETON, NEW JERSEY
TORONTO   LONDON
NEW YORK

D. VAN NOSTRAND COMPANY, INC.
120 Alexander St., Princeton, New Jersey (*Principal office*)
257 Fourth Avenue, New York 10, New York

D. VAN NOSTRAND COMPANY, LTD.
358, Kensington High Street, London, W.14, England

D. VAN NOSTRAND COMPANY (Canada), LTD.
25 Hollinger Road, Toronto 16, Canada

The Library of Congress has catalogued this publication as follows:

Curtiss, Leon Francis, 1895–
 An introduction to neutron physics. [1st ed.] Princeton,
N. J., Van Nostrand [1959]

 369 p. illus. 24 cm. (Van Nostrand nuclear science series)

 1. Neutrons. I. Title: Neutron physics.

QC721.C9828   *539.72   59–7558 ‡

Library of Congress

PREFACE

Much information, both theoretical and experimental, has now accumulated concerning the neutron and its behavior. Most of the facts have come to light in the last decade. A student approaching this accretion of knowledge may well be deterred by its magnitude and ramifications. A need seems to exist for an introduction to the more basic features of the experimental science of the neutron, with elementary explanations of the role which theory has played in expanding the structure of this science. The aim in this text is to provide such an introduction to some of the principles of what can be termed *neutron physics*.

In this book, emphasis has been placed on experimentally demonstrated facts and methods by which the data were obtained. Where desirable to show the value of study of the neutron in the development of nuclear physics, abbreviated discussions of theory are included. References to original literature are made in all cases to permit the specializing student to pursue topics beyond the scope of this volume.

To keep the size of the book within manageable limits, many equations are presented without derivation; they are derived in the references. But to acquaint the student with a few of the applications of mathematics to the development of theories used in neutron physics, some frequently used equations are derived in the Appendices. Because some readers may desire to use this text for self-instruction, numerous illustrations are provided. Problems are placed at the ends of chapters to permit the reader to test his understanding of some of the topics.

Garrett Park, Maryland   L. F. Curtiss
November, 1958

CONTENTS

CHAPTER I—INTRODUCTION

CHAPTER II—PARTICLE AND NUCLEAR INTERACTIONS

Chapter III—SOURCES

Chapter VII—CALIBRATIONS AND STANDARDS

Chapter VIII—NEUTRON SHIELDING AND PROTECTION OF PERSONNEL

Appendices—SOME FORMULAS OF NEUTRON PHYSICS

Chapter I

INTRODUCTION

1.1. Discovery of the Neutron

The discovery of the neutron by Chadwick (1) was the culmination of investigations in several European laboratories. The story of these experiments is one of the most interesting in the brief history of nuclear physics. The principal participants, in addition to Chadwick, were Bothe and Becker in Germany and the Joliot-Curies in Paris. All were studying a peculiarly penetrating radiation generated by the impact of polonium alpha particles on beryllium. In viewing the work in retrospect, it is clearly evident that both laboratories on the Continent had been unwittingly experimenting with neutrons for more than a year before Chadwick announced the true nature of the "beryllium radiation." The error of the observers on the Continent had consisted in trying to to explain their observations in terms of radiation already known. The nature of their data therefore led them to think they were dealing with a highly penetrating gamma radiation.

The arguments and experimental evidence used by Chadwick to prove that the penetrating radiation consists of neutral particles with a mass approximately equal to that of the proton are extremely instructive. They well illustrate how a careful correlation of experimental facts leads to a correct interpretation of data. Irène Curie and Frédéric Joliot observed that the beryllium radiation ejected protons in relatively large numbers from paraffin. The ranges of the protons extended up to 26 cm in air. Using the simple apparatus sketched in Fig. 1.1, Chadwick also measured the ranges of the protons and obtained data represented by the typical curve shown in Fig. 1.2. He noted that the frequency of the scattering of the hypothetical gamma radiation greatly exceeded the prediction of the Klein-Nishina formula for the scattering of gamma rays by protons. A further difficulty was presented by the fact that a gamma ray must have a computed energy of the order of 50 Mev to produce Compton recoils of the observed velocities. He failed to discover how so energetic a gamma ray could be generated by the impact of alpha particles with energy of about

1

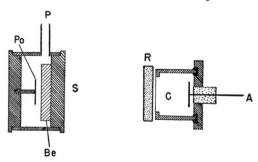

FIG. 1.1. *Apparatus used by Chadwick in experiments leading to the discovery of the neutron. S is the source of neutrons in which* Po *is a disk coated with polonium, and* Be *is a block of beryllium. A vacuum pump was connected at* P. C *is a pulse ionization chamber connected to an amplifier and oscillograph at* A. R *is a sheet of paraffin in which the neutrons produced recoil protons.*

5 Mev on beryllium. The situation was further complicated by observations on recoil particles of different masses. It was found that protons were ejected from paraffin with energies of about 5.7 Mev. Since the maximum energy E which can be given to a particle of mass m in Compton scattering by a quantum of energy $h\nu$ is

$$E = \frac{2h\nu}{2 + mc^2/h\nu} \tag{1.1}$$

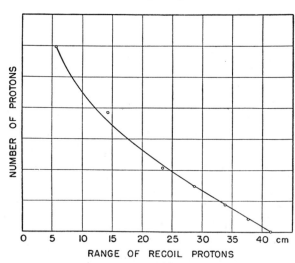

FIG. 1.2. *Curve showing the relative numbers of protons of various ranges ejected from paraffin placed in front of the ionization chamber shown in Fig. 1.1. Ranges are measured in equivalent centimeters of air.*

it can be computed that the value of $h\nu$ required to produce protons with energy of 5.7 Mev is about 55 Mev. In similar experiments with nitrogen nuclei the recoil energy was found to be about 1.2 Mev. Applying the above formula to the same radiation under these circumstances yielded a value of $h\nu$ of about 90 Mev. In other words, as the mass of the target particle increased, the quantum energy for the same radiation also increased.

If the momentum and energy are conserved in these interactions, the foregoing interpretation of the radiation as a form of gamma radiation makes no sense at all. However, Chadwick found that a simple interpretation was available, consistent with the laws of conservation, if the gamma-ray hypothesis for the beryllium radiation was abandoned. In particular, if the unknown radiation consisted of particles of a mass about equal to that of the proton, all difficulties disappeared. It was also necessary to assume these particles to be without electric charge to account for their great penetrating power. Therefore they could correctly be called *neutrons*, assumed to be each a proton and an electron in close association, as described by Rutherford (2) in 1920. Perhaps the most remarkable incident in the events leading to the discovery of the neutron is this accurate prediction of the nature of the neutron a dozen years before it was identified.

1.2. Preliminary Estimates of the Mass of the Neutron

It is easy now to see how introducing the neutron simplified the interpretation of the observations on the radiation generated by the impact of alpha particles on beryllium. Now with a particle of a mass nearly equal to the proton mass incident on paraffin, the recoil protons could have all velocities up to the original velocities of the neutrons. The maximum velocity of the recoil protons was estimated to be about 3.3×10^9 cm per sec. This would also be the velocity of the neutrons which ejected these protons. Furthermore, the energy of the protons at this velocity is about 1.4 Mev, consistent with all other data in the experiment. From the information obtained in collisions of neutrons with protons on the one hand and with nitrogen nuclei on the other, a rough estimate of the mass of the neutron could be calculated. The maximum velocity V_p for a recoil proton is given by

$$V_p = \frac{2M}{M+1} V \tag{1.2}$$

where M is the mass of the neutron and V its velocity. Similarly, the maximum velocity for a recoil nitrogen nucleus, V_N, is

$$V_N = \frac{2M}{M+14} V \tag{1.3}$$

The estimated velocity of the nitrogen recoil nuclei was 4.7×10^8 cm per sec. Therefore

$$\frac{M + 14}{M + 1} = \frac{V_p}{V_N} = \frac{3.3 \times 10^9}{4.7 \times 10^8}$$

from which

$$M = 1.15 \text{ amu (atomic mass units)}$$

A more precise value for the mass of the neutron was obtained by Chadwick from a study of the nuclear reaction

$$B^{11} + He^4 \rightarrow N^{14} + n^1 \tag{1.4}$$

in which the masses of B^{11} and N^{14} were at the time known with fair accuracy. The energy equation for Reaction 1.4 is

$$M_{B^{11}} + M_{He^4} + E_{He^4} = M_{N^{14}} + M_{n^1} + E_{N^{14}} + E_{n^1} \tag{1.5}$$

The M's are the masses and the E's the kinetic energies of the respective particles. Putting all values in terms of atomic mass units, the available data were

$$M_{B^{11}} = 11.00825, \ M_{He^4} = 4.00106, \ M_{N^{14}} = 14.0042$$

$$E_{He^4} = 0.00565, \ E_{n^1} = 0.0035, \ E_{N^{14}} = 0.00061.$$

Substituting these values in Eq. 1.5 yielded a value of $M_{n^1} = 1.0067$. This figure is to be compared with the currently accepted value, $M_{n^1} = 1.008982$.

1.3. Consequences of the Discovery of the Neutron

Even if the unraveling of the experimental enigma which the so-called beryllium radiation presented had been the only result of the discovery of the neutron, the accomplishment would have been of some significance. Actually the impact of this discovery on ideas of nuclear structure was so far-reaching that the last chapter may not be written for many years to come. As an example, one of the most perplexing problems concerning the nucleus prior to 1932 was that of explaining the ratio of mass to charge for all nuclei except that of the hydrogen atom. The only massive constituent particle available for nuclei was the proton. Therefore it seemed logical to conclude that each type of nucleus contained a number of protons equal to its mass number. On the other hand the atomic number, equal to the nuclear charge number, was always in the neighborhood of one-half the mass number. Hence the next logical step called for the introduction of a number of electrons into the nuclei to bring their net charge down to the proper value.

This proposal caused considerable dismay to theoreticians who were applying the principles of wave mechanics to nuclear structure. The wavelength associated with electrons under conditions assumed to exist within a nucleus greatly exceeded known nuclear dimensions. The difficulty immediately vanished when, by adding neutrons to the appropriate number of protons, nuclei with correct mass and atomic numbers could be constructed.

Other consequences of the discovery of the neutron have been at least equally momentous. The study of neutrons and their interactions is now a large part of nuclear physics. It will be the aim of this book to outline the current status of some of the more significant and well-established methods for measurement of neutrons and of investigations in which neutrons play an important role. As this statement implies, the main emphasis will be on the experimental point of view. Although the exact nature of the neutron is even now scarcely well understood, an effort will be made to avoid details that are still unsettled and to confine the attention to features of neutron studies which are likely to remain valid regardless of the interpretations which they may ultimately receive.

2.1. Fundamental Properties of the Neutron

The detailed properties peculiar to the neutron control its behavior. Although it is no longer strictly correct to speak of the neutron as a fundamental particle, in the ultimate sense, it is readily identifiable by its properties as an entity in its own right. Moreover, nuclear physics as it is known today may legitimately be considered to have begun with the discovery of the neutron. This is true not only because of the resulting simplification of concepts of nuclear structure; equally important is the value of the neutron as a probe for exploring the structure of nuclei, a role previously assigned necessarily to charged particles requiring considerable kinetic energy to penetrate the nucleus.

2.2. Mass of the Neutron

We have seen that in his paper announcing the discovery of the neutron, Chadwick was able to deduce a mass for the neutron which is within about 0.2% of the current value. Whereas in many commonly encountered situations such accuracy would be quite adequate, in the present case a much better value is desirable. The need for higher accuracy arises mainly from the energy scale associated with mass, in accordance with the principle of the equivalence of mass and energy. One atomic mass unit is the equivalent of 931×10^6 electron volts. Therefore the comparatively small difference between Chadwick's estimate and the present value for the mass of the neutron, 0.00228 mass units, represents 2.1×10^6 ev. This difference could cause serious discrepancies in determining the energy balance of a nuclear interaction in which a neutron is involved. Even the present uncertainty in the mass of the neutron, usually assumed to be about ± 0.000003 mass units, represents 2.8×10^3 ev.

The currently accepted value for the mass of the neutron is based on information of the same kind as that used by Chadwick in his original estimate. The value is deduced indirectly from mass-spectrometer measurements of stable nuclei and the release of energy involving the emission of a neutron when these nuclei enter into selected nuclear reactions. For example, Chadwick and Goldhaber (3) investigated the photonuclear reaction

$$_1H^2 + h\nu \rightarrow {}_1H^1 + {}_0n^1 \tag{2.1}$$

using gamma rays of ThC″, with $h\nu = 2.62 \times 10^6$ ev. Since the mass of the deuteron and of the proton were known, the only measurement required to determine the mass of the neutron is of the kinetic energy of the proton and of the neutron. Actually, since the kinetic energies of the proton and of the neutron will be nearly equal, it was sufficient to determine the energy for the proton alone. The measurement of the kinetic energy of the proton was accomplished by determining the total number of ion pairs produced when the protons were absorbed in an ionization chamber. The sum of the kinetic energies of the proton and the neutron was found to be 2.1×10^6 ev, or 0.0023 atomic mass units. This energy represents the binding energy of the deuteron. The measurement was not very precise, and there was a greater uncertainty than at present regarding the masses of the proton and the deuteron. In spite of these uncertainties, the authors were able to limit the mass of the neutron between the values 1.0084 and 1.0090 mass units. As we have seen, the present value lies within these limits, being only slightly lower than the larger value. As mass spectrometric measurements establishing the masses of the proton and deuteron increased in accuracy, it only remained for a better value for the binding energy of the deuteron to appear to improve the accuracy of the value for the mass of the neutron. The most accurate determination of the binding energy to date has been made by Bell and Elliott (4) from a study of the inverse reaction to that of the photodisintegration of the deuteron. When a proton captures a neutron to form a deuteron, a gamma ray is emitted with energy equal to the binding energy of the deuteron, if all particles are essentially at rest. In this case no kinetic energies are involved which must be measured. An experiment satisfying the requirement of zero kinetic energies can for practical purposes be performed with thermal neutrons. The reaction is then represented by

$$_0n^1 + {}_1H^1 \rightarrow {}_1H^2 + h\nu \tag{2.2}$$

where $h\nu$ is the gamma ray with energy equal to the binding energy. Bell and Elliott obtained the value 2.230 ± 0.007 Mev for the energy of the gamma ray in Eq. 2.2. In mass units this figure is 0.002395. Therefore the mass of the neutron from Eq. 2.2 becomes

$$_0n^1 = {}_1H^2 - {}_1H^1 + h\nu = 2.014735 - 1.008142 + 0.002395$$
$$= 1.008988 \text{ amu}$$

However, Bainbridge (5) combines the results of a series of values for the binding energy of the deuteron to obtain an average value of 0.002489 amu, which give the value of M_n, the mass of the neutron, as

$$M_n = 1.008982 \text{ amu.}$$

2.3. Charge of the Neutron and Electron Interaction

From the earliest mention in the literature, the neutron has been considered to be some type of combination of a proton with an electron. We now know that this is not an accurate picture in detail, but it serves as a first approximation. The equality in the magnitude of the charges carried by electrons and protons leads to the assumption that the net charge on the neutron must be zero. As far as fields of Coulomb type are concerned, all efforts to detect a charge on the neutron have failed. Thus it has been found impossible to detect ionization, attributable to the direct action of neutrons on electrons, in a gas traversed by neutrons (6). The fact that atoms, throughout the periodic table, are electrically neutral, in spite of the various combinations of neutrons and protons in their nuclei, is also consistent with absence of electrical charge for the neutron. Any other assumption leads to considerable difficulty in obtaining over-all neutrality for the atom.

When we turn to a consideration of short-range forces, such as exist within the nucleus, the neutron takes on a slightly different aspect. The composite nature of the neutron (just how complex it may be is still comparatively unknown) requires the existence of short-range forces within the neutron. The structure must also account for the magnetic dipole moment of the neutron which is responsible for a small but measurable interaction between neutrons and electrons at distances comparable with nuclear dimensions. From a study of the neutron-electron interaction comes additional evidence for the absence of net electrical charge on the neutron. The scattering experiments of Fermi and Marshall (7), for example, show that the scattering of neutrons from xenon atoms is spherically symmetrical within limits of experimental error. This symmetry reduces the possible value of the electric charge on the neutron to a vanishingly small value which has been estimated to be of the order of 10^{-18} times the charge of an electron.

2.4. Wavelength and Neutrons

In certain situations the De Broglie wavelengths associated with neutrons are of importance. Wave properties are not peculiar to neutrons but are assigned by the theory of wave mechanics to all particles. In wave theory, now generally familiar to physicists, any material particle may be represented by a wave equation. One of the more significant characteristics of the waves associated with matter is the wavelength. This wavelength is defined in wave-mechanical theory as

$$\lambda = \frac{h}{mv} \tag{2.3}$$

where h is Planck's constant and mv is the momentum of the particle. The form given in Eq. 2.3 holds only for velocities low enough that relativistic corrections are negligible. It is convenient to express the momentum in terms of the energy of the neutron in electron volts. Introducing M_n for the mass of the neutron, we can write

$$\lambda = \frac{h}{M_n v} = \frac{h}{\sqrt{2M_n E}} = \frac{6.625 \times 10^{-27}}{1.83 \times 10^{-12}\sqrt{E}}$$

which yields λ when E is in ergs. Since 1 erg is 0.624×10^{12} ev, we can convert to electron volts by multiplying the numerator of the right-hand member by the factor $\sqrt{0.624 \times 10^{12}} = 0.79 \times 10^6$, which yields

$$\lambda = \frac{2.86 \times 10^{-9}}{\sqrt{E}} \text{ cm} \tag{2.4}$$

with E in electron volts. Converting to express λ in angstrom units we have

$$\lambda = \frac{0.286}{\sqrt{E}} \text{ Å} \tag{2.5}$$

Because it happens that the wave properties of neutrons are mainly important at low velocities, the nonrelativistic expression for the wavelength will be found adequate for most applications. For example, when $E = 0.025$ ev, corresponding to thermal velocities for the neutron,

$$\lambda = 1.82 \text{ Å}$$

comparable with atomic dimensions. For $E = 1$ Mev, where the nonrelativistic expression still gives a good approximation,

$$\lambda = 2.86 \times 10^{-12} \text{ cm}$$

approaching nuclear dimensions. This small wavelength partially explains the ready acceptance, theoretically, of the neutron as a constituent of the nucleus. Frequently the wavelength of the neutron is expressed in terms of the Dirac notation in which $\lambdabar$, the Dirac wavelength, is

$$\lambdabar = \frac{\lambda}{2\pi} \tag{2.6}$$

Nonrelativistic equations for the wavelength fail to give correct values as the energy of the neutron approaches the energy corresponding to the rest mass of the neutron, which is

$$M_n c^2 = 939.5 \text{ Mev.}$$

The failure of the simple equation at higher energies is illustrated in Fig. 2.1, where the relativistically computed wavelengths, corresponding to the energy of the neutron in electron volts, is indicated by the circles and the straight line represents the computation of the wavelength according to the simple formula. It can be seen that this formula begins to fail at an energy of 100 Mev.

From the general nature of the interaction of waves with matter, it is obvious that phenomena associated with the wave properties of the neutron will become prominent when the dimensions of the material

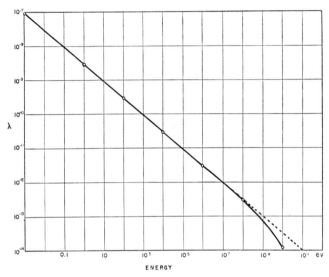

FIG. 2.1. *The wavelength* λ *of the neutron at various energies plotted against the energy of the neutron in electron volts. The deviation from a straight line at about* 10^8 *ev indicates the beginning of the effect of the relativistic correction at high energies.*

structure with which neutrons interact are comparable with the neutron wavelength. Thermal neutrons have wavelengths about equal to the atomic spacings in crystals, for example, and a Bragg type of reflection can be expected when thermal neutrons interact with crystals. Thus neutron spectrometers, analogous to x-ray crystal spectrometers, have been constructed to operate on the principles of Bragg reflections. The chief difference, in fact, between the reflection of neutrons and of x-rays is that the neutrons interact with the nuclei of the atoms and x-rays with the orbital electrons. Neutrons with energies from 1 Mev to 100 Mev have wavelengths of the order of nuclear dimensions. By increasing the velocity of the neutrons to the relativistic region, 10 to 100 Bev, the wavelengths can be made comparable with the spacing of nucleons within the nucleus, which provides a method for investigating the structure of the nucleus.

2.5. Statistics of the Neutron and Spin

Another characteristic of the neutron which may be determined experimentally is referred to as the statistics. There are two kinds of statistics, Fermi statistics and Bose statistics, arising from symmetry properties of the wave functions in the wave theory. In Fermi statistics, two identical particles cannot exist in the same state and thus conform to the Pauli exclusion principle. Electrons obey Fermi statistics, as is familiar from the study of atomic spectra. On the other hand, any number of the same particles with Bose statistics may be in the same state. Neutrons have been found to obey Fermi statistics. There is much evidence to support this conclusion. Qualitatively the fact that all nuclei with odd mass numbers obey Fermi statistics, and those with even mass numbers Bose statistics, is consistent with the assignment of Fermi statistics to the neutron. The most direct confirmation on this point comes from measurements of band spectra of molecules containing deuterium. Once the statistics has been determined as of the Fermi type, the spin of the neutron is fixed as $\frac{1}{2}$. The value of $\frac{1}{2}$ for the spin of the neutron has been confirmed by reflection of neutrons from magnetized mirrors by Hughes and Burgy (8).

2.6. Decay of the Neutron

We have seen that the neutron may be considered a combination of an electron with a proton. When careful measurements of the mass of the neutron showed it to be significantly greater than that of the proton, the hypothesis of a complex structure for the neutron was strengthened. It was also evident that the neutron outside the nucleus is unstable and could be expected to decay with the emission of a beta particle plus a neutrino, leaving a proton. It was also assumed that a similar process accounted for the beta emission of beta-unstable radioactive nuclei. Nevertheless it was nearly twenty years after the discovery of the neutron that the beta decay was definitely confirmed with the measurement of the decay energy and of the half-life.

The major features of the radioactive decay of the neutron were firmly established by Robson (9). The plan of the experimental arrangement is shown in Fig. 2.2. A collimated beam of pile neutrons, filtered through a 5-inch bismuth plug to reduce the gamma-ray intensity, passed from a nuclear reactor into a "beam catcher," at B, which absorbed the neutrons and the accompanying gamma radiation. In traveling from the reactor to the beam catcher, the neutrons traversed the evacuated tank T. Two lateral and opposite openings in the tank communicated, the one on the right with a proton spectrometer, the one on the left with a conventional beta-ray spectrometer. The proton spectrometer was provided with an electron multiplier for the detection of the protons and the beta-ray spectrometer used a scintillation crystal to detect beta rays. A high-voltage electrode E in the tank provided the accelerating field to drive protons

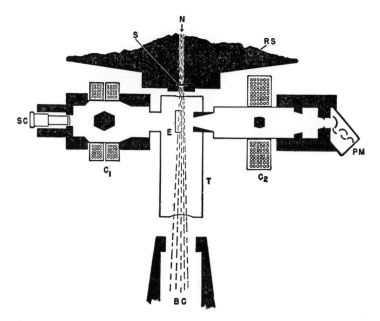

FIG. 2.2. *Diagram of the apparatus used by Robson to determine the disintegration energy of the neutron. N—beam of thermal neutrons from the reactor. S—shutter in the path of the neutron beam. RS—radiation shield. E—electrode for accelerating the protons from the decay of neutrons to the right into the proton spectrometer C_2. PM—electron multiplier for detecting protons. C_1—beta-ray spectrometer. SC—scintillation detector. T—evacuated tank connected with both spectrometers. B—beam catcher for emergent neutrons. Heavily shaded parts are lead.*

into the proton spectrometer. First the creation of protons in the tank was confirmed when a beam of approximately 1.5×10^{10} thermal neutrons per second was passing through the tank. An accelerating potential of 13 kv was applied to the electrode E. Under these conditions, if protons were created in the tank, the proton spectrometer should show a single peak as the current in the electromagnet of the proton spectrometer was varied. Furthermore the peak should disappear when the neutron beam is shut off by the boron shutter at S. Fig. 2.3 shows that these expectations were realized. The lower dotted curve B represents the rate of the response of the electron multiplier with S closed. In the next stage of the experiment the coincidences between recorded protons and beta particles were observed. These data yielded the curve sketched in Fig. 2.4, where the number of proton–beta-particle coincidences is plotted against the energy of the beta particles. Then the beta-ray spectrum was measured in the beta spectrometer leading to the allowed Fermi plot shown in Fig. 2.5. Extra-

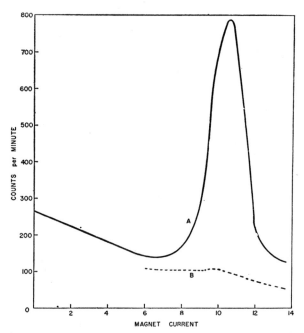

FIG. 2.3. *The solid curve shows the number of protons detected plotted against the current through the coils of the proton spectrometer. The dotted curve is the counting rate with the neutron shutter closed.*

polation of the curve of Fig. 2.5 gives a value for the maximum energy of the spectrum as 782 ± 13 kev. Adding the energy required to create an electron gives a value for the total energy closely approximating the mass difference between the neutron and the proton.

Finally an estimate of the half-life of the neutron was obtained by calculating the number of neutrons decaying per minute per unit volume of the beam. The calculation involved a determination of the volume of the beam from which protons reached the multiplier and were recorded. From the value of n, representing the number of neutrons decaying per cm³ per

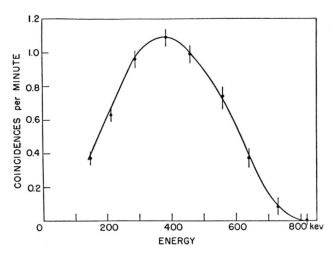

FIG. 2.4. *The coincidence rate between the beta particles and the protons resulting from neutron decay plotted against the energy of the beta particles in kilovolts.*

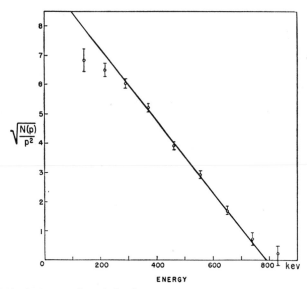

FIG. 2.5. *A Fermi plot of the beta spectrum of the neutron.* $N(p)$ *is the number of coincidences per unit interval of momentum.*

minute in the beam and the measured density ρ of the neutrons in the beam, the half-life, $T_{1/2}$, becomes

$$T_{1/2} = \frac{\rho}{n} \times 0.0693 = 12.8 \text{ min} \tag{2.7}$$

2.7. Moment of the Neutron

The neutron has a magnetic dipole moment associated with its spin. The value of this moment was measured with considerable accuracy as early as 1940 by Alvarez and Bloch (10). The measurement was based on determining the intensity of a steady magnetic field in which the neutrons were made to precess by the superposition of an oscillating magnetic field of fixed frequency. Designating the angular frequency of the oscillating field by ω and the intensity of the fixed field by H_0, the frequency of the Larmor precession, equal to $2H_0\mu/\hbar$, will be in resonance with the oscillating field at some value H^*_0 of H_0. Hence

$$\frac{2H^*_0\mu}{\hbar} = \omega \tag{2.8}$$

where μ is the magnetic moment of the neutron and $\hbar$ is Planck's constant over 2π. From Eq. 2.8

$$\mu = \frac{\hbar\omega}{2H^*_0} \tag{2.9}$$

The apparatus used to measure μ is sketched in Fig. 2.6. Thermalized neutrons from a carefully stabilized cyclotron were passed through the polarizing magnet P to the neutron-flipping solenoid F and the magnet H_0.

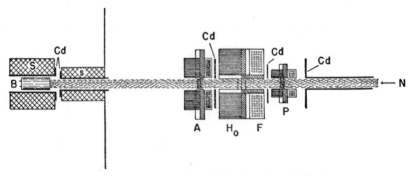

FIG. 2.6 *Plan of the apparatus used by Alvarez and Bloch to measure the magnetic moment of the neutron. N—beam of thermal neutrons. Cd—cadmium screens. P—polarizing magnet. H_o—steady field magnet. F—neutron flipping solenoid. A—analyzing magnet. S—neutron shield of water or paraffin. B—boron trifluoride ionization chamber.*

Then the neutrons proceeded through the analyzing magnet A into the BF$_3$ counting chamber B. The fractional change in the number of neutrons transmitted, $\Delta I/I$, is proportional to the probability of a change in polarization in passing from the polarizer to the analyzer. This probability will have a maximum value when $H_0 = H^*_0$. The observations consisted in varying the current through the coils of the magnet H_0 until a minimum number of neutrons reached the detector. Measurement of the field H_0 at

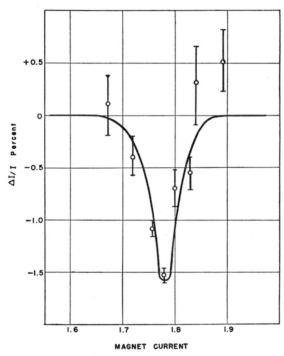

FIG. 2.7. *Typical resonance dip for neutrons obtained by varying the current through the magnet* H_o.

this point gave the value of H^*_0. A typical curve is shown in Fig. 2.7 where $\Delta I/I$ in percent is plotted against the current in the H_0 magnet for a frequency $\omega/2\pi = 1843$ kilocycles per second. The measurements lead to a value for μ of $\mu = -1.935$ nuclear magnetons, a value somewhat higher than that currently accepted. The more recent value comes from the work of Cohen, Corngold, and Ramsey (11), who used a resonance method similar to that of Alvarez and Bloch to determine the ratio of the neutron magnetic moment to that of the proton. Advances in techniques for developing polarized neutrons permitted them to obtain more precise values than were realized from earlier experiments. They found

$$\frac{\mu_n}{\mu_p} = 0.685057 \pm 0.000017$$

from which they deduced

$$\mu_n = -1.913148 \pm 0.000066$$

nuclear magnetons. It is to be noted that the simple relation

$$\mu_d = \mu_p + \mu_n$$

with μ_d the magnetic moment of the deuteron, which seemed confirmed in earlier measurements, no longer holds for the recent, more accurate measurements.

To date no measurable electric dipole moment has been found for the neutron. Attempts to measure such a moment by Smith (12) yielded an upper limit for the electric dipole moment as that of a positive and negative electronic charge separated by 5×10^{-21} cm.

2.8. Nucleons

Because neutrons and protons within an atomic nucleus have similar properties, especially from a theoretical point of view, the term nucleon is often applied to both. The characteristic of neutrons by which they are able to transform into the proton state inside and outside of the nucleus, and the ability of protons to transform into neutrons within the nucleus, ties these two particles together as different aspects of a more basic structure. The investigation of the nucleon structure is now one of the most challenging problems of nuclear physics.

3.1. Classification of Neutrons as to Energy

The preceding summary of the fundamental properties of the neutron is a sufficient basis for the explanation of the more general features of its behavior. For more detailed examination of the results of the interactions of neutrons with matter it is also desirable to classify them according to their kinetic energy. It is possible to separate neutrons of a variety of energies into fairly definite groups. The divisions, in general, occur naturally as a result of the interactions peculiar to certain ranges of energy. Although these different regions merge into each other, and sometimes overlap, the division into categories which has developed is convenient and often necessary for an understanding of particular types of interactions.

3.2. Slow Neutrons

Neutrons with energies from zero to about 1000 ev are usually included in the category of slow neutrons. In this range a number of subclassifications occur. The more important are listed below.

3.3. "Cold" Neutrons

The adjective "cold" has been applied to neutrons with an average energy less than that of thermal neutrons. The quotation marks indicate that these neutrons are not produced by refrigeration but by a device which depends on the coherent scattering of slow neutrons. From the Bragg law

$$n\lambda = 2d \sin \theta \tag{3.1}$$

It is apparent that when λ, the neutron wavelength, exceeds $2d$, where d is the grating spacing of the crystal, the value of $\sin \theta$ becomes greater than unity, which is impossible mathematically. Therefore there is no reflection. If a beam of thermal neutrons traverses a column of poly-crystalline graphite, the neutrons which have wavelengths less than $2d$ will be reflected and ultimately be removed from the column. Thus the neutrons with the higher energies are not transmitted. Since $2d$ for graphite is 6.7 Å the computed maximum energy of the transmitted neutrons is 0.002 ev. This is well below the average energy of thermal agitation for neutrons at room temperature.

3.4. Thermal Neutrons

When fast neutrons have been slowed down until the average energy of the neutrons is equal to the average thermal energy of the atoms of the medium, the neutrons are called thermal neutrons. The energies and corresponding velocities of the neutrons then depend upon the temperature of the medium. The distribution of the velocities approaches the Maxwell distribution,

$$dn(v) = Av^2 e^{-Mv^2/2kT} dv \tag{3.2}$$

where v is the neutron velocity, M its mass, k is Boltzmann's constant and T the absolute temperature. The maximum number of neutrons will have the energy kT. The value of kT at 20°C is approximately 0.025 ev.

3.5. Epithermal Neutrons

Consider an arrangement in which neutrons are being produced at energies much greater than thermal—say, by a source of fission neutrons. Also assume that the source of fission neutrons is surrounded by a moderator which slows the neutrons down until eventually they have energies in thermal equilibrium with the molecules of the moderator. At any location where complete thermal equilibrium has not been established, the distribution of neutron velocities will contain velocities which exceed any permitted by a Maxwell distribution for the temperature of the moderator. Such a distribution is called epithermal and the neutrons in it are called epithermal neutrons.

3.6. Resonance Neutrons

In the approximate range of energies between 1 and 100 electron volts, various nuclei exhibit strong absorption of neutrons at fairly well-defined energies. These absorptions are called resonance absorptions, and the neutrons having the corresponding energies are known as resonance neutrons.

3.7. Intermediate Neutrons

The region of energy between 1000 ev and 0.5 Mev is often considered the intermediate range of neutron energies. Less information has been accumulated about intermediate neutrons than about neutrons of lower energies because of difficulty of finding efficient detectors for the intermediate neutrons. In addition, sources of neutrons with energies in this intermediate range are not plentiful and there has been until recently little progress in studying their interactions.

3.8. High-Energy and Ultra-High-Energy Neutrons

In the region of higher energies, neutron classifications based on energy are somewhat less sharply defined. Ordinarily, high-energy neutrons are assumed to have energies in the region from 0.5 to 10 Mev. Accelerators for producing particles of 50 Mev and above, often called the very-high-energy range, are not yet numerous. Relatively few sources of neutrons with this range of energies are available. Therefore much remains to be learned regarding the properties of very-high-energy neutrons. As efforts multiply in the development of accelerators to generate charged-particle radiations of energies greatly exceeding 50 Mev, the production of neutrons in the ultra-high-energy range becomes possible. It is impossible to predict the ultimate limit of the upward extension of neutron energies. Enough exploratory work in the 1-to-5 Bev region has been done to indicate the general tendencies of interactions of ultra-high-energy neutrons with nuclei. Fission and spallation of nuclei with atomic numbers below bismuth, as well as above it, are produced in this region. Also most nuclei appear to be relatively transparent to neutrons in the Bev range of energy. The cosmic radiation is also a source of neutrons with energies well above those which are likely to be produced by accelerators. However these cosmic-ray neutrons are not as accessible for study as neutrons generated by accelerators.

SYMBOLS USED IN CHAPTER I

Bev	billion electron volts
c	velocity of light
d	atomic lattice spacing in crystals
E	energy
E_n	energy of a neutron
ev	electron volts
h	Planck's constant
$\hbar$	$h/2\pi$
k	Boltzmann's constant
m	mass of any particle
M, M_n	mass of the neutron
Mev	million electron volts
n	number of neutrons
n, n^1	neutron
T	absolute temperature in degrees K
v, V	velocity of a neutron
V_N	velocity of a nitrogen nucleus
V_p	velocity of a proton
θ	Bragg angle of crystal reflection
λ	wavelength
λ	$\lambda/2\pi$
μ, μ_n	magnetic moment of the neutron
μ_d	magnetic moment of the deuteron
μ_p	magnetic moment of the proton
ν	frequency in cycles per second
ρ	neutron density
ω	angular frequency in radians per second

PROBLEMS FOR CHAPTER I

1. Compute the mass of the neutron from the nuclear reaction

$$N^{14} + n^1 \rightarrow C^{14} + H^1 + 0.61 \text{ Mev}$$

2. Compute the reaction energy Q in the nuclear reaction

$$Cl^{35} + n^1 \rightarrow P^{32} + He^4 + Q$$

3. Compute the energy required to create an electron with rest mass of 9.1085×10^{-28} g.

REFERENCES FOR CHAPTER I

1. J. Chadwick. *Proc. Roy. Soc.* **A136,** 692 (1932).
2. E. Rutherford. *Proc. Roy. Soc.* **A97,** 373 (1920).
3. J. Chadwick and M. Goldhaber. *Proc. Roy. Soc.* **A151,** 479 (1935).
4. R. E. Bell and L. G. Elliott. *Phys. Rev.* **74,** 1552 (1948); *Phys. Rev.* **79,** 282 (1950).
5. K. T. Bainbridge. *Experimental Nuclear Physics,* Wiley (1953), Vol. I, p. 745.
6. P. I. Dee. *Proc. Roy. Soc.* **A136,** 727 (1932).
7. E. Fermi and L. Marshall. *Phys. Rev.* **72,** 1139 (1947).
8. D. J. Hughes and M. T. Burgy. *Phys. Rev.* **81,** 498 (1951).
9. J. M. Robson. *Phys. Rev.* **83,** 349 (1951).
10. L. W. Alvarez and F. Bloch. *Phys. Rev.* **57,** 111 (1940).
11. V. W. Cohen, N. R. Corngold, and N. F. Ramsey. *Phys. Rev.* **104,** 283 (1956).
12. J. H. Smith. Harvard University Thesis (1951).

Chapter II

PARTICLE AND NUCLEAR INTERACTIONS

4.1. Particle Interactions

The study of the interactions of neutrons with other nuclear particles has revealed information regarding the properties of neutrons and details of nuclear structure. A discussion of the main features of the interactions of neutrons with particles is essential to a description of the neutron and its behavior.

4.2. Cross Sections

In the investigation of the interactions of neutrons with other forms of matter, the concept of a cross section has been introduced. Although cross section is now a relatively familiar term, we will review here some of the elementary aspects of this concept. The most direct and simple definition of a cross section is given by the equation

$$r = F\sigma N \tag{4.1}$$

Here F represents a flux of particles in an incident collimated beam, σ is the complete probability of a particular interaction occurring with a number N of entities exposed to the beam. These entities may be, for example, the atoms in a thin absorbing layer of matter. Then r is the rate at which, on the average for a large number of events, the particular type of interactions are occurring. A dimensional analysis of Eq. 4.1 reveals σ to be an area. This fictitious area results from the framework in which the probability has been specified. Nevertheless, σ is an area, customarily expressed in square centimeters. A convenient size of this unit for most interactions is 10^{-24} cm^2, now universally called the barn. Neutron flux is commonly represented by nv, expressed in number of neutrons per second per square centimeter, with n the number of neutrons and v their velocity. If the number of atoms N are changed from their original state to some other condition by the interaction, we may replace r by dN/dt. Then

$$\frac{dN}{dt} = -nv\sigma N \tag{4.2}$$

21

which on integration gives

$$N = N_0 e^{-nv\sigma t} \tag{4.3}$$

where N is the number of atoms in the target area in their original state at time t, and N_0 is the number at $t = 0$. This result, of course, assumes nv to be constant throughout the target area.

The cross section is also used to describe the removal of neutrons from a collimated beam—say, by absorption or scattering. This situation may be approached by comparing the area A of the beam with the cross-sectional area of the target atoms. If N now is the number of atoms per cm^3 in a target of thickness x, the total number of atoms exposed to the beam is NAx. The cross-sectional area of these atoms is $NAx\sigma$. The fraction of the neutrons removed from the incident beam is $NA\sigma x/A$ or $N\sigma x$. The fraction removed in an element of path dx in the target is

$$\frac{dn}{n} = -N\sigma dx \tag{4.4}$$

which on integration gives

$$n = n_0 e^{-N\sigma x} \tag{4.5}$$

where n_0 is the neutron intensity in the incident beam and n the intensity after traversing a layer of thickness x. Here again σ is assumed to be constant, and this assumes no change in the velocity of the neutrons. N is also assumed constant, which is usually true to a high degree of approximation. It is to be noted that the type of interaction considered here must completely remove the neutron from the well-collimated beam at the first encounter. As an example of the use of Eq. 4.5, consider a beam of thermal neutrons with a flux density of 4×10^3 neutrons per cm^2 per sec incident on a sheet of cobalt in a plane at right angles to the beam. The cobalt is assumed to be 0.5 cm thick with a density of 8.71 g/cm^3. One gram of cobalt contains

$$\frac{6.02 \times 10^{23}}{59} = 1.02 \times 10^{22} \text{ atoms}$$

Therefore $N = (1.02 \times 10^{22}) \times 8.71 = 8.88 \times 10^{22}$ atoms per cm^3. The thermal neutron absorption cross section for cobalt is 37 barns. Therefore we have $N\sigma x = (8.88 \times 10^{22}) \times (37 \times 10^{-24}) \times 0.5 = 1.64$. Introducing this value of $N\sigma x$ into Eq. 4.5 we have

$$n = (4 \times 10^3) \cdot e^{-1.64} = 4 \times 10^3 \times 0.71 = 2.84 \times 10^3 \text{ neutrons}$$
$$\text{per } cm^2 \text{ per sec transmitted through the cobalt}$$

4.3. The Macroscopic Cross Section

The symbol σ, as just defined, represents the atomic or nuclear cross section. The "macroscopic cross section," as it is commonly called, represented by Σ is defined by the relation

$$N\sigma = \Sigma \tag{4.6}$$

In spite of the common use of the term "cross section" in connection with Σ, Σ does not represent an area but is expressed in cm^{-1} and is therefore an absorption coefficient.

From Eq. 4.4 we then have

$$\frac{dn}{n} = -\Sigma dx \tag{4.7}$$

and Σdx is the probability that a neutron will be captured in a path length dx. Hence the average distance neutrons will travel before capture is the statistical average

$$\frac{\int_0^\infty x e^{-\Sigma x} dx}{\int_0^\infty e^{-\Sigma x} dx} = \frac{1}{\Sigma} = \lambda \tag{4.8}$$

where λ is the mean free path for capture in a target for which the macroscopic cross section is Σ. Eq. 4.5, stated in terms of λ, becomes

$$\frac{n}{n_0} = e^{-x/\lambda} \tag{4.9}$$

Hence for a beam of neutrons, λ is obviously the distance the neutrons will travel before they are reduced to $1/e$ times their initial intensity. Thus λ is frequently called the relaxation length.

The value of Σ must, of course, be calculated for each sample of absorbing material. Usually it is simpler to take values of σ from tables for practical computations. For example, N for a sheet of gold of density 19.3 g/cm^3

$$N = \frac{19.3 \times 6.02 \times 10^{23}}{197} = 59 \times 10^{21} \text{ atoms per cm}^3.$$

The atomic absorption cross section of gold for thermal neutrons is 98 barns. Hence $N\sigma = (59 \times 10^{21})(98 \times 10^{-24}) = 5.8 \quad \text{cm}^{-1} = \Sigma$. Then $n/n_0 = e^{-\Sigma x} = e^{-0.58} = 0.25$.

When introducing Eq. 4.1 to define σ it was stated that σ represents the probability for a particular interaction. As this statement implies, there is a separate σ for each type of interaction. It is customary to indicate the type of interaction by a subscript. Thus σ_a usually represents the cross section for neutron absorption, σ_s the cross section for scattering, σ_{el} the cross section for elastic scattering, and a number of similar additional examples could be cited.

4.4. The Neutron-Proton Interaction

This interaction is of basic importance to nuclear reactions induced by neutrons. Because the deuteron consists of a neutron bound to a proton by nuclear forces, it offers a natural system for the investigation of the mutual interaction between the neutron and the proton. The manner in which the proton and the neutron split apart in the disintegration of the deuteron is particularly significant. The binding energy of this combination is known from a variety of observations to be approximately 2.23 Mev. Any reaction which can introduce an amount of energy greater than 2.23 Mev offers the possibility of disintegrating the deuteron. The fact that the spin of the deuteron is equal to the numerical sum of the spin of the proton plus that of the neutron also shows that the spins of the proton and the neutron must be aligned parallel to each other in the deuteron. Of the possible ways of splitting the deuteron, that offered by the (γ,n) reaction, sometimes called the photoeffect, is most attractive. The only particles involved are the proton and the neutron. Consequently the disintegration of the deuteron has been investigated extensively both in theory and in experiment. This disintegration is, in principle, a dual process in which both the electric and magnetic fields of the photons play a role. The electric field reacts with the instantaneous dipole moment to split the neutron from the proton, leaving the spins still parallel. At photon energies a few Mev above the threshold, the magnetic field of the photon radiation reacts with the magnetic dipole moments of the neutron and of the proton to produce antiparallel spins. This spin-flip, originally pointed out by Fermi (1), is called the photomagnetic process. It becomes important at photon energies in excess of 20 Mev. The electric separation of the proton and neutron involves properties of the neutron-proton potential in the triplet state (parallel spins) and the photomagnetic process involves the singlet state (antiparallel spins). Schiff (2) and Marshall and Guth (3) have shown that Yukawa and exponential potentials yield the same dipole cross section for this reaction and that the angular distribution $f(\theta)$ is of the form $A + \sin^2 \theta$. Halpern and Weinstock (4) have investigated the distribution of the recoil protons, using bremsstrahlung photons of 20 Mev from a betatron target. The photomagnetic effect, represented by A in the distribution function, is relatively small at this energy. The electric quadrupole transition $^3S \rightarrow {}^3D$ introduces a modification of the transition by interference with ^3P waves producing an asymmetry represented by $\sin^2 \theta(1 + 2\beta \cos \theta)$ where $\beta = \sqrt{(h\nu - \epsilon)/Mc^2}$, in which $h\nu$ = photon energy, ϵ = binding energy of the deuteron, and M = the mass of the proton or neutron. Thus the distribution function becomes $f(\theta) = A + \sin^2 \theta(1 + 2\beta \cos \theta)$. Measurement of the number of recoil protons per neutron were made with the arrangement sketched in Fig. 4.1. G is a collimated beam of 20-Mev bremsstrahlung which traverses a target T of deuterated paraffin. Two scintillation counters DD, for detecting the protons, are mounted rigidly with respect to the target and to each other. The assembly may be rotated with respect to the photon beam on an axis at right angles to the beam. The results of the measurements are plotted in Fig. 4.2, in which the solid curve is $f(\theta)$ and the circles are the numbers of protons at various angles in the center-of-mass system. A similar agreement with theory is found in other investigations of the disintegration of the deuteron and represents one of the more satisfactory situations in the complicated studies of nuclear forces.

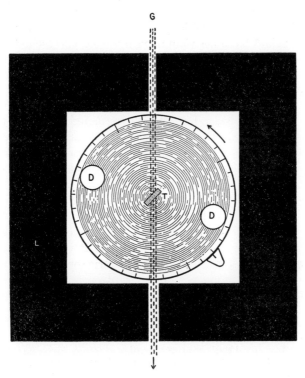

FIG. 4.1. *Plan of the apparatus used by Halpern and Weinstock in the study of the photodisintegration of the deuteron. G—beam of 22-Mev bremsstrahlung. D-D—zinc sulfide scintillators. T—deuterated paraffin target. L—lead shield. The target and detectors rotate as a unit with respect to the gamma-ray beam.*

The radioactive capture of neutrons by protons is the inverse process to the photodisintegration of the deuteron, and theory applicable to one also fits the other. Because the theory predicts a vanishingly small cross section for the photoelectric process of slow neutrons, some other explanation is required for the observations which proved that neutrons have a measurable cross section for capture by hydrogen. It was the search for the explanation which led Fermi to the development of the theory of the photomagnetic process. With only S states ($l = 0$) involved, instead of

P states ($l = 1$), infrequent for slow neutrons, Fermi could show that the cross section should follow the $1/v$ law. Furthermore the photomagnetic process was adequate to explain the observed cross section of hydrogen for thermal neutrons. In spite of the theoretical as well as practical interest in the value of the absorption cross section of hydrogen for thermal neutrons, no very precise values have become available. The absence of information arises mainly from the difficulties in measuring such a small effect in a nuclear reaction which leads to a nonradioactive product. The best current values have been obtained by using pile oscillators in which the absorption of neutrons is detected by a decrease in the reactivity of

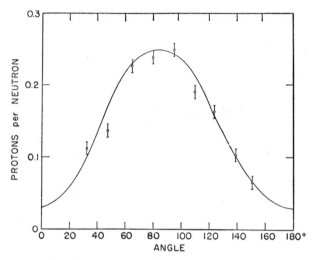

FIG. 4.2. *Angular distribution of the photoprotons in terms of center mass angle. Indicated errors refer to the statistics of the counting.*

the reactor and by measurement of the diffusion length of thermal neutrons in water.

Scott, Thomson, and Wright (5) have reported an ingenious application of the diffusion method to the measurement of σ_H, the absorption cross section for hydrogen. As sketched in Fig. 4.3, a betatron with target at T was used to generate bremsstrahlung as a means of producing a pulsed neutron source. The burst of gamma radiation from T struck the uranium absorber U and released the neutrons. These neutrons, produced by (γ,n) and (γ,f) reactions in the uranium, diffused into the tank of water W. A proportional counter tube lined with a layer of B^{10} was mounted at C. By changing the depth of the water in the tank, the mean life of the neutrons, as measured by an eight-channel electronic time analyzer, could

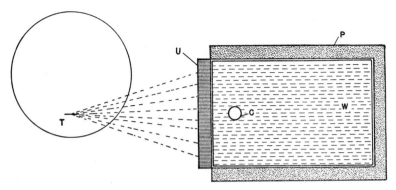

FIG. 4.3. *Sketch of the arrangement used by Scott, Thomson, and Wright to measure* σ_H *by determining the mean life of neutrons in a finite volume of water. T—betatron target. U—uranium irradiated by gamma rays. W—water. C—B^{10} proportional counter. P—paraffin shield. A layer of cadmium separates the water tank from the paraffin shield.*

be correlated with the "buckling factor" B of the tank. The buckling factor may be defined by the relation

$$B^2 = \left(\frac{\pi}{a}\right)^2 + \left(\frac{\pi}{b}\right)^2 \tag{4.10}$$

where a and b are the linear dimensions of the rectangular mass of water. From simple diffusion theory

$$\frac{1}{t} = (1 + B^2 L^2)\Sigma_a v \tag{4.11}$$

in which L is the diffusion length, that is, the distance over which the neutron density drops to $1/e$ of its initial value, as expressed in Eq. 13.4. Σ_a is the macroscopic absorption cross section in water, and v the velocity of the neutrons, with t the mean life of the neutrons. The value of B approaches zero as the volume of the tank approaches infinity. In the limit

$$\frac{1}{t} = \Sigma_a v \tag{4.12}$$

The value of $1/t$ is obtained by extrapolating to $B = 0$ in the plot of $1/t$ versus B^2, as shown in Fig. 4.4. The extrapolation yields the value of 213 ± 4 sec for t. Since $\Sigma_a = N\sigma_a$, where σ_a is the atomic absorption cross section, and N is the number of atoms per cm³, Eq. 4.12 yields $1/213 = (3.33 \times 10^{16})\sigma_H(2.2 \times 10^5)$; or $\sigma_H = 0.323 \pm 0.008$ barn for $v = 2200$ meters per sec.

Using a method by which the average power level $\bar{p}$ of a reactor is made

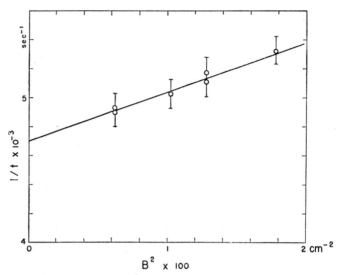

FIG. 4.4. *The thermal neutron decay constant plotted against the buckling factor* B^2.

to oscillate by propelling an absorbing sample in and out of the reactor, Harris and co-workers (6) have compared the value of σ_H with that of σ_B, the absorption cross section for boron, using a standardized sample of boron. The value of σ_B for the standardized sample was known from transmission measurements to be 755 ± 3 barns. In theory the change in the power level of the reactor varies as the product $\bar{p}N_a\sigma_a$ where N_a is the number of absorbing nuclei and σ_a is their absorption cross section. Measurements in the reactor are complicated by the necessity of knowing certain constants of the reactor which are not easily determined accurately. However, these authors obtained the value $\sigma_H = 0.332 \pm 0.007$ barn at $v = 2200$ meters per sec.

To avoid the difficulties associated with the pile oscillator method, Hamermesh, Ringo, and Wexler (7) studied the competition for neutron capture in boron and hydrogen in a solution irradiated by neutrons from a constant source. The activation by neutron capture of NaI added to the solution was used to measure the neutron density in the solution. In one experiment the solution consisted of sodium iodide in water, and in the second experiment boric acid was also added to this solution. Under the conditions of the experiments the 25-minute nuclide I^{128} was the predominant activity generated by the neutrons. If R is the ratio of the iodine activities in the two experiments for identical times of irradiation, and the number of atoms per cm³ of iodine N_I are also the same, then

$$R - 1 = \frac{N'_B\sigma_B + (N'_H - N_H)\sigma_H}{N_I\sigma_I + N_H\sigma_H} \tag{4.13}$$

In each case the N represents the numbers of atoms per cm³ without boron in the solution and the N' refers to the experiment with boron present. Because $(N'_H - N_H)\sigma_H$ is small, and the sodium iodide concentration was chosen to keep $N_I\sigma_I$ also small, the value of σ_B/σ_H is easily computed from Eq. 4.13. This method, with the same standard boron used by Harris (6), yielded a value of $\sigma_H = 0.329 \pm 0.004$ barn at 2200 meters per sec.

Combining the results of the foregoing measurements with others which differ but slightly from them, Hughes and Harvey (8) give the best current value for the cross section of hydrogen for thermal neutrons as

$$\sigma_H = 0.330 \pm 0.003 \text{ barn}$$

This value is in good agreement with the theoretical computation of the capture cross section for hydrogen, on the assumption that the capture is a photomagnetic process which is concerned with the properties of the neutron-proton interaction in the singlet state and that the $^1S_0$ state of the deuteron is unbound.

4.5. Neutron-Proton Scattering

A vast amount of experimental data on the result of scattering of neutrons by protons has accumulated. Interest in this interaction has been stimulated by the possibilities of learning much about nuclear forces from the characteristics of the neutron-proton scattering interaction at different energies. There is also ample opportunity to compare the experimental results with a variety of theories in this area. In many instances theoretical calculations can now predict measured values of a number of parameters accurately. A good example is the scattering cross section of the proton for neutrons over a range of energies extending from thermal neutrons up to at least 200 Mev. Fig. 4.5 shows the theoretical curve, taken from Hughes and Harvey (8). This curve has been confirmed at many points by experimental observations. The agreement of theory with experiment in this area is sometimes illusory because only recently have experimental measurements of cross sections been made with an accuracy which permits differentiation between various refinements of the theory. In other situations experimental measurements have indicated where improvement in the theory is required. For example, Wigner (9) developed an expression for the scattering cross section of the proton, which may be represented by

$$\sigma_s = \frac{4\pi\hbar^2}{M(E/2 + |\epsilon|)} \tag{4.14}$$

in which ϵ is the binding energy of the deuteron. Whereas Eq. 4.14 agreed well with measured cross sections for neutrons with energies of the order of 1 Mev, it gave values much too small for slow neutrons. This discrepancy has been ascribed to the difference in the neutron-proton force for the

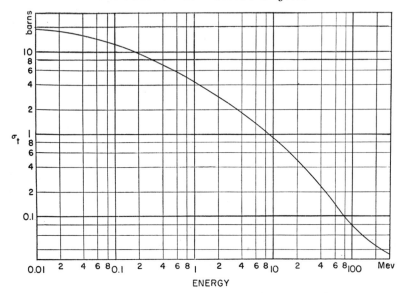

FIG. 4.5. *The total neutron cross section for hydrogen in the range 0.01 to 100 Mev.*

singlet and triplet states. Because the scattering of slow neutrons must occur in the singlet state, the expression Eq. 4.14 should be modified. In fact $\sigma_s = \frac{3}{4}\sigma_3 + \frac{1}{4}\sigma_1$, where σ_3 refers to the triplet state and σ_1 to the singlet state.

4.6. Effect of Chemical Binding on the Neutron-Proton Scattering Cross Section

Early in the investigations of neutron-proton scattering, fluctuations in the measured values of the cross sections were observed. These variations were later found to be mainly the effect of the chemical binding of the hydrogen atoms in chemical compounds. This effect was noted particularly for slow neutrons. As soon as the energy of the neutrons greatly exceeded that of the chemical bonds, the variations in the cross sections disappeared. This situation led to experiments intended to measure σ_0, defined as the total cross section of free protons for slow neutrons. Melkonian (10) made use of the then unpublished theory developed by Placzek to determine σ_0 experimentally. According to this theory, the measured cross section σ is given by

$$\sigma = \sigma_0 + \frac{\beta}{E} \tag{4.15}$$

where β is a constant dependent on well-known characteristics of the hydrogen molecule, and E the energy of the neutron. Consequently a graph of σ versus $1/E$ should give a straight line with σ_0 as the y-intercept at $1/E = 0$. Typical data obtained by Melkonian are plotted in Fig. 4.6, showing $\sigma_0 = 20.36 \pm 0.10$ barns. An example of the effect of chemical binding on σ is revealed by the data of Jones (11). His results are summarized in Fig. 4.7, where the value of the total cross section per hydrogen atom of water is plotted as a function of the energy of the neutron. Following the curve from right to left, it begins at a neutron energy of 100 ev,

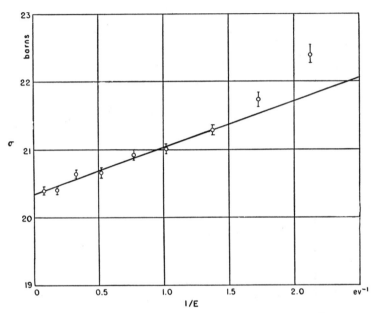

FIG. 4.6. *The slow neutron cross section of* H_2 *gas in the energy range 0.5 to 15 ev according to Melkonian.*

where σ has the value 20.4 barns, corresponding to that of σ_0 for free protons. Proceeding further along the curve in the direction of decreasing neutron energy, at 0.5 ev the curve begins to rise and continues sharply upward. A small part of the rise at very low energies is contributed by the thermal motions of the water molecules and by the proton capture cross section, which is of the order of 1 barn at the lowest energy. As might be expected, the importance of chemical binding in relation to the scattering cross section decreases with increasing mass of the scattering nucleus. The situation is illustrated by the graph in Fig. 4.8, where the ratio of the observed cross section σ for bound nuclei to σ_0 for free nuclei is plotted against the mass number.

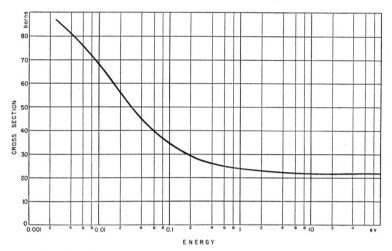

FIG. 4.7. *Total cross section per hydrogen atom of water for neutron energies from 0.002 to 100 ev.*

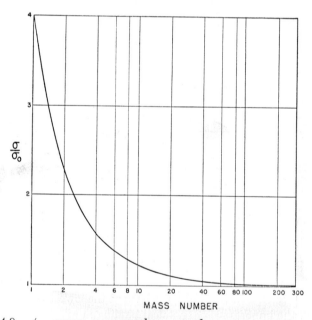

FIG. 4.8. σ/σ_0 *versus mass number.* σ *is the scattering cross section for a bound nucleus in liquids or solids, and* σ_0 *the scattering cross section for the free nucleus. The equation of the curve is*
$$\sigma = \left(\frac{A+1}{A}\right)^2 \sigma_0 \text{ where A is the mass number.}$$

4.7. Neutron-Proton Scattering at High Energies

Contrasted with the spherical symmetry in the center-of-mass system of the scattering of slow neutrons by protons, at high energies, in excess of 10 Mev, large deviations from spherical symmetry appear experimentally. An example is shown in Fig. 4.9, representing observations by De Pangher (12) at 300 Mev. The current explanation for this asymmetry is that at high energies, states of higher angular momentum of the neutron-proton

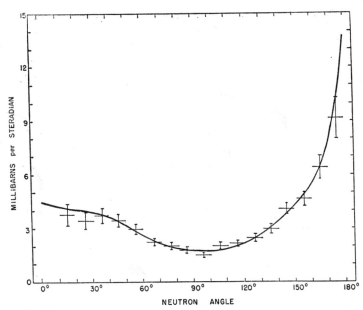

FIG. 4.9. *The angular distribution of the differential cross section in the center-of-mass system for neutrons scattered by protons, according to De Pangher. The smooth curve is intended to represent the experimental data.*

are involved. In the S state the angular momentum is zero and scattering is spherically symmetrical in the center-of-mass system. Theoreticians have used the shape of the angular distribution curves of the scattering to infer the nature of the potential of nuclear forces. The distributions seem to favor an exchange force of the type ascribed to Serber (13) in the form

$$V = \tfrac{1}{2}(1 + P^M)V(r) \tag{4.16}$$

where V is the potential of the nuclear force and P^M is the Majorana exchange operator. However, the nature of the observations and the incompleteness of the theory leave considerable gaps in the information regarding nuclear forces.

4.8. The Neutron-Neutron Interaction

Almost nothing is known directly from experiment regarding the neutron-neutron interaction. The lack of free neutron densities sufficiently high to permit observations of the scattering of free neutrons by free neutrons has made direct observation of the neutron-neutron interaction impossible. Inferences from forces between nucleons within nuclei are not conclusively applicable to free neutrons. Within nuclei, neutron-neutron forces seem to be equal to proton-proton forces, neglecting the Coulomb repulsion between protons. Definite experimental information on the existence, or the nonexistence, of the hypothetical di-neutron (two neutrons bound together) would throw some light on the neutron-neutron interaction. At present definite proof regarding the di-neutron is lacking, but most indirect evidence indicates that it is unstable. In an indirect measurement of the n-n interaction, Phillips and Crowe (14) have compared the gamma-ray spectra in the two reactions

$$\pi^- + d \rightarrow 2n + \gamma$$

$$\pi^- + p \rightarrow n + \gamma$$

using negative pions produced by 335-Mev protons in the Berkeley cyclotron. From the broadening of the gamma-ray spectrum in the deuteron reaction, they determine the scattering length a for the S-state neutron-neutron scattering as $a = -15.9 \times 10^{-13}$ cm. This corresponds approximately to 160 kev as the binding energy of the assumed di-neutron.

In the region of ultra-high energies, say from 100 to 1500 Mev, the wavelength of the neutron becomes comparable with the assumed average separation of the neutron and the proton in the deuteron. It might be supposed that the two nucleons would scatter neutrons independently and thus afford an insight into the neutron-neutron interaction. On this simple assumption, $\sigma(\text{n-n}) = \sigma(\text{n-d}) - \sigma(\text{n-p})$. Therefore measurements of scattering of neutrons by deuterons and by protons might yield the value of $\sigma(\text{n-n})$. However, there are many obstacles to such a simple interpretation. Coherent elastic scattering from the two nucleons might develop interference, the Pauli exclusion principle may not allow some of the final states in the analysis, or complicated three-body interactions may occur. In Fig. 4.10 are plotted some of the observations by various authors on the total cross sections of deuterons and of protons for neutrons with energies from 40 to 1400 Mev. The data are taken from Coor and co-workers (15) who also measured the two points at 1400 Mev.

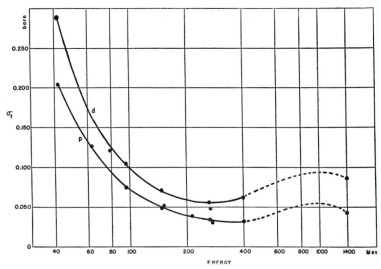

FIG. 4.10. *Total cross sections of deuterons (curve* d) *and of protons (curve* p) *for neutrons with energies from* 40 *Mev to* 1400 *Mev, according to Coor et al.*

4.9. The Neutron-Electron Interaction

That there is an interaction between neutrons and electrons related in some way to short-range forces seems beyond dispute. However, the magnitude and theoretical interpretation of this interaction are subjects of widespread disagreements. Reported experimental measurements are very imprecise and the theory is equally confused. The neutron-electron interaction here considered must be distinguished from the magnetic interaction of neutrons with electrons resulting from the magnetic moment of the neutron, a comparatively much stronger and well-understood effect. The nature of the electron interaction with neutrons involved here becomes clearer from a consideration of some of the explanations which have been offered for it. One explanation is based on an assumed structure for the neutron. This structure is visualized as a reversible interaction within a system involving a proton and a pion. It may be represented by the reversible equation

$$n \rightleftarrows p + \pi^- \tag{4.17}$$

When in the dissociated state, represented by the right-hand side of Eq. 4.17, the structure is still a closely bound system scarcely distinguishable from the completely bound state represented by n. Furthermore, the theory stipulates that the spontaneously dissociated state exists only for a fraction of the time. In the dissociated condition there is a very small separation of the positive and negative electric charges which can account for an interaction with electrons at distances of the order of those over which nuclear forces are effective. The neutron-electron interaction also differs from the magnetic interaction of two dipoles in that it is independent of spin. The interaction was investigated experimentally by Fermi and Marshall (16) and interpreted on the dissociation hypothesis. Assuming a potential energy between the neutron and the electron represented by the function $U(r)$, with r the distance between them, the volume integral of the potential becomes

$$b = 4\pi \int_0^\infty U(r)\,r^2 dr \qquad (4.18)$$

Further assuming arbitrarily that this volume integral is equal to that for the classical electron and introducing experimental data on the asymmetry of thermal neutron scattering by xenon, these authors found the depth of the potential well to be $V = 300 \pm 5000$ ev. More recently Hughes and co-workers (17) have determined the magnitude of the neutron-electron interaction by measuring the critical angle for total reflection of slow neutrons at the interface between bismuth and liquid oxygen. These elements were selected because of their large difference in atomic number and therefore in the number of electrons in their atoms and because their nuclear interactions are nearly equal. Fig. 4.11 is a diagram of the arrangement for measuring the critical angle of reflection θ_c. The data for determining θ_c are plotted in Fig. 4.12 from which $\theta_c = 3.66$ minutes of arc. The angle θ_c is related to the coherent bound scattering amplitude a_e of electrons scattered by neutrons by the equation

$$\frac{\pi}{\lambda^2}\theta^2{}_c = N_1 a_1 \left(\frac{N_2 a_2}{N_1 a_1} - 1\right) + (N_1 Z_1 - N_2 Z_2)a_e \qquad (4.19)$$

where the subscripts 1 refer to bismuth and the subscripts 2 refer to oxygen. N is the respective numbers of atoms per cm^3, Z the atomic number, a the neutron coherent scattering amplitudes, and λ the wave-

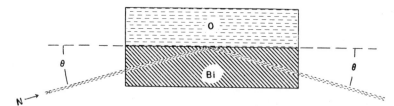

FIG. 4.11. *Geometrical arrangement used by Hughes and co-workers to investigate the neutron-electron interaction. N—collimated beam of thermal neutrons. O—liquid oxygen Bi—bismuth metal. θ—angle between the neutron beam and the bismuth-oxygen interface.*

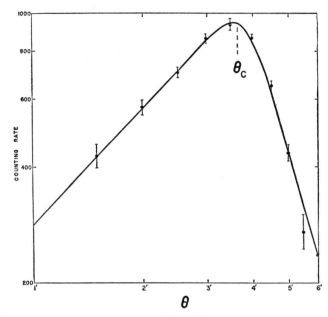

FIG. 4.12. *The intensity of the reflected beam of neutrons from the bismuth-oxygen interface as a function of the angle* θ *of incidence.*

length of the neutrons. Experimentally the ratio $N_2 a_2 / N_1 a_1$ was found to have the value 1.0204 ± 0.0008. Introducing this value and the appropriate values of Z into Eq. 4.19 we obtain

$$a_e = \frac{(\pi/\lambda^2)\theta^2{}_c - 0.0204 N_1 a_1}{83 N_1 - 8 N_2}$$

On introducing the experimental values of θ_c, N_1, N_2, and λ into this equation, the authors obtained $a_e = 1.40 \times 10^{-16}$ cm. This value corresponds to $V = 3860 \pm 370$ ev for the depth of the potential well and is the most precise measurement of V which has been published to date.

5.1. Nuclear Interactions

Using a source of neutrons consisting of radon sealed in a glass tube with some beryllium powder, Fermi (18) discovered that strong radioactivity was induced in such common elements as phosphorus, iron, silicon, and iodine when exposed to this source. The list of elements which showed some radioactivity after exposure to neutrons was considerably longer. These experiments marked the beginning of an entirely new method of producing so-called artificial radioactivity. The irradiation of stable isotopes with neutrons to produce radioactive isotopes was ultimately developed into the most prolific means of manufacturing radioisotopes in use today. In early investigations no mention was made of a moderator to slow down the relatively fast neutrons from the source. However, within a short time, it was realized that neutrons do not require kinetic energy to overcome Coulomb forces in penetrating the nucleus. Hence the chance of a reaction should increase as the transit time through the force-field of the nucleus became longer. In the original experiments in which neutrons were identified, the transfer of kinetic energy from neutrons to protons played an important role. Collision with protons is also the most effective means available for slowing neutrons. Consequently Moon and Tillman (19) were able to show that neutrons from a Ra-Be neutron source were 30 per cent more effective in producing radioactivity in silver and rhodium with 1.5 cm of paraffin between the source and the target, as compared with the bare source. The strongest sources of slow neutrons generally available for the greater part of the next decade consisted of Ra-Be sources in a paraffin moderator.

The nature of the processes occurring when slow neutrons reacted with nuclei was also under investigation. Whereas Fermi originally assumed that an alpha particle or a proton was expelled when a neutron entered a nucleus, Lea (20) found that gamma rays were generated when neutrons were absorbed by some of the elements of intermediate atomic number. This observation was confirmed by Amaldi and co-workers (21) with particular reference to cobalt, cadmium, chlorine, and gold. They also noted that fast neutrons did not stimulate these elements to emit gamma rays. A glance at some of the papers of the early period of neutron studies reveals the uncertainties which existed for a time regarding the nature of the interactions of neutrons with nuclei and the specific properties of the neutrons which influenced the results of the observations. However, within a few years the significance of the principal processes began to be understood. The existence for slow neutrons of (n,γ) reactions for a large number of elements, of (n,α) reactions for some of the light elements, and a rare (n,p) reaction for nitrogen, became firmly established. These developments were followed by the discovery of resonance capture for slow neutrons at particular values of the neutron energy. The exact value of the resonance energy was found to be a characteristic of the capturing nucleus. In these studies it was often difficult to interpret the results of observations correctly. Means of resolving the energies of the neutrons were imperfect, monochromatic sources were still largely nonexistent, and scattering and capturing effects were often confused. Thus many of the early reports in this field seem contradictory. It would be difficult to trace the course of the gradual development of currently accepted views. Therefore the best course seems to be to proceed with an outline of the present status of our information.

5.2. The Compound Nucleus

The vast complex of experimental data on interactions of neutrons with nuclei now available has accumulated along with the development of a number of theories on the various features of these interactions. Because we are concerned here primarily with the results of experiments, any extended discussion of these theories is out of place. However, some of the simpler forms can be most helpful in understanding the data. This is true even when, as at present, theory is undergoing rapid modifications.

Possibly the most important concept in the theories has been that of the compound nucleus. On this concept the interaction of a neutron with a nucleus cannot be said to have begun until the neutron and nucleus have approached to within the very short range of their mutual nuclear forces. The interaction is completed as soon as the products of the interaction depart from this region. In the interim, while the powerful nuclear forces are shaping the consequences of the interaction, the nucleus is in the compound state, usually called simply the compound nucleus. Bohr (22) suggested that it is useful to consider the compound nucleus in two stages, (1) the formation of the compound nucleus and (2) the separation of this system into its products. Furthermore it is usually assumed that the incident particle loses its identity in state (1) and becomes assimilated into the newly formed unstable system. The energy introduced by the arrival of the incident particle is statistically shared among all components of the compound nucleus until one or more constituents acquire sufficient energy to escape. In some instances, where there is insufficient energy to expel a particle, the excess energy is carried off by photon radiation. Frequently the product nucleus is unstable and undergoes radioactive transformations until a stable form of nucleus results. This simple picture of the compound nucleus is beginning to lose favor in some quarters as new information comes to light in support of the nuclear shell theory. The shell theory assumes independent orbits for the nucleons in the nucleus and suggests that the interaction of the nucleons in the compound state is not as strong or effective as the Bohr model would require. Still the statistical concept of the compound nucleus remains useful, and many experimental results have been correlated within its framework. At present, the independent particle model is able to predict experimental results in some areas but fails in others. A similar statement can be made concerning the compound nucleus model. It may turn out that some combination of the independent particle and statistical models will ultimately be found to be most useful. An extensive discussion of the various theories of nuclear interactions will be found in the book by Blatt and Weisskopf (23).

5.3. Nuclear Resonance

One of the phenomena occurring when neutrons interact with nuclei with which nuclear theories must deal is that of nuclear resonance. In analogy to the corresponding situation in atomic physics, the term resonance has found a place in describing the nucleus. A neutron resonance is observed experimentally by a sharp increase in the cross section of the target nucleus at discrete energies of the incident neutrons. The increased probability of interaction is assumed to result from a corresponding energy level in the target nucleus. Therefore resonance is a property of nuclei. An example of data for a resonance level, taken from Seidl and co-workers (24) is shown by the curve plotted in Fig. 5.1. It shows the neutron transmission for a sample of silver in the slow-neutron region with a resonance level at 5.2 ev. The transmission T is defined as

$$T = \frac{n}{n_0} = e^{-N\sigma_t x} \tag{5.1}$$

where n_0 is the incident intensity of neutrons, n is the transmitted intensity, N is the number of target nuclei per cm³, σ_t is the total absorption cross section, that is, the sum of the absorption and scattering cross sections, and x is the thickness of the target sample. The resonance in Fig. 5.1 is

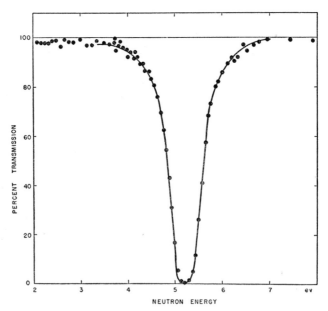

FIG. 5.1. *Data obtained by Seidl and co-workers on the absorption of neutrons by the 5.2-ev resonance level in silver.*

predominantly a capture resonance, but resonances also occur for both elastic and inelastic scattering.

5.4. Bound and Virtual Levels

When the energy of the newly formed level of the compound nucleus is insufficient to expel a particle, the level is said to be bound. The excess energy of a bound level is dissipated by the emission of photon radiation. If the neutron is captured in the process, it is called a radiative capture and is represented by (n,γ). This abbreviation stands for a process in which a neutron is incorporated into the nucleus with the subsequent emission of gamma rays.

Levels of the compound nucleus with excitation energies sufficient for the expulsion of particle radiation are called virtual levels. Decay by particle emission leads toward the ground state of some nuclide other than the one under discussion. Hence the name "virtual level." An example of a nuclear level scheme for Ne^{20}, adapted from Ajzenberg and Lauritsen (25), is shown in Fig. 5.2.

5.5. Level Width

The energy state of the compound nucleus formed by the interaction of a neutron with a stable nucleus, on the statistical model, must have a finite lifetime. The compound nucleus continues in existence long enough to permit the recently acquired energy to be shared among the components of the nucleus, prior to the release of radiation or particles in the de-excitation process. The uncertainty principle of Heisenberg, which has its basis in the wave properties of matter, requires that the uncertainty ΔE in the energy E of a state be given by

$$\Delta E = \frac{\hbar}{\Delta t} \text{ ergs} \qquad (5.2)$$

where Δt is the lifetime of the state and $\hbar$ is Planck's constant over 2π. The ΔE is the level width, usually represented by Γ. The significance of Γ can be further illustrated by considering the wave equation for an energy level. If the probability of deexcitation is included, the level can be represented by a wave function of the form

$$\Psi = \psi e^{\frac{(w - i\Gamma/2)t}{\hbar}} \qquad (5.3)$$

with the total energy represented by the complex quantity $w - i\Gamma/2$. Hence the probability for the level continuing for a time t is proportional to $e^{-(\Gamma t/\hbar)}$ and $\Gamma/\hbar$ is the probability of the decay of the level per unit time. Since $\Gamma/\hbar$ is equal to $1/\tau$ where τ is the mean life of the level, we may write, if τ is measured in seconds,

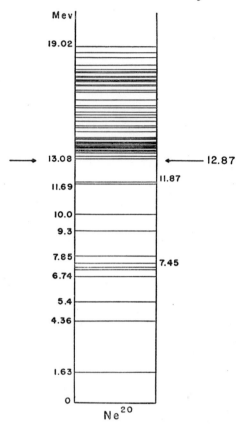

FIG. 5.2. *A nuclear energy-level diagram for Ne²⁰, adapted from Ajzenberg and Lauritsen* (25). *The levels below* 12.87 *Mev are bound levels because they can only decay to the ground state of Ne²⁰ by emission of gamma rays. The energies of levels below* 12.87 *Mev are insufficient for the expulsion of a particle. The levels above* 12.87 *Mev are virtual levels because by particle emission they can decay to some nuclide other than Ne²⁰.*

$$\Gamma = \frac{0.6579 \times 10^{-15}}{\tau} \text{ ev} \tag{5.4}$$

Eq. 5.4 indicates that a level with a long mean life will have a very well defined energy. As the excitation energy becomes larger, the mean life of a level decreases and the levels broaden and begin to overlap to an extent that discrete levels no longer exist. Stated in another way, the value of Γ exceeds the average level spacing D.

5.6. Breit-Wigner Formula

One of the earlier theories, based on quantum mechanics, of the resonance effects in the nucleus was developed by Breit and Wigner (26). Here we follow the Bohr assumption for the division of the interaction into two parts, first the formation of the compound nucleus, then the emission of energy in the form of a particle or of radiation. Representing the emission by a, the cross section $\sigma(n,a)$ for a neutron interaction becomes

$$\sigma(n,a) = \sigma_c \frac{\Gamma_a}{\Gamma} \qquad (5.5)$$

where σ_c is the cross section for the neutron entering the compound nucleus, Γ_a is the partial level width for emission, and Γ the total level width. The Breit-Wigner theory yields for a single isolated level a value of the cross section for formation of a compound nucleus given by

$$\sigma_c = \pi \lambda^2 g \frac{\Gamma_n \Gamma}{(E - E_0)^2 + (\Gamma/2)^2} \qquad (5.6)$$

so that

$$\sigma(n,a) = \pi \lambda^2 g \frac{\Gamma_n \Gamma_a}{(E - E_0)^2 + (\Gamma/2)^2} \qquad (5.7)$$

Eq. 5.7 represents the well-known one-level formula in which it is assumed that the level under discussion is not affected by any other levels. In the formula $2\pi\lambda$ is the wavelength of the incident neutron, g is a statistical weighting factor, E is the kinetic energy of the neutron, and E_0 is the excitation energy of the resonance level. The one-level formula, in cases where $\Gamma = \Gamma_n + \Gamma_\gamma$, may also be written

$$\sigma_a = \pi \lambda_0^2 g \frac{\Gamma_n \Gamma_\gamma}{(E - E_0)^2 + (\Gamma/2)^2} \qquad (5.8)$$

where σ_a is the cross section for radiative capture of the neutron (n,γ). The corresponding form for σ_s, the scattering cross section, is

$$\sigma_s = 4\pi \lambda_0^2 g \left| \frac{\Gamma_n/2}{E - E_0 + i(\Gamma/2)} + \frac{R}{\lambda_0} \right|^2 + 4\pi(1 - g)R^2 \qquad (5.9)$$

with $g = \frac{1}{2}\left[1 \pm \frac{1}{2I + 1}\right]$ where $I = \pm\frac{1}{2}$ is the spin of the target nucleus, $2\pi\lambda_0$ is the wavelength of the neutron with kinetic energy E_0, and R is the nuclear radius. In more general terms, the statistical factor g, which expresses the probability that the neutron angular momentum $j\hbar$ and that of the nucleus $I\hbar$ will be oriented properly to give $J\hbar$ for the total angular momentum of the level of the compound nucleus involved, may be expressed

$$g_l = \frac{2J+1}{2(2I+1)} \qquad (5.10)$$

Since for slow neutrons, $l = 0$, $j = \frac{1}{2}$ and $J = I + \frac{1}{2}$, we have $g_0 \approx \frac{1}{2}$ for large I and $g_0 = 1$ for $I = 0$.

The usefulness of the Breit-Wigner formula, in spite of its restricted application, is well demonstrated by data published by Sailor (27) on the 1.26-ev resonance level in rhodium. The data are plotted as open circles in Fig. 5.3. Superposed is a solid curve drawn to correspond to the Breit-Wigner one-level formula in the form

$$\sigma_t(E) = \sigma_{\text{fa}} + (E_0/E)^{1/2}\sigma_0 \frac{\Gamma^2}{4(E - E_0)^2 + \Gamma^2} \qquad (5.11)$$

where $\sigma_t(E)$ is the total cross section at energy E, σ_{fa} is the free atom scattering cross section and σ_0 is the cross section at E_0, the resonance

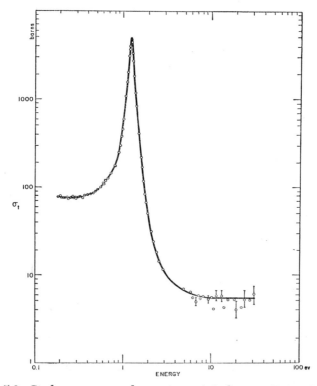

FIG. 5.3. *Circles represent observations of Sailor on the total cross section of rhodium for neutrons. The curve is computed from the Breit-Wigner one-level formula with* $E_0 = 1.260$ *ev,* $\sigma_0 = 5000$ *barns,* $\Gamma = 0.156$ *ev and* $\sigma_{\text{fa}} = 5.5$ *barns.*

energy. The agreement of the plotted points with the solid curve is remarkably precise. The excellence of the fit to the curve is mainly attributable to the fact that there are no other levels of rhodium in this region. Sailor also gives the details of an analysis of the data in terms of the Breit-Wigner formula.

The general expression for $\sigma(n,a)$ of Eq. 5.7 can be modified to apply to the scattering of a neutron by a nucleus. The scattering process, however, as indicated in Eq. 5.9, is usually assumed to be made up of two parts, one capture scattering involving the formation of a compound nucleus, the other potential scattering in which the neutron is assumed not to enter the nucleus, but to be reflected from its surface. The probability of a slow neutron entering a nucleus is actually much less than unity. The interaction is supposed to result mainly from the long wavelength of slow neutrons. The probability P of penetrating the nucleus may be expressed as

$$P = \frac{4kK}{(k + K)^2} \tag{5.12}$$

where k is the wave number, the reciprocal of the wavelength, of the neutron outside the nucleus and K its wave number inside the nucleus. K and k may be defined by the following relations

$$k^2 = 2M_nE/\hbar^2 = 1/\lambda^2 \quad K^2 = 2M_n(E + \epsilon)/\hbar^2 = k^2 + K^2_0$$

where $K^2_0 = 2M_n\epsilon/\hbar^2$ and ϵ is the average kinetic energy of the neutron within the nucleus, with $\epsilon \gg E$. Because for slow neutrons k is approximately equal to K_0, Eq. 5.12 becomes approximately $P \approx 4k/K_0$, where K_0 is of the order of 10^{13} cm^{-1}. The potential scattering is usually represented by

$$\sigma_p = 4\pi\lambda^2 \sum_l (2l + 1) \sin^2\xi_l \tag{5.13}$$

with ξ_l the phase shift of the scattered partial wave of orbital angular momentum $l\hbar$. Eq. 5.13 is a very general formula which also covers the case of coherent scattering. Because the radius R of the nuclear sphere is much less than λ for slow neutrons and $\xi_0 = kR$, with ξ_l for $l > 0$ much less than ξ_0, Eq. 5.13 becomes approximately

$$\sigma_p \approx 4\pi\lambda^2 \sin^2 kR \approx 4\pi R^2 \tag{5.14}$$

The relation between potential and capture scattering may be represented schematically as in Fig. 5.4, taken from Feshbach, Peaslee, and Weisskopf (28). The origin in each diagram is at the center of the nucleus which has a boundary at $r = R$. The example at (a) is intended to represent the situation far from a resonance. Here the incident partial wave is reflected at the boundary of the nucleus. At (b) an intermediate case is sketched as a resonance is approached. The conditions at a resonance are shown at (c) where the external and internal waves meet at full amplitude. Conse-

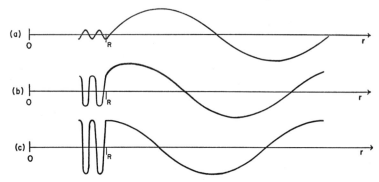

FIG. 5.4. *Diagram of the neutron wave function at the surface of the nucleus. o—center of nucleus. r—radial distance from center of nucleus; r = R — surface of the nucleus. (a) represents conditions remote from a resonance level, (c) those at a resonance level and (b) an intermediate situation. At resonance the internal and external waves join at full amplitude.*

quently when the energy of the incident neutron is remote from a resonance energy, the potential scattering is the predominant process, but at resonance the capture scattering becomes more important. However, capture and potential scattering are coherent and interfere. Therefore the expression for the elastic scattering cross section $\sigma(n,n)$ becomes

$$\sigma(n,n) = \pi\lambdabar^2 g_l \left| \frac{i\Gamma_{nl}}{(E - E_0) + i\Gamma/2} + e^{2i\xi_l} - 1 \right|^2 + \sigma'_p \qquad (5.15)$$

in which $\sigma'_p = \sigma_p - \pi\lambdabar^2 g_l |e^{2i\xi_l} - 1|^2$ is the incoherent part of the potential scattering. Eq. 5.15 leads directly to expressions of the form of Eq. 5.9. These expressions are not symmetrical with respect to E_0. Fig. 5.5 is a sketch illustrating the asymmetry in the case of slow neutron scattering near a resonance level. The value of the scattering cross section σ_s passes through a minimum at an energy E_{min} less than E_0. If we assume $\Gamma_n \lambdabar / R \ll \Gamma$,

$$E_0 - E_{min} \approx \frac{\Gamma_n \lambdabar}{2R} \approx \frac{D}{\pi K_0 R} \qquad (5.16)$$

where D is the level spacing, and the value of $\sigma(n,n) = \sigma_s$ is at E_{min}

$$\sigma_s \approx 4\pi R^2 \left(1 - g_0 + \frac{g_0 R^2 \Gamma^2}{\lambdabar^2 \Gamma_n^2} \right) \qquad (5.17)$$

Again the Breit-Wigner formula is very successful in predicting the cross sections for neutron scattering in the neighborhood of an isolated resonance. Fig. 5.6, taken from Sheer and Moore (29), shows the observed values of σ_s/σ_t for the 5.19-ev resonance level of silver plotted as open circles. The

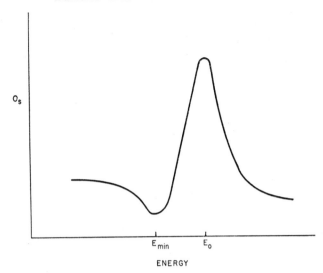

FIG. 5.5. *Diagram of the variation of the scattering cross section for neutrons in the vicinity of a resonance.* E_{min}—*value of the neutron energy at which the cross section is a minimum.* E_0—*resonance energy.*

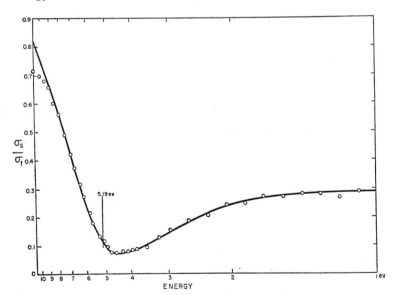

FIG. 5.6. *Circles are observations by Sheer and Moore on the ratio of the scattering cross section to the total cross section at various neutron energies near the 5.19-ev resonance of silver. The solid curve is computed by the Breit-Wigner formula, using parameters given in the text.*

solid curve represents values computed from the two Breit-Wigner formulas for capture and scattering

$$\sigma_a = \frac{\sigma_{c0}\Gamma^2(E_0/E)^{1/2}}{4(E - E_0)^2 + \Gamma^2} \tag{5.18}$$

and

$$\sigma_s = \sigma_p + \frac{X + Y(E - E_0)}{4(E - E_0)^2 + \Gamma^2} \tag{5.19}$$

where σ_{c0} is the capture cross section at resonance, $\Gamma = \Gamma_n + \Gamma_\gamma = $ total level width, $\Gamma_n = $ neutron width, $\Gamma_\gamma = $ radiative capture width, $X = 4\pi G_J \lambda_0^2 \Gamma_n^2$, $Y = 16\pi G_J \lambda_0^2{}_n R$, and $\sigma_p = 4\pi G_J R^2 + 4\pi G'_J R'^2 = $ total potential scattering cross section. G_J and G'_J are spin weighting factors for resonant and nonresonant states of the compound nucleus. R and R' are effective nuclear radii for the resonant and nonresonant spin states. The values of these parameters to be substituted in Eq. 5.19 and Eq. 5.18 were obtained from the experimental cross section curve or other measurements. The values are:

$$E_0 = 5.193 \text{ ev}$$
$$\sigma_{to}\Gamma^2 = 366 \text{ barns-ev}^2 = \frac{\sigma_{c0}\Gamma^2}{1 - \Gamma_n/\Gamma}$$
$$J = 1$$
$$\Gamma = 0.128 \text{ ev}$$
$$\Gamma_n = 0.0155 \text{ ev}$$
$$\sigma_p = 5.90 \text{ barns}$$
$$\sigma_{to} = 22,200 \text{ barns}$$
$$R = 0.66 \text{ barn}^{1/2}$$
$$R' = 0.42 \text{ barn}^{1/2}$$
$$\sigma_p \text{ (isotope)} = 4.64 \text{ barns}$$
$$X = 44.43 \text{ barns-ev}^2$$
$$Y = 37.8 \text{ barns-ev}^2$$

where σ_{to} is the total cross section at resonance.

5.7. The Independent Particle Model of the Nucleus

Feshbach, Porter, and Weisskopf (30) have called attention to the deficiencies of theories based on the compound nucleus with strong coupling between a particle entering the nucleus and all other particles within it. Certain qualitative conclusions have developed from this strong-coupling model.

(A) The particle widths of nuclear resonances are generally considered to be related in some way to the average level spacing D of the levels of the compound nucleus. This width Γ_n, for the emission of neutrons with zero orbital angular momentum, is

$$\Gamma_n \approx \frac{2}{\pi}\frac{k}{K} D \tag{5.20}$$

where k is the wave number of the incident neutron and K the wave number after it has entered the nucleus.

(B) Elastic scattering is assumed to result from the addition of a resonance amplitude and a slowly varying potential scattering amplitude. The resonance amplitude is only important near a resonance, and the potential scattering amplitude is equal to that from an impenetrable sphere of radius approximately equal to the nuclear radius.

(C) The total neutron cross section, averaged over a resonance, is equal to the total cross section of a spherical potential well with a depth which will give rise to wave numbers of the order of $K = 10^{13}$ cm^{-1} and an ability to absorb the incoming waves within distances of the order of $1/K$. Although Eq. 5.20 gives correct orders of magnitude, according to (C) the total neutron cross sections, averaged over resonances, should all be smooth functions of the energy and decrease monotonically with increasing energy. Moreover, the form should be similar for all atomic numbers A and should show a continuous, slowly increasing, trend with increasing A. These predictions of the strong-coupling model have not been verified, even approximately, by experimental observations.

Considerations of the kind just mentioned, added to the success of the independent-particle shell model in other areas, led Feshbach and his collaborators to study the consequences of a weaker interaction between nucleons in the nucleus. This study resulted in a hypothesis that an incident neutron can enter, and move about inside, a nucleus without necessarily forming a compound nucleus. The compound state only occurs, with a probability less than unity, after the particle has entered the nucleus. The target nucleus is supposed to act on the incident nucleon as a potential well. If a compound nucleus is subsequently formed, this process adds an absorption effect. The authors admit that this oversimplification of the picture will not predict all features of nuclear interactions, but it should be useful for results which can be obtained after averaging over resonances of the compound nucleus.

In the formulation of this simplified model, a special set of cross sections is introduced and the definition of the cross section for the formation of the compound nucleus is clarified. The total cross section σ_t is defined as

$$\sigma_t = \sigma_{\text{el}} + \sigma_r \tag{5.21}$$

where σ_{el} is the elastic scattering cross section and σ_r is the reaction cross section. The elastic cross section is defined as the cross section for scattering without change of quantum state of the nucleus, the particle leaving in the same channel by which it entered.

We digress here briefly to explain the meaning of the term *channel*. We may represent possible results of a nuclear reaction schematically by

$$a + X \rightarrow \begin{cases} X + a \\ X^* + a \\ Y + b \\ Z + c \end{cases}$$

etc.

Here a represents an incident particle, X the target nucleus, b, c, . . . the emitted particles, and Y, Z, . . . the product nuclei. In the first reaction the incident particle emerges from the reaction with its initial energy in the center-of-mass system. Thus this reaction represents elastic scattering. In the second reaction, representing inelastic scattering, the incident particle emerges with less than its initial energy, leaving the target nucleus in an excited state. In all other cases the product nucleus differs from the target nucleus. The concept of channels offers a means of sub-dividing the reactions according to the quantum state of the product nucleus and of the emergent particle for all cases except elastic scattering. The channel system may be illustrated, following the example of Blatt and Weisskopf (23), by a scheme similar to the reaction scheme above but with Greek subscripts to indicate the quantum states. α', β', γ', . . . refer to quantum states of nuclei and α'', β'', γ'', . . . to quantum states of particles. If a, b, and c represent elementary particles, then α'', β'', γ'' describe their spin orientation. This leads to the scheme

$$a_{\alpha''} + X_{\alpha'} \rightarrow \begin{cases} X_{\alpha'} + a_{\alpha''} \\ X_{\beta'} + a_{\beta''} \\ Y_{\gamma'} + b_{\gamma''} \end{cases}$$

etc.

in which the left-hand member represents the entrance channel and the right-hand members the possible exit, or reaction, channels. The possible pairs of product nucleus and emergent particle are restricted, of course, by the various laws of conservation of energy, angular momentum, and parity. It is customary to refer to the channel itself by unprimed letters. Thus the channel α stands for reaction components with subscripts α' and α''.

To resume our original discussion, the elastic cross section has an angular dependence defined as

$$\sigma_{el} = \int \frac{d\sigma_{el}}{d\Omega} (\theta) d\Omega \tag{5.22}$$

The reaction cross section includes all processes in which the residual nucleus differs from the target nucleus, or is in a different quantum state. The elastic cross section σ_{el} is divided into two parts as

$$\sigma_{el} = \sigma_{se} + \sigma_{ce} \tag{5.23}$$

in which σ_{se} is the "shape elastic" cross section which refers to scattering occurring without the formation of a compound nucleus. The cross section σ_{ce} is the "compound elastic" cross section referring to scattering resulting from the formation of a compound nucleus and subsequent emission of the particle into the entrance channel. All reactions σ_{ce} are assumed to occur after the formation of a compound nucleus. This leads to a cross section σ_c for the formation of a compound nucleus where

$$\sigma_c = \sigma_{ce} + \sigma_r \tag{5.24}$$

Therefore

$$\sigma_t = \sigma_{se} + \sigma_c \tag{5.25}$$

The model proposed is expected to predict only σ_{se} and σ_c. This approach deals only with that part of the phase space in which the target nucleus is in its initial state. Formation of a compound nucleus is regarded as an absorption of the incident beam, but a part of the absorption, represented by σ_{ce}, leads to an elastic scattering process.

In this independent-particle model the nucleus is replaced by a complex potential

$$V = V_0 + iV_1 \tag{5.26}$$

which confronts the approaching neutron. The scattering from this model should predict the shape of σ_{se} and the absorption produced by the imaginary term iV_1 should predict the shape of σ_c. The term V_0 describes the average potential energy of the neutron within the nucleus and its shape should reveal the form of the potential well inside the nucleus. V can be expected to depend in some simple way on the mass number A, and the relation between V and r, the radial distance from the center of the nucleus, should be the same for all nuclei. The simplest choice, that of a square-well potential was selected. Thus

$$V_0 = -U \text{ for } r < R \qquad V_0 = 0 \text{ for } r > R \qquad V_1 = \zeta V_0$$

with ζ a fractional coefficient determining the depth of the potential well. With a given $U(r)$, the potential energy function inside the nucleus, and its dependence on A, the cross sections σ_t, σ_{se}, and σ_c can be computed as a function of the neutron energy and the mass number of the target nucleus. Using values of $R = (1.45 \times 10^{-13})A^{1/3}$ cm, $V_0 = 42$ Mev and $\zeta = 0.03$, this model predicts quite well the variation of the total neutron cross section as a function of energy and of the mass number of the nucleus. It also does almost as well with the angular distribution of elastically scattered neutrons as a function of $\cos \theta$ and of mass number. The agreement with experiment is not quite as good for values of σ_c. The theoretical curves for total cross sections are reproduced in Fig. 5.7 and the corresponding experimental curves in Fig. 5.8.

Whereas the modification of the continuum theory of nuclear cross sec-

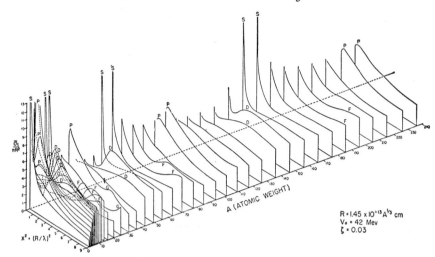

FIG. 5.7. *Total neutron cross sections computed from the continuum theory by Feshbach, Porter, and Weisskopf as a function of the energy and mass number. The parameters selected for the computation are shown at the lower right. The energy ϵ is expressed by $x^2 = [A^{2/3}(A/10)(A+1)]\epsilon$.*

tions, a name derived from the fact that cross sections are averaged over many resonances, reproduces the broad features of the dependence of the cross sections on energy and atomic number, it fails in many instances to predict particular data. An example is provided by the study of the angular distribution of neutrons scattered elastically from cadmium, tin, and bis-

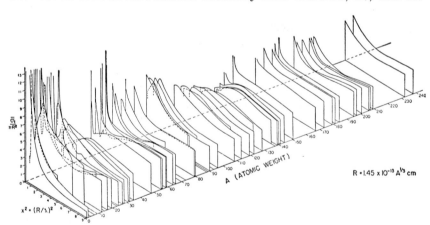

FIG. 5.8. *Experimental observations of total cross sections as a function of energy and mass number. Units are the same as in Fig. 5.7, with which this graph is to be compared.*

muth by Snowdon and Whitehead (31). In describing angular distributions, it is convenient to use the differential scattering cross section for scattering into unit solid angle at an angle θ. The differential scattering cross section $\sigma_{el}(\theta)$ may be defined by the relation

$$\sigma_{el} = \int \sigma_{el}(\theta)d\Omega \tag{5.27}$$

where Ω is the solid angle into which the neutrons are scattered. The theoretical expression from the modified continuum theory for values of $\sigma_{el}(\theta)$, averaged over an energy interval containing many resonances, is

$$\sigma_{el}(\theta) = \tfrac{1}{4}\lambda^2\sum_l\sum_m(2l+1)(2m+1)$$

$$[(1-\bar{\eta}_l)(1-\bar{\eta}^*_m) + (\langle\eta_l\eta^*_m\rangle_{av} - \bar{\eta}_l\bar{\eta}^*_m)]P_l(\cos\theta)P_m(\cos\theta) \tag{5.28}$$

where η is a phase constant and $P_l(\cos\theta)P_m(\cos\theta)$ are Legendre polynomials of the form

$$P_n(x) = \frac{1}{2^n n!}\frac{d^n}{dx^n}(x^2-1)^n$$

The term $(1-\bar{\eta}_l)(1-\bar{\eta}^*)$ controls the shape elastic scattering distribution and the term $(\langle\eta_l\eta^*_m\rangle_{av} - \bar{\eta}_l\bar{\eta}^*_m)$ controls the compound elastic scattering. In applying this theory, it is necessary to select the constants for the nuclear model of Eq. 5.26. The constants chosen, to give best over-all agreement with the data, are $V = -19(1 + i\zeta)$ Mev, with $\zeta = 0.05$ for the potential energy within the nucleus and $R = (1.45 \times 10^{-13})A^{1/3}$ cm for the nuclear radius.

The measurements were made in an arrangement sketched in Fig. 5.9

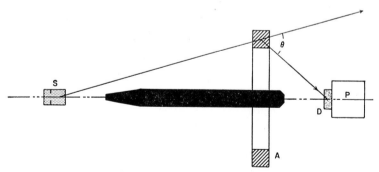

FIG. 5.9. *Arrangement for using a ring scatterer for the measurement of the angular distribution of elastically scattered neutrons. S—source of neutrons, consisting of deuterium gas bombarded by deuterons. D—Lucite–zinc sulfide neutron scintillation detector. P—photomultiplier. A—ring scatterer. The opaque tapered cylinder is an iron shield to screen the detector from direct radiation from the source.*

S is a source of 3.7-Mev neutrons, consisting of deuterium gas bombarded by deuterons of 1-Mev energy. The ring of scattering material is located at A and D is a Lucite–zinc sulfide scintillation detector for the neutrons. The scintillator is mounted in front of the photomultiplier tube P. The scattering angle θ was varied by moving the ring A along its axis. The results of the measurements on cadmium, tin, and bismuth are shown by the curves in Fig. 5.10. The two theoretical curves for the differential cross sections, one for shape elastic scattering, the other for shape elastic plus compound elastic scattering, are also plotted as lighter continuous curves. The agreement between theory and experiment is in general not

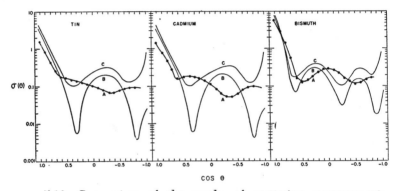

FIG. 5.10. *Comparison of the results of scattering measurements with theory. In each case, curve A represents the experimental data obtained with 3.7-Mev neutrons on the variation of the differential cross section for elastic scattering with cos θ where θ is the angle of scattering in the center-of-mass system. Likewise, curve B is the shape-elastic distribution predicted by the continuum theory and curve C is the shape-elastic plus the compound-elastic distribution predicted by the continuum theory.*

very good. The real nature of the disagreement becomes more apparent when it is explained that by adjusting the parameters of the nuclear model to a different set of values, better agreement could be obtained for one of the elements. This adjustment, however, would make the divergence between theory and experiment greater for the other two elements.

5.8. The Transport Cross Section

The differential scattering cross section can be used to compute the quantity known as the transport cross section σ_{tr}. The transport cross section may be defined by the relation

$$\sigma_{\text{tr}} = \sigma_t - \int \sigma_{\text{el}}(\theta) \cos\theta \, d\Omega \tag{5.29}$$

Essentially σ_{tr} expresses the rate at which neutrons lose their forward momentum. Feshbach and Weisskopf (32) have computed the theoretical values of the transport cross section, in units of πR^2 where R is the nuclear radius equal to $(1.5 \times 10^{-13}) A^{1/3}$ cm, in terms of x where $x = kR = 0.22 R E_n^{1/2}$. Here E_n is the kinetic energy of the incident neutron and k is its wave number. Curves for two nuclear models, $X_0 = 5$ and $X_0 = 8$, are shown in Fig. 5.11. $X_0 = K_0 R$ and K_0 is related to K, the wave number of the neutron inside the nucleus, by the expression $K^2 = K_0^2 + k^2$. The

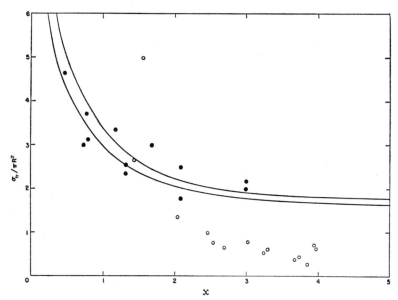

FIG. 5.11. *Transport cross sections in units of* πR^2 *as a function of* $x = 0.222 R (\epsilon)^{1/2}$ *where* ϵ *is the kinetic energy of the incoming neutron in Mev. The upper curve is for* $X_0 = 5$ *and the lower curve for* $X_0 = 8$, *where* $X_0 = kR$. *Closed circles represent measurements by Barschall et al. (33). Open circles are measurements by Walt and Beyster (34).*

closed circles in Fig. 5.11 represent measurements by Barschall and co-workers (33) for neutrons of 1.5-Mev energy. These points show fair agreement with theory. However, more recent measurements of σ_{tr} for a number of elements with 4.1-Mev neutrons do not seem to agree as well with the theory. These points at the higher energies were determined by Walt and Beyster (34) and are shown as open circles. It is apparent that only approximate values for σ_{tr} can be predicted by the theory. This defect of the theory appears to be the result of the special assumptions required in the derivation of the theory in terms of a simplified nuclear model.

5.9. Elastic Neutron Scattering

From the discussion of the Breit-Wigner formula for scattering of neutrons it developed that the scattering cross section could be considered as the sum of the capture scattering and potential scattering cross sections, taking account of the spin states where coherent effects are involved. In the case of slow neutrons it has been noted that interactions in the $l = 0$ state predominate and the potential scattering cross section is approximately equal to $4\pi R^2$ and the elastic scattering cross section is given theoretically by Eq. 5.15. The measured scattering cross sections deviate considerably from $4\pi R^2$. The divergence is generally attributed to the effects of resonance levels in the region of the measurement so that reso-

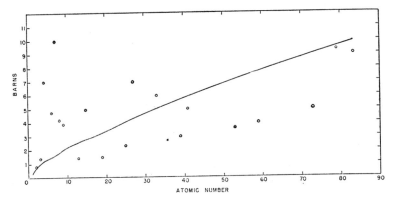

FIG. 5.12. A *graph of* $4\pi R^2$, *where* R $= 1.5A^{1/3} \times 10^{-13}$ *cm, against* A. *The circles represent values of* σ_s *taken from Hughes and Harvey (8).*

nance scattering contributes to the measured values of the cross sections. In Fig. 5.12 the curve represents values of $4\pi R^2$ where $R = 1.5A^{1/3} \times 10^{-13}$ cm. The circles are values of σ_s taken from Hughes and Harvey (8) for a few elements composed of a single isotope. The graph of Fig. 5.12 gives a fairly representative picture of the degree of agreement to be expected.

Proceeding to higher neutron energies and to higher values of atomic numbers of the scattering nuclei, scattering resonances become a characteristic feature of the scattering process. In the intermediate region of atomic numbers, the distance between levels is frequently comparatively large and the maximum cross section for a resonance is given approximately by $4\pi \lambda_0^2 g$. When the level spacing becomes smaller this approximation no longer holds. Measured maximum cross sections at resonances deviate from the predicted values for at least two reasons. One is the limited resolving power of the device used to measure the neutron energies.

The other is the interference between resonance scattering and potential scattering. Fig. 5.13 shows a curve obtained by Stelson and Preston (35) for the variation of the total neutron cross section of sodium in the range of neutron energies from 120 kev to 1000 kev. The resolution of the neutron energies is in the range 2.5 to 5 kev and shows a number of peaks very clearly. The dotted curve A represents $4\pi\lambda^2$, and the dotted curve B shows the calculated potential scattering cross section. At still higher atomic numbers, the density of the resonance levels in nuclei becomes so great

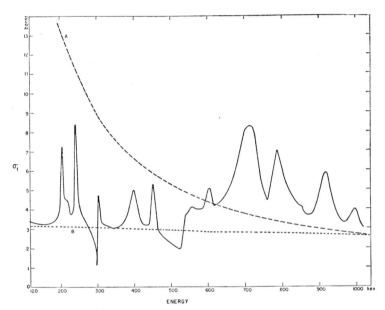

FIG. 5.13. *Total neutron cross section of sodium. Curve* B *is the calculated potential scattering for an interactive radius of 5.1 × 10^{-13}cm. Curve* A *represents $4\pi\lambda^2$ as a function of neutron energy.*

that no means has yet been devised to resolve them experimentally. The total cross section curve therefore becomes smoothly continuous, revealing only general trends. An example is given in Fig. 5.14, taken from Henkel and co-workers (36), of the total cross section for normal uranium in the range of neutron energy from 20 kev to 20 Mev. There is some indication that this particular curve approaches the prediction of the theory of Feshbach, Porter, and Weisskopf (30).

The term elastic scattering has been used to refer to either of two processes. One, already discussed, assumes that the incident neutron is captured and a compound nucleus formed. Then this neutron is re-emitted with nearly its original energy. The other type of elastic scattering assumes

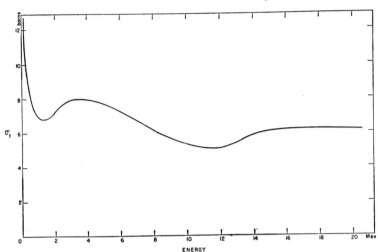

FIG. 5.14. *Total neutron cross section of uranium as a function of neutron energy.*

that the change is merely in the direction of motion of the neutron. No compound nucleus is formed. This scattering is sometimes called diffraction scattering, since the wavelength of the incident neutrons is one of the controlling parameters in this scattering process. The dependence on neutron wavelength distinguishes diffraction scattering from capture scattering where the structure of the compound nucleus has a strong influence on the behavior of the scattered neutrons. Diffraction scattering becomes clearly distinguishable from capture scattering for fast neutrons, where λ is less than R. Actually the different angular distributions for the two types of scattered neutrons are often used to separate them experimentally. Blatt and Weisskopf (23) have derived the expression

$$\frac{d\sigma_{el}(\theta)}{d\Omega} = \pi\lambda^2 \left| \sum_{l=0}^{\infty} \sqrt{2l+1}\, e^{2i\xi} \left(A_{res}^l + A_{pot}^l\right) Y_{l,0}(\theta) \right|^2$$

for the cross section per unit solid angle for scattering at the angle θ. Here the A's are the scattering amplitudes, ξ is a phase constant and $Y_{l,0}(\theta)$ is a spherical harmonic defined on page 782 of reference (23). When λ becomes very much smaller than R, corresponding to neutrons with energies of 10^8 ev or higher, the value of $\sigma_{el} = \int d\sigma(\theta)$ is approximately equal to $\pi(R + \lambda)^2$. Since in this high-energy region σ_t is approximately equal to $2\pi(R + \lambda)^2$, diffraction scattering contributes roughly one-half to the total cross section. Fernbach, Serber, and Taylor (37) have proposed an optical model of the nucleus in which the neutron is assumed to be scattered by a sphere having an absorption coefficient and an index of refraction. Recently, Culler, Fernbach, and Sherman (38) have applied this optical model to the elastic scattering of 14-Mev neutrons. By suitable choice of nuclear well potential, remarkably close fits to the experimental data were obtained. An example is shown in Fig. 5.15 which represents the distribution of $\sigma(\theta)$ as a function of θ. Fig. 5.16 shows the

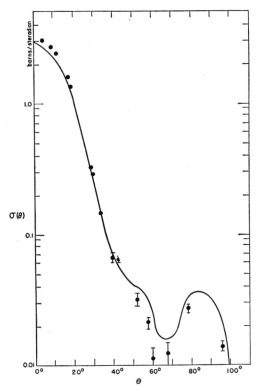

FIG. 5.15. *Differential scattering cross sections computed from an optical model of the nucleus plotted against θ, the laboratory angle of scattering. The curve is for a non-square well as sketched in (a) Fig. 5.16. Dots represent experimental observations.*

types of potential wells which gave theoretical values of the differential scattering cross section in reasonable agreement with the observations.

5.10. Inelastic Neutron Scattering

The so-called capture scattering, a term used to describe the re-emission of a neutron which has been captured by a nucleus, may be elastic or inelastic. If the kinetic energy of the incident neutron is insufficient to excite the lowest level of the nucleus, the neutron is emitted with approximately

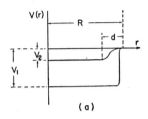

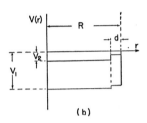

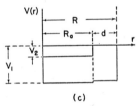

FIG. 5.16. *Types of nuclear wells used in computing the variation of $\sigma(\theta)$ with θ on the optical model of the nucleus.*

(a) *Non-square well where*

$$V(r) = \begin{cases} -V_1 - iV_2 & r \leq R - d \\ \sum_{n=0}^{4} a_n r^n + \sum_{n=0}^{4} b_n r^n & R - d \leq r \leq R \\ 0 & R \leq r \end{cases}$$

(b) *Step well where*

$$V(r) = \begin{cases} -V_1 - iV_2 & r \leq R - d \\ -V'_1 - iV'_2 & R - d \leq r \leq R \\ 0 & R \leq r \end{cases}$$

(c) *Step-well potential, which yielded best agreement with experimental data where*

$$V(r) = V_1 + iV_2, \quad V_1 = -42 \text{ Mev}, \quad V_2 = -11 \text{ Mev},$$
$$R_a = 1.22A^{1/3} \times 10^{-13} \text{ cm}, \quad d = 0.74 \times 10^{-13} \text{ cm},$$
$$R = R_a + d.$$

the same kinetic energy which it had when it entered the nucleus. Hence this process is called elastic capture scattering. On the other hand, if the neutron energy is sufficient to excite the nucleus, the nucleus may be left in an excited state after the neutron departs. Then the kinetic energy of the emergent neutron is correspondingly less than that with which it entered the nucleus.

This scattering process in which the incident neutrons give up a part of their initial energy to the nucleus is called *inelastic capture scattering,* or simply *inelastic scattering.* It is obvious that inelastic scattering should offer a means of investigating nuclear structure in some detail. In fact the process has been used to determine the values of the energy of low-lying nuclear levels from the loss in kinetic energy of the inelastically scattered neutrons. Another application is the determination of level spacings. In the inelastic scattering process the scattering nuclei are left in an excited state from which they decay by the emission of gamma rays. The determination of the energies of these gamma rays leads directly to a level scheme for the portion of the level structure involved. To date only a small part of the information which might be obtained from studies of inelastic neutron scattering has become available. This lack of information is the result of the technical difficulties which surround investigations of inelastic scattering. The required monoenergetic sources of neutrons are not available over a sufficient range of energies. The energy resolution of detecting arrangements falls far short of the minimum requirements for obtaining precise data. Even the relative intensities of the scattered neutrons, which could throw light on neutron emission widths for specific processes, are sometimes difficult to establish reliably. These and similar instrumental difficulties account for the small number of successful experiments in this field.

5.11. Measurement of Inelastic Scattering Cross Sections

A number of geometrical arrangements of source, scattering material, and detector have been used in the measurement of inelastic scattering cross sections. These arrangements include the ring-scatterer used frequently also in the study of elastic scattering. A considerable improvement in the intensity of the scattered neutrons can be achieved by using the scattering substance in the form of a spherical shell. In this case, it is customary to place the detector within the shell and the source outside, as represented in the diagram of Fig. 5.17. This advantageous experimental arrangement may be treated mathematically with the positions of source and detector reversed. The mathematics is simplified by this transposal, and the results of the computations are identical for either case. There is

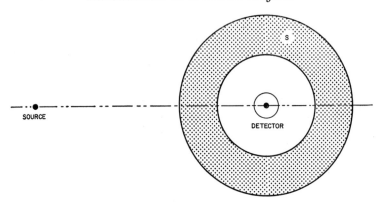

FIG. 5.17. *Diagram of the arrangement to measure the neutron transmission of a spherical shell of material.*

a straightforward relation, although somewhat complicated, between the transmission and the value of σ_i, the inelastic scattering cross section. The transmission of the spherical shell is defined as the ratio of the counting rate of the neutron detector with the shell surrounding the detector to the counting rate with the shell removed. This definition of the transmission, naturally, assumes a constant flux of neutrons from the source during the observations to be compared. An example of the shell method is the arrangement used by Beyster and co-workers (39) for measuring σ_i sketched in Fig. 5.18. The incident neutrons in this experiment had energies of 4.0 and 4.5 Mev. The detector D in Fig. 5.18 consisted of small spheres of a plastic phosphor supported by suitably formed quartz disks. The light, stimulated in the phosphor by recoil protons, was conducted down the quartz light pipe L to the photomultiplier PM. This particular

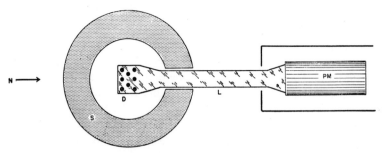

FIG. 5.18. *Sketch of the apparatus used by Beyster and co-workers for the measurement of the transmission of a spherical shell S. D—scintillation detector. L—quartz light tube. PM—photomultiplier. Neutrons are incident in the direction N.*

design of neutron detector was intended to reduce the response of the phosphor to the gamma rays from the scattering material.

One of the more serious problems in the measurement of inelastic scattering cross sections is the correction of the observations for the loss of energy by neutrons which have been elastically scattered. Although neutrons lose comparatively little energy in the elastic scattering process, this small difference may alter considerably the sensitivity with which the neutrons are detected. Because the neutrons which have lost energy have a lower probability of detection in most proton recoil methods, a spurious increase in the observed value of the inelastic scattering cross section results. This spurious effect is particularly noticeable for proton recoil counters biased to detect only those neutrons with energies close to the energy of the incident neutrons. The magnitude of the effect on the cross section may be computed from

$$\Delta\sigma = \sigma_{el}(1 - S(\overline{E})) \tag{5.31}$$

where $\overline{E}$ is the average energy after an elastic collision and $S(\overline{E})$ is the relative sensitivity for detecting a neutron of this average energy. The importance of corrections for loss of energy in elastic collisions is illustrated in Fig. 5.19 from reference (39).

As has been mentioned, an interaction of the type (n,n'), "n" representing the incident neutron and "n'" its re-emission at lowered energy, leaves the bombarded nucleus in an excited state. Measurement of the energies and intensities of the gamma rays emitted by the nucleus on return to the ground state may also be used to determine the values of σ_i. Studies at fixed neutron energy give data on the energy levels and the cross section. By varying the neutron energy, the threshold may be measured and the excitation curve obtained for a particular interaction. The gamma-ray method of measuring inelastic scattering cross sections, while simple in principle, involves some fundamental experimental difficulties. Both the gamma-ray emission from the scatterer and the neutron flux through it must be measured absolutely. The ratio of these two measurements is used in computing σ_i. If several nuclear levels are excited simultaneously, resulting in gamma rays of several different energies, comparatively high resolution of energy on the part of the gamma-ray detector is required to obtain reasonably precise data. Using apparatus sketched in Fig. 5.20, Van Loef and Lind (40) have measured σ_i by the gamma-ray method. The response of their NaI(Tl) crystal detector for the gamma rays is shown in Fig. 5.21 for a typical case. Curve A represents the output of the photomultiplier with the scatterer absent. Curve B is the response of the photomultiplier with the scatterer in place. C is the difference curve, B − A, showing the effect to be attributed to the gamma rays from the scatterer, in this case Fe^{56}. The arrow indicates the position of the 850-kev peak,

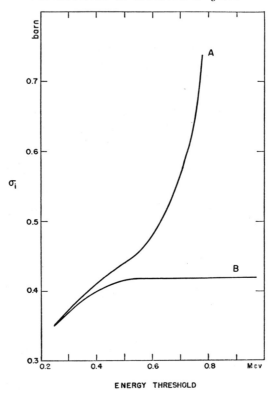

FIG. 5.19. *Measured inelastic cross sections for iron at 1 Mev neutron energy. Curve* A *represents values before correcting for loss of energy in elastic collisions. Curve* B *represents values after correcting for this loss of energy.*

corresponding to the decay of the single excited level in the target. The equation for this reaction may be written

$$Fe^{56}(n,n')Fe^{56*} \rightarrow Fe^{56} + \gamma(850 \text{ kev}) \qquad (5.32)$$

(The asterisk is commonly used to indicate a nuclide in an excited state.) The results of measurements of σ_i at neutron energies from 0.8 to 1.8 Mev are shown in Fig. 5.22. The dotted curve follows values computed from the theory of Hauser and Feshbach (41) on the basis of a statistical nuclear model. In this case spin and parity states of 0^+ for the ground state and 2^+ for the excited state are assumed.

5.12. Nonelastic Scattering of Neutrons

As the details of inelastic scattering become more evident, special terminology has been developed to describe them. Because this nomencla-

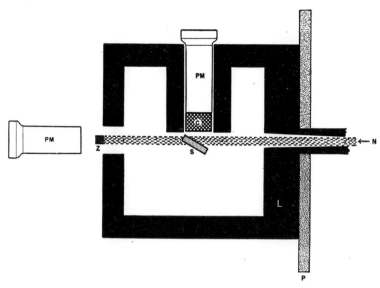

FIG. 5.20. *Apparatus for measuring inelastic scattering cross sections in terms of gamma rays emitted by the scattering substance. PM—photomultipliers. L—lead shield. N—neutron beam. S—scattering target. P—borated paraffin shield. C—NaI crystal for detecting gamma rays. Z—zinc sulfide button for detecting neutrons.*

ture is in a formative stage, it is frequently necessary to restate definitions which sometimes change as new facts are discovered or new interpretations are made of existing observations. The term nonelastic scattering as applied to neutrons deserves some attention in this connection. In the experimental observations of the total cross section, particularly in the neutron energy range from 3 to 15 Mev, the quantity actually measured is the total cross section minus the elastic cross section. This cross section, defined as $(\sigma_t - \sigma_{el})$, is now commonly called the nonelastic cross section. It includes all processes in which the neutron loses energy. These processes include, for example, inelastic scattering and the (n,2n) reaction. At high energies, the nonelastic cross section approaches the value of the reaction cross section. At low energies, where only a few states may be excited in the bombarded nucleus, the nonelastic cross section plus the compound elastic cross section equal the value of the reaction cross section. The term inelastic cross section, on the other hand is reserved for the (n,n') process. The (n,n') symbol merely indicates that a neutron enters a nucleus and emerges at a lower energy than that at which it entered the nucleus. When changes of spin are involved in these processes, a further complication develops in the differentiation of individual processes. Ultimately, generally acceptable definitions and symbols can be expected to emerge.

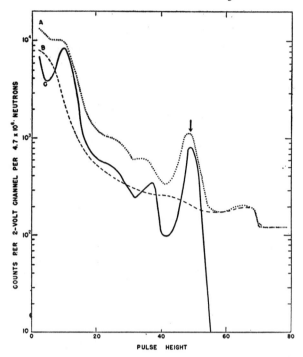

FIG. 5.21. *Pulse-height spectrum for the gamma rays observed from Fe^{56} at a neutron energy of 1.2 Mev. Curve A represents observations with scattering target in place, and curve B observations with the target removed. Curve C is the difference between curve A and curve B and represents the gamma-ray spectrum.*

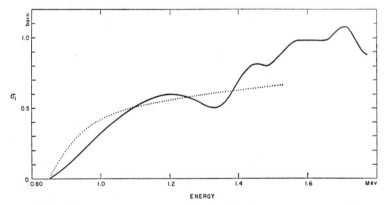

FIG. 5.22. *The excitation curve for the 850-kev gamma rays following inelastic scattering of neutrons by Fe^{56}. The dotted curve is calculated from the Hauser and Feshbach (41) theory for an opaque nucleus.*

6.1. Nuclear Reactions

Although the terms interaction and reaction are sometimes used interchangeably, there is tendency to use the term reaction to refer to those interactions in which the product nucleus differs either in mass number or atomic number from the target nucleus. Hence in this more restricted use of the term, a nuclear reaction bears some resemblance to a chemical reaction. In this section we will consider some nuclear reactions in which neutrons are involved and in which the product nuclide is a different nuclide from the target nuclide. The reactions which occur when atomic nuclei are exposed to neutrons of various energies are divided into a number of types. The exact nature of the reaction depends on many factors, most prominent of which are the structure of the nucleus involved and the energy of the neutrons. Some of these reactions are possible for neutrons of any energy, as for example radiative capture, represented by (n,γ). Other neutron reactions, such as those in which charged particles are emitted from the compound nucleus, represented by (n,p) and (n,α) as examples, have threshold energies which the kinetic energy of the neutron must exceed before the reaction is energetically possible. The final nature of the reaction products depends upon the competition within the compound nucleus of the various possible deexcitation processes. We have seen that the probability of a particular reaction is defined by the cross section for this type of reaction in a given nucleus. Experimentally these cross sections may be measured even if the details of the competition responsible for them are not always well understood.

6.2. The Equation of a Nuclear Reaction

In analogy with the equation for a chemical reaction, there is an expression for the nuclear process. The equation for a nuclear reaction expresses the balance of mass and energy between the components entering the reaction and those emerging from it. In the case of a nuclear reaction involving a neutron, the terms on the left of the equation represent the masses of the neutron and of the target nucleus. The terms on the right represent the masses of the products plus the kinetic energy released or absorbed in the reaction. The energy absorbed or released is called the reaction energy represented by Q. Thus for an (n,γ) reaction with a target nucleus X with atomic number Z and mass number A, written as $_Z X^A$, it is usual to write

$$_Z X^A + {}_0 n^1 \rightarrow {}_Z X^{A+1} + \gamma \qquad (6.1)$$

Here the gamma radiation represents the Q of the reaction. The value of Q in Mev will be equal to the difference in the masses on the two sides of the equation multiplied by 931 Mev, the energy equivalent of 1 atomic mass unit. For an (n,p) reaction the nuclear equation becomes

$$_zX^A + _0n^1 \rightarrow _{z-1}X^A + _1H^1 + Q \qquad (6.2)$$

where Q now represents the nuclear reaction energy, usually expressed in Mev. Similarly for the (n,α) reaction

$$_zX^A + _0n^1 \rightarrow _{z-2}X^{A-3} + _2He^4 + Q \qquad (6.3)$$

It is to be noted that these equations also balance with respect to atomic number and mass number. Because Q is determined by the change of mass in the individual components of the reaction, it can be computed for any reaction where the masses of the constituents are known. Explicitly

$$Q = 931[M_n + M_X - (M_x + M_Y)] \text{ Mev} \qquad (6.4)$$

where M_n is the mass of the neutron, M_x the mass of any particle released in the reaction, M_X the mass of the target nucleus, and M_Y the mass of the product nucleus, all in atomic mass units. For a numerical illustration we may take the actual nuclear reaction

$$N^{14} + n^1 \rightarrow C^{14} + H^1 + Q$$

Introducing the appropriate atomic mass units into Eq. 6.4, we have

$$Q = 931[1.00892 + 14.007515 - (1.008142 + 14.007682)]$$
$$= 0.627 \text{ Mev}$$

Eq. 6.4 of course can also be used to determine the mass of any one component when the value of Q and of the other masses are known. It is important to note that Q may be positive or negative. When it is positive the neutron requires no kinetic energy to produce the reaction. Again in analogy with the chemical terminology, the reaction is then called exoergic. When Q is negative, and the reaction endoergic, the neutron must have sufficient kinetic energy to make up the deficit. The value of the kinetic energy of the neutron at which an endoergic reaction first becomes possible is called the threshold energy E_T, given by

$$E_T = \frac{M_X + M_n}{M_X} Q \qquad (6.5)$$

6.3. Radiative Capture

The capture of slow neutrons by nuclei has become familiar as the reaction by which large numbers of radioactive isotopes have become available from nuclear reactors. The compound nucleus resulting from the capture of a neutron has a high energy of excitation. As we will see in § 6.5, this excitation is of the order of 8 Mev. If the neutron is not reemitted, this energy must be dissipated in some other form of deexcitation. Most commonly this deexcitation is accomplished by the emission of gamma rays and the reaction in consequence is known as radiative capture. This process is always in competition with capture scattering and related phenomena, the relative frequency of the various processes being defined · by the corresponding partial level widths in the compound nucleus, often called radiation widths. The partial width for radiative capture Γ_γ, as we have already seen, is given theoretically by

$$\Gamma_\gamma = \frac{\hbar}{\tau} \tag{6.6}$$

where τ is the mean lifetime of the excited state. For slow neutrons, Γ_γ is of the order of 0.1 ev which means that τ is of the order of 10^{-14} sec for the prompt emission of gamma rays. The production of radioactive nuclides by radiative capture is a consequence of the fact that this prompt emission of gamma rays does not usually remove all of the excitation energy leaving the product nucleus unstable. The excess energy is then dissipated by the familiar processes known collectively as radioactivity. The spectrum of the (n,γ) gamma rays is not limited to a single energy but contains a number of lines. The energies of these lines can be identified occasionally with nuclear levels determined by other methods of measurement. This independent confirmation gives additional confidence in the study of (n,γ) spectra as a means of investigating nuclear energy levels. Kinsey, Bartholomew, and Walker (42) have described equipment used to determine the (n,γ) spectra of a number of nuclides. Using a nuclear reactor as a source of slow neutrons, they assembled a system of filters and collimators shown in the diagram of Fig. 6.1. For the gamma rays of energies ranging from 2 to 8 Mev encountered in this work, pair production is a more efficient method of detection than scintillators or ion chambers. Therefore a pair spectrometer, containing a metal foil to convert the

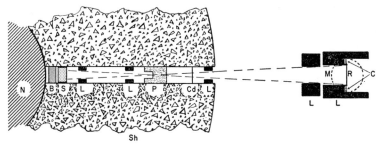

FIG. 6.1. *Pair spectrometer and collimating system used by Kinsey in measuring the gamma-ray spectrum from the (n,γ) process. N— reactor core serving as source of slow neutrons. Sh—reactor shield. B—bismuth plug to absorb gamma rays from the reactor. S—sample in which neutron capture occurs. P—borated paraffin. Cd—cadmium filter. M—magnet poles of pair spectrometer. R—radiator in which pair production by gamma rays to be measured occurs. C—counters for electrons and positrons. L-L—lead collimators.*

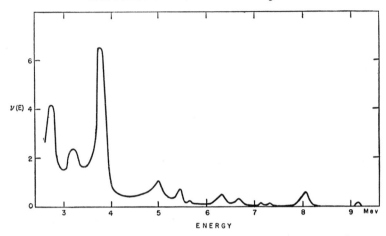

FIG. 6.2. *The energy spectrum of capture gamma rays from the reaction* $Mg^{25}(n,\gamma)Mg^{26}$.

gamma rays into electron pairs, was used to measure the (n,γ) gamma rays. The spectrometer was calibrated in terms of the energies of the incident gamma rays. A typical spectrum is shown in Fig. 6.2. The curve represents the corrected gamma-ray spectrum for $Mg^{25}(n,\gamma)Mg^{26}$.

6.4. (n,γ) Cross Sections

The knowledge of the value of the cross sections of nuclei for the (n,γ) process is of considerable practical importance. The (n,γ) cross section is used in computing the yield of radioisotopes from various target material in a reactor. In many experiments with slow neutrons, materials of low or high (n,γ) cross section are used depending on whether the material is to be used as a window for slow neutrons or as a screen to exclude slow neutrons. The usefulness of (n,γ) cross sections has led over recent years to numerous compilations of known values. At the moment the most recent and extensive compilation is contained in reference (8), to which the reader is referred. Because of the $1/v$ law dependence of the cross section for slow neutrons in most nuclei, it is convenient to give the value of the neutron capture cross section for a particular velocity of the neutron in the tables. Thermal neutrons are, for this purpose, defined as those having a velocity of 2200 meters per sec. We shall see later that this corresponds to an absolute temperature $T = 293°K$. At neutron energies of 1 Mev or greater the capture cross section varies as $1/E_n$. This $1/E$ dependence of the cross section results partly from the fact that the measured values represent averages over a great many nuclear levels. It should also be noted that a nuclear cross section is a property of a specific nuclide. Therefore there is a different (n,γ) cross section for each isotope of a multi-isotopic element. The cross section for the element is an average of the values of the separate cross sections of the isotopes, determined in accordance with the relative abundance of the isotopes in the element.

6.5. The Binding Energy of the Neutron

In the (n,γ) reaction a neutron is captured, and the excess energy of the compound nucleus is emitted as gamma radiation. The energy balance of the equation of this reaction leads to a quantitative measurement of the binding energy of the neutron in the product nucleus. On the left-hand side of Eq. 6.1 we have the masses $M_n + M_X$. On the right-hand side we have $M_Y + Q$, where Q represents the energy of gamma-ray emission and also the binding energy on the neutron in the nucleus $_zX^{A+1}$ of mass M_Y. Therefore the binding energy of the neutron in the product nucleus may be obtained from

$$E_B = 931 \left[(M_n + M_X) - M_Y\right] \text{Mev} \tag{6.7}$$

with all masses expressed in atomic mass units. When Eq. 6.7 is applied to typical (n,γ) reactions, it is found that E_B is of the order of 8 Mev, which is also the magnitude of the excitation energy of the compound nucleus resulting from slow neutron capture.

6.6. The (n,2n) Reaction

The threshold of the (n,2n) reaction is approximately the binding energy of a neutron in the target nucleus. Therefore the occurrence of the (n,2n) reaction is limited to neutrons with high kinetic energies, roughly from 10 Mev upward. As in the (n,γ) reaction, the product nucleus is isotopic with the target nucleus, and is also frequently radioactive. The induced radioactivity assists considerably in the study of yields and excitation curves. In some instances the (n,2n) reaction has also been used in measurements of energies and intensities of fast neutrons. Because of the technical difficulties in the measurements, as well as the lack of numerous sources of very high energy neutrons, the (n,2n) reaction has not yet received a great deal of attention experimentally. The chief activity in this direction has been the reporting of a number of radioisotopes resulting from the (n,2n) reaction. The values for the threshold energies E_T for the (n,2n) reaction may be obtained from observations on (γ,n) reactions. With betatrons to provide gamma rays of the required energy, there has been more opportunity to study (γ,n) reactions. The threshold for the (γ,n) reaction $E_{T(\gamma,n)}$ may be converted to the threshold for the (n,2n) reaction $E_{T(n,2n)}$ by the simple relation

$$E_{T(n,2n)} = \frac{A+1}{A} E_{T(\gamma,n)} \tag{6.8}$$

with A the mass number of the nuclide in question. A few values for the (n,2n) threshold in a number of nuclides are given in Table 6.1. These values are selected from Feld (43) to illustrate the magnitudes and general trends.

Table 6.1

THRESHOLDS FOR THE (n,2n) REACTION

Target	E_T (Mev)	Target	E_T (Mev)
$_1H^2$	3.34	$_{14}Si^{29}$	8.7
$_3Li^6$	6.2	$_{15}P^{31}$	12.6
$_3Li^7$	8.2	$_{16}S^{32}$	15.3
$_4Be^9$	1.85	$_{16}S^{34}$	11.2
$_5B^{10}$	9.4	$_{23}V^{51}$	11.4
$_5B^{11}$	12.6	$_{25}Mn^{55}$	10.3
$_6C^{12}$	20.3	$_{27}Co^{59}$	10.5
$_7N^{14}$	11.3	$_{33}As^{75}$	10.4
$_8O^{16}$	17.3	$_{48}Cd^{113}$	6.6
$_9F^{19}$	10.9	$_{57}La^{139}$	8.9
$_{11}Na^{23}$	12.6	$_{73}Ta^{181}$	7.6
$_{12}Mg^{24}$	17.1	$_{77}Ir^{193}$	7.8
$_{12}Mg^{25}$	7.5	$_{79}Au^{197}$	8.1
$_{12}Mg^{26}$	11.6	$_{83}Bi^{209}$	7.4
$_{13}Al^{27}$	13.2	$_{90}Th^{232}$	6.4
$_{14}Si^{28}$	17.4	$_{92}U^{238}$	6.0

6.7. Cross Sections for the (n,2n) Reaction

For nuclides with mass numbers greater than 50, and for incident neutrons with energies greater than 1 Mev, Weisskopf and Ewing (44) have developed a relatively simple theoretical expression for computing $\sigma(n,2n)$. If the residual nucleus, remaining after an (n,n) reaction, still has excitation energy greater than the binding energy of a neutron, a second neutron will be emitted. The probability of the emission of the second neutron exceeds considerably the probability of deexcitation by emitting gamma radiation. The computation of the (n,2n) cross section may then be made in terms of the energy distribution of the outgoing neutrons. This gives

$$\sigma(n,2n) = \pi R^2 \frac{\displaystyle\int_0^{\epsilon'} I(\epsilon)d\epsilon}{\displaystyle\int_0^{\epsilon_{n(max)}} I(\epsilon)d\epsilon} \qquad (6.9)$$

where $I(\epsilon)$ is the intensity of the outgoing neutrons with energy ϵ, ϵ' is the maximum energy of the outgoing neutron for which the residual nucleus is still able to emit another neutron, and $\epsilon_{n(\max)}$ is the maximum energy which an outgoing neutron can have. Hence

$$\epsilon' = \epsilon_{n(\max)} - E_{T(n,2n)} \tag{6.10}$$

The integration of Eq. 6.9 yields

$$\sigma(n,2n) \approx \pi R^2 \left[1 - \left(1 + \frac{\Delta \epsilon}{\Theta} \right) e^{-\Delta \epsilon / \Theta} \right] \tag{6.11}$$

where $\Delta \epsilon$ is the excess of the energy of the incident neutron over the threshold energy $E_{T(n,2n)}$ and $\Theta = 2(5\epsilon/A)^{1/2}$ Mev if ϵ is in Mev. To test

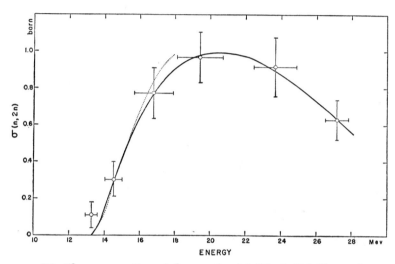

FIG. 6.3. *The cross section of the reaction* $Mo^{92}(n,2n)Mo^{91}$ *as a function of neutron energy. Corrections have been made for the isotopic abundance of* Mo^{92} *and for K-capture in competition with positron emission in the product nucleus. The dotted line is the prediction of the statistical theory, disregarding competitive proton emission from the target nucleus.*

this theory and provide information regarding the (n,2n) reaction, Brolley, Fowler, and Schlacks (45) have measured the (n,2n) cross sections in several elements as a function of the energy of the incident neutrons. The nuclei investigated all became radioactive as a result of the reaction. Hence the yields of the reactions were determined by measuring the absolute activity induced in the target. An example of the experimental results is shown in Fig. 6.3, where the value of $\sigma(n,2n)$ is plotted against the energy of the incident neutrons. The dotted curve represents the prediction of Eq. 6.11. The value of the threshold for the (n,2n) reaction $Mo^{92}(n,2n)Mo^{91}$ is also indicated in Fig. 6.3 at 13.2 Mev.

6.8. The (n,p) and (n,α) Reactions

Experiments have revealed that charged particles may frequently be emitted from the compound nucleus formed by the capture of a neutron. Although charged-particle reactions for neutrons are mainly restricted to neutrons of energies in the Mev range, there is one very well known (n,p) reaction in which slow neutrons are captured, the (n,p) reaction in nitrogen. In any case, the excitation of the compound nucleus by the entering neutron must be sufficient to give a charged particle an appreciable probability of penetrating the nuclear Coulomb barrier, if a charged-particle reaction is to result. This fact explains why charged-particle reactions for slow neutrons are limited to the lighter nuclei where the Coulomb barrier is low. Furthermore, the charged-particle reaction with slow neutrons must be fundamentally exoergic, since the incident neutron cannot supply the energy in kinetic form required for the expulsion of a charged particle from the nucleus. The known number of charged-particle reactions for slow neutrons is small. The more important of them include two methods of preparing tritium,

$$_2\text{He}^3 + \text{n}^1 \rightarrow \text{H}^3 + \text{H}^1 + Q \quad (Q = 0.764 \text{ Mev})$$

$$_3\text{Li}^6 + \text{n}^1 \rightarrow \text{H}^3 + \text{He}^4 + Q \quad (Q = 4.785 \text{ Mev})$$

He³ has a natural percentage abundance of 0.00013 and the cross section for the (n,p) reaction is 5400 barns. Li⁶ has a natural percentage abundance of 7.52 and an (n,α) cross section of 945 barns for thermal neutrons. Another charged-particle, slow neutron reaction of practical importance is B¹⁰(n,α)Li⁷, representing a common means of detecting slow neutrons by alpha-counting methods. B¹⁰ is very useful for detecting slow neutrons because, in addition to a large thermal neutron capture cross section, the cross section follows the $1/v$ law for a range of neutron energies extending over more than 10^4 ev, as shown in Fig. 6.4, taken from reference (8). The B¹⁰ reaction may be written

$$_5\text{B}^{10} + \text{n}^1 \rightarrow _3\text{Li}^7 + \text{He}^4 + Q \quad (Q = 2.791 \text{ Mev})$$

The natural percentage isotopic abundance of B¹⁰ is 18.8 and the thermal neutron capture cross section is 4010 barns. C¹⁴ is usually prepared by the reaction

$$_7\text{N}^{14} + \text{n}^1 \rightarrow _6\text{C}^{14} + \text{H}^1 + Q \quad (Q = 0.626 \text{ Mev})$$

N¹⁴ has a percentage isotopic abundance of 99.6 and an (n,p) cross section of 1.75 barns for thermal neutrons. Among the charged-particle reactions for slow neutrons, the reaction by which S³⁵ is prepared should be mentioned

$$_{17}\text{Cl}^{35} + \text{n}^1 \rightarrow _{16}\text{S}^{35} + \text{H}^1 + Q \quad (Q = 0.62 \text{ Mev})$$

The percentage isotopic abundance of Cl³⁵ is 75.4 and the (n,p) cross section for thermal neutrons is 0.3 barn.

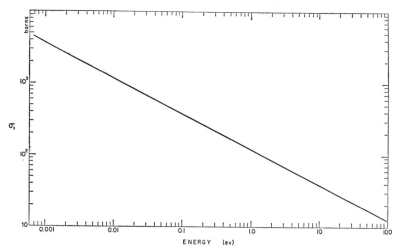

FIG. 6.4. *Total slow neutron cross section for boron as a function of neutron energy in ev over the region where the 1/v law holds. This graph is taken from the experimental curve in reference (8).*

At intermediate energies of the incident neutrons, the charged-particle reactions exhibit the expected resonances. The results of the competition between (n,p) and (n,α) decay of the compound nucleus can also be seen in the variation of the cross sections with neutron energy. The separation of the resonance peaks for the two types of charged-particle decay

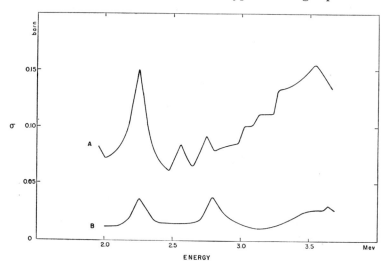

FIG. 6.5. *Curve A represents the cross section for the section $N^{14}(n,a)B^{11}$ and curve B represents the cross section for the reaction $N^{14}(n,p)C^{14}$ over the same range of energy for the incident neutrons.*

can be used to interpret the intricate spin and parity relations in the compound nucleus under these conditions. The $1/v$ law no longer holds in the region of intermediate neutron energies. Typical cross-section curves are shown in Fig. 6.5, from Bollman and Zünti (46). Curve A represents the cross section for the reaction $N^{14}(n,\alpha)B^{11}$ and curve B that for the reaction $N^{14}(n,p)C^{14}$—thus for the same compound nucleus. It is also of interest to compare the course of the (n,α) cross section with a curve showing the probability for an alpha particle to penetrate the Coulomb barrier of the nucleus in question. In some instances the two curves run quite parallel to each other, giving some evidence of the role which the Coulomb barrier plays in charged-particle reactions. Fig. 6.6, from Seitz and Huber (47), shows by the solid curve the results of experimental observations on the cross section for the reaction $O^{16}(n,\alpha)C^{13}$. The dotted curve represents the results of calculation of the probability for an alpha particle to penetrate

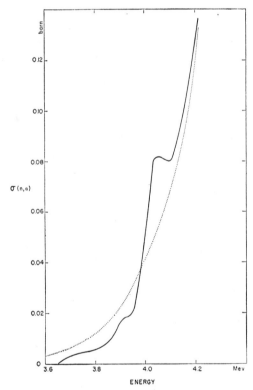

FIG. 6.6. *The solid curve represents the experimental data for the variation with neutron energy of the cross section for the reaction* $O^{16}(n,a)C^{13}$. *The dotted line is the result of computation of the probability of penetration of the Coulomb barrier by an alpha particle.*

the Coulomb barrier. In the calculation it was assumed that the alpha particle would be emitted with $l = 0$, and the nuclear radius is 4.02×10^{-13} cm. The similarity between the two curves is evident.

6.9. Fission

Probably the most spectacular effect produced by neutrons when captured in nuclei is nuclear fission. The (n,f) reaction results from the peculiar property of nuclei in which the binding energy per nucleon decreases with increasing mass number, beginning at about $A = 60$. Hence at the upper end of the periodic table of the elements the division of a nucleus approximately in half will result in the release of energy due to the increase in binding energy in the products of the reaction. This increase of the binding energy explains why fission is energetically possible with a high value of Q. Such an explanation gives little or no information regarding the internal details of the process. A liquid-drop model of the nucleus has been proposed to explain the division of the nucleus into two approximately equal parts. The excitation energy provided by the neutron is supposed to set this model into oscillations, which continue until the model breaks apart. This liquid-drop model explanation of fission also ignores entirely the internal structure of the drop and therefore of the nucleus. Once the nucleus has split, the consequences can be computed. For example, if a U^{238} nucleus is divided into two nuclei, each with $A = 119$, the binding energy of the products has increased by about 0.9 Mev per nucleon. Multiplying by the total number of nucleons we obtain approximately 214 Mev for the energy which should be released. This value of the energy release is quite close to the average value observed. Because of the asymmetry in the products there is the possibility also of the release, on the average, of two or three neutrons per fission. The release of neutrons has been confirmed by observation and makes possible the development of a chain reaction, now the familiar process fundamental to the operation of nuclear reactors. The fact that fission does occur on neutron capture in a few heavy elements indicates a definite instability of these nuclei for division into two parts. The questions then arise (1) why fission does not occur spontaneously and (2) why it is not induced in more of the heavy elements by slow neutron capture. The answer is that spontaneous fission does occur, but that half-lives for the elements with atomic number less than about 96 are so long that they are difficult to measure. However in the transuranium elements, particularly among those recently discovered, several examples of relatively short half-lives for spontaneous fission have been found. The situation regarding spontaneous fission is illustrated in Fig. 6.7, taken from Huizenga (48), summarizing the measurements of the half-life for spontaneous fission for some of the heaviest nuclides. The graph also reveals

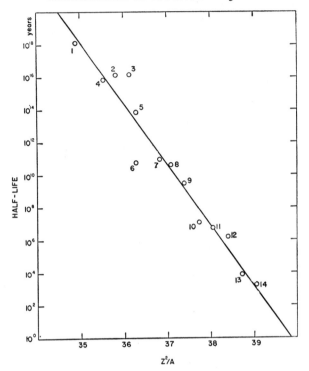

FIG. 6.7. *Spontaneous fission rates plotted as a function of Z^2/A.*

1—Th^{232}	6—Pu^{242}	10—Cm^{244}
2—U^{235}	7—Pu^{240}	11—Cm^{242}
3—U^{234}	8—Pu^{238}	12—Cm^{240}
4—U^{238}	9—Pu^{236}	13—Cf^{248}
5—U^{232}		14—Cf^{246}

an empirical exponential relation between Z^2/A and the spontaneous fission half-life. The answer to question (2) is that there is a type of potential barrier, sometimes called the Gamow barrier, in nuclei which opposes fission. The excitation energy must exceed this barrier before fission can occur. The nature and origin of the Gamow barrier is explained in terms of Coulomb and nuclear forces by Evans (49). Whereas a few nuclei can be induced to undergo fission by slow neutrons, the majority have threshold energies for the incident neutron. These reactions thus join the class of reactions that can be used to investigate neutron energies, known as threshold reactions. When used to determine neutron energies, these targets are frequently called threshold detectors. Examples of the variation of σ_f with neutron energy are shown in Fig. 6.8, as measured by Lamphere and Greene (50). The graph also shows the positions of the thresholds.

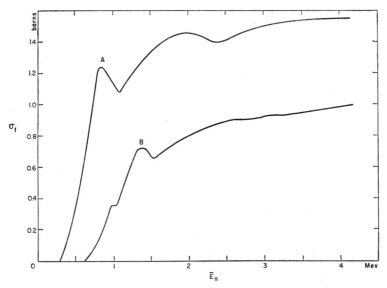

FIG. 6.8. *Fission cross sections as a function of neutron energy. Curve A—U²³⁴, curve B—U²³⁶.*

6.10. Asymmetry in Fission

The cleavage of heavy nuclei in fission is predominantly asymmetrical. There are comparatively few fissions which yield products of equal masses, and the curve showing the percentage yield plotted against mass number has a deep saddle depression in the center with humps on each side. Swiatecki (51) has called attention to an apparently linear relation between the degree of asymmetry and Z^2/A. On the basis of the liquid-drop model there are two asymmetric saddle-point shapes which can be expressed as

$$\text{Asymmetry} = \pm c[(Z^2/A_0) - Z^2/A]^{1/2} \tag{6.12}$$

where c is a constant and $(Z^2/A)_0$ is the limiting value of the ratio beyond which the liquid-drop model is no longer stable with respect to deformations of the simplest type. The degree of asymmetry may also be represented in terms of $M_2 - M_1$, the separation measured in mass difference between the two humps of the fission yield curve. We may write

$$\text{Asymmetry}^2 = b[(Z^2/A)_0 - Z^2/A] = \left[\frac{M_2 - M_1}{A}\right]^2$$

and select $[(M_2 - M_1)/A]^2$ as a parameter for the ordinates of a curve such as is shown in Fig. 6.9. The equation of the straight line in Fig. 6.9 leads to the semi-empirical formula

$$M_2 - M_1 = 0.090(40.2 - Z^2/A)^{1/2}A. \tag{6.13}$$

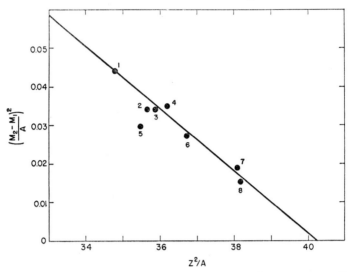

FIG. 6.9. *The square of the relative symmetry in fission, expressed as* $(M_2—M_1)/A$ *as a function of* Z^2/A.

1—Th^{233}	5—U^{239}
2—U^{238}	6—Pu^{240}
3—U^{236}	7—Cm^{242}
4—U^{234}	8—Cf^{252}

SYMBOLS FOR CHAPTER II

A	mass number
c	velocity of light
D	nuclear level spacing
E	kinetic energy
E_0	kinetic energy of a neutron at resonance
E_n	kinetic energy of a neutron
F	flux in general
G, g	spin weighting factors in nuclear interactions
H^1	proton
h	Planck's constant
$\hbar$	$h/2\pi$
$h\nu$	photon energy
I	angular momentum quantum number of a nucleus
$j = l \pm \frac{1}{2}$	total angular momentum quantum number of a neutron
J	total angular momentum quantum number of a level in a compound nucleus
k	wave number of a neutron outside the nucleus

K	wave number of a neutron inside the nucleus
l	orbital angular momentum quantum number of a neutron
M	mass
M_n	mass of the neutron
N	number of target nuclei, number of atoms per cm^3 in a target
n	neutron
n	number of neutrons
nv	neutron flux
P	probability of a neutron penetrating a nucleus
p	proton
$\bar{p}$	average power level of a reactor
$P_m (\cos \theta)$	Legendre polynomial
Q	nuclear reaction energy
r	rate of an interaction, radial distance
R	nuclear radius
$U(r)$	potential energy function within a nucleus
V	potential energy
Z	atomic number
α	alpha particle
γ	gamma ray
Γ	total width of a nuclear energy level
Γ_a	partial level width for particle or photon emission
Γ_n	partial level width for neutron emission
Γ_γ	partial level width for photon emission
ϵ	binding energy of the deuteron, average energy of a neutron within a nucleus, neutron energy in a nuclear interaction
ζ	a fractional coefficient determining depth of nuclear potential well
η	phase shift angle in neutron scattering
θ	direction of scattering of a neutron with respect to incident direction
θ_c	critical angle for total reflection of a neutron from a mirror
λ	neutron wavelength, mean free path of a neutron
$\lambdabar$	$\lambda/2\pi$
ν	frequency in cycles per second
ξ	phase shift angle in potential scattering of neutrons
π^-, π^+	pions
Σ	macroscopic cross section

Σ_a	macroscopic cross section for absorption
σ	nuclear cross section
σ_a	nuclear cross section for absorption
σ_{tr}	transport cross section
σ_s	neutron scattering cross section
σ_i	inelastic neutron scattering cross section
σ_{el}	elastic neutron scattering cross section
σ_c	cross section for a neutron entering a compound nucleus
σ_t	total nuclear cross section
σ_0	resonance cross section, free atom cross section
σ_{fa}	free atom cross section
$\sigma(n,a)$	cross section for interaction of a neutron with a nucleus
τ	mean life of a nuclear energy level
Ψ, ψ	wave function symbols

PROBLEMS FOR CHAPTER II

1. Compute the value of Q in the nuclear reaction

$$N^{14} + n^1 \rightarrow C^{14} + H^1 + Q$$

using the mass tables to be found in the Appendix.

2. Make the numerical computations required to obtain the energy level of 12.87 Mev of Fig. 5.2 and explain the steps.

3. Compute the values of Q in the following reactions:

$$Br^{81} + n^1 \rightarrow Br^{82} + \gamma$$

$$Br^{81} + n^1 \rightarrow Se^{81} + H^1 + Q$$

$$Br^{81} + n^1 \rightarrow As^{78} + He^4 + Q$$

$$Br^{81} + n^1 \rightarrow Br^{80} + 2n + Q$$

4. In a neutron transmission experiment the ratio $n/n_0 = 0.67$. The absorption layer has a thickness of 1.5×10^{20} atoms per cm^2. Compute the value of the absorption cross section σ_a in barns.

5. In an absorbing medium the density of thermal neutrons is found to decrease by a factor of 0.45 over a distance of 10 cm in a direction away from the source of thermal neutrons: that is, if n_0 represents the neutron density at the beginning of the 10-cm length, $0.45n_0$ is the density at the end of it. Compute λ_a, the mean free path for absorption in centimeters.

6. If a single gamma ray were emitted to leave the product nucleus in the ground state in the hypothetical reaction $Ca^{42} + n^1 \rightarrow Ca^{43} + \gamma$, compute the energy of the gamma ray in Mev.

7. If the potential neutron scattering cross section of a nucleus has the value of 7 barns, compute the approximate value of the nuclear radius in centimeters.

8. Compute the binding energy of a neutron in Ca^{43}.

REFERENCES FOR CHAPTER II

1. E. Fermi. *Phys. Rev.* **48**, 570 (1935).
2. L. I. Schiff. *Phys. Rev.* **78**, 733 (1950).
3. J. F. Marshall and E. Guth. *Phys. Rev.* **78**, 738 (1950).
4. J. Halpern and E. V. Weinstock. *Phys. Rev.* **91**, 934 (1953).
5. F. R. Scott, D. E. Thomson, and W. Wright. *Phys. Rev.* **95**, 582 (1954).
6. S. P. Harris, C. O. Muehlhause, D. Rose, H. P. Schroder, G. E. Thomas, Jr., and S. Wexler. *Phys. Rev.* **91**, 125 (1953).
7. B. Hamermesh, G. R. Ringo, and S. Wexler. *Phys. Rev.* **90**, 603 (1953).
8. D. J. Hughes and J. A. Harvey. *Neutron Cross Sections*, McGraw-Hill (1955).
9. E. P. Wigner. *Z. Phys.* **83**, 253 (1933).
10. E. Melkonian. *Phys. Rev.* **76**, 1744 (1949).
11. W. B. Jones. *Phys. Rev.* **74**, 364 (1948).
12. J. De Pangher. *Phys. Rev.* **99**, 1447 (1955).
13. R. S. Christian and E. W. Hart. *Phys. Rev.* **77**, 441 (1950).
14. R. H. Phillips and K. M. Crowe. *Phys. Rev.* **96**, 484 (1954).
15. T. Coor, D. A. Hill, W. F. Hornyak, L. W. Smith, and G. Snow. *Phys. Rev.* **98**, 1369 (1955).
16. E. Fermi and L. Marshall. *Phys. Rev.* **72**, 1139 (1947).
17. D. J. Hughes, J. A. Harvey, M. D. Goldberg, and M. J. Stafne. *Phys. Rev.* **90**, 497 (1953).
18. E. Fermi. *Nature* **133**, 757 (1934).
19. P. B. Moon and J. R. Tillman. *Nature* **135**, 904 (1935).
20. D. E. Lea. *Proc. Roy. Soc.* **150**, 637 (1935).
21. E. Amaldi, O. D'Agustino, E. Fermi, B. Pontecorvo, F. Rasetti, and E. Segrè. *Proc. Roy. Soc.* **149**, 522 (1935).
22. N. Bohr. *Nature* **137**, 344 (1936).
23. J. M. Blatt and V. F. Weisskopf. *Theoretical Nuclear Physics*, Wiley (1952).
24. F. G. P. Seidl, D. J. Hughes, H. Palevsky, J. S. Levin, W. Y. Kato, and N. G. Sjöstrand. *Phys. Rev.* **95**, 476 (1954).
25. F. Ajzenberg and T. Lauritsen. *Rev. Mod. Phys.* **27**, 77 (1955).
26. G. Breit and E. P. Wigner. *Phys. Rev.* **49**, 519 (1936).
27. V. L. Sailor. *Phys. Rev.* **91**, 53 (1953).
28. H. Feshbach, D. C. Peaslee, and V. F. Weisskopf. *Phys. Rev.* **71**, 145 (1947).
29. C. Sheer and G. Moore. *Phys. Rev.* **98**, 565 (1955).
30. H. Feshbach, C. E. Porter, and V. F. Weisskopf. *Phys. Rev.* **96**, 448 (1954).
31. S. C. Snowdon and W. D. Whitehead. *Phys. Rev.* **94**, 1267 (1954).
32. H. Feshbach and V. F. Weisskopf. *Phys. Rev.* **76**, 1550 (1949).
33. H. H. Barschall, M. E. Battat, W. C. Bright, E. R. Graves, T. Jorgensen, and J. H. Manley. *Phys. Rev.* **72**, 881 (1947).
34. M. Walt and J. R. Beyster. *Phys. Rev.* **98**, 677 (1955).
35. P. H. Stelson and W. M. Preston. *Phys. Rev.* **88**, 1354 (1952).
36. R. L. Henkel, L. Cranberg, G. A. Jarvis, R. Nobles, and J. E. Perry, Jr. *Phys. Rev.* **94**, 141 (1954).
37. S. Fernbach, R. Serber, and T. B. Taylor. *Phys. Rev.* **75**, 1352 (1949).
38. G. Culler, S. Fernbach, and N. Sherman. *Phys. Rev.* **101**, 1047 (1956).
39. J. R. Beyster, R. L. Henkel, R. A. Nobles, and J. M. Kister. *Phys. Rev.* **98**, 1216 (1955).
40. J. J. Van Loef and D. A. Lind. *Phys. Rev.* **101**, 103 (1956).

41. W. Hauser and H. Feshbach. *Phys. Rev.* **87,** 366 (1952).
42. B. B. Kinsey, G. A. Bartholomew, and W. H. Walker. *Phys. Rev.* **83,** 519 (1951).
43. B. T. Feld, in E. Segrè (Ed.). *Experimental Nuclear Physics,* Wiley (1953), Vol. 2.
44. V. F. Weisskopf and D. H. Ewing. *Phys. Rev.* **57,** 472 (1940).
45. J. E. Brolley, Jr., J. L. Fowler, and L. K. Schlacks. *Phys. Rev.* **88,** 618 (1952).
46. W. Bollman and W. Zünti. *Helv. Phys. Acta* **24,** 517 (1951).
47. J. Seitz and P. Huber. *Helv. Phys. Acta* **28,** 227 (1955).
48. J. R. Huizenga. *Phys. Rev.* **94,** 158 (1954).
49. R. D. Evans. *The Atomic Nucleus,* McGraw-Hill (1955), p. 387.
50. R. W. Lamphere and R. E. Greene. *Phys. Rev.* **100,** 763 (1955).
51. W. J. Swiatecki. *Phys. Rev.* **100,** 936 (1955).

Chapter III

SOURCES

7.1. Radioactive Sources

In this category we will consider sources of neutrons made up of a target material mixed or alloyed with a naturally decaying radioactive component which supplies the bombarding radiation for the release of neutrons. Radioactive sources are usually of relatively small volume. Thus they are readily portable and adaptable to particular experimental arrangements. These sources also can be calibrated quite accurately, and the neutron output is either practically constant or its variation with the decay of the radioactive component can be estimated reliably.

There are several types of radioactive neutron sources, differentiated both by the nature of the target material and of the radioactive nuclide producing the bombarding radiation. Those radioactive sources which have been found useful will be described. In general it may be said that neutron sources which depend upon a radioactive preparation for the bombarding radiation are limited in the rate of neutron emission which can be conveniently achieved. Most of these sources would become awkwardly large for a total emission of neutrons of the order of 10^8 neutrons per sec. Unwieldy size would impair one of the main advantages of these sources even if they were otherwise acceptable. Therefore the radioactive sources which have been used in the past have an order of neutron emission not greatly exceeding 10^7 neutrons per sec.

The discussion will begin with radioactive (α,n) sources not merely because of their historical significance in connection with the discovery of neutrons but also because (α,n) sources have been found to be the most useful of the radioactive sources. The fact that alpha particles from radioactive substances do not have energies extending much above 5 Mev automatically limits the useful target elements for these sources. Those nuclides which have thresholds for the (α,n) reaction within this region of energy at first show a slow rise in the neutron yield as the alpha-particle energy increases beyond the threshold. This excitation curve rises more rapidly as the alpha-particle energy approaches the maximum energy of the alpha particles from the radioactive preparation.

Beryllium has the highest yield of all the elements for polonium alpha particles, the yield for thick targets being nearly four times the yield from boron, its nearest competitor. Beryllium also has a neutron yield more than six times that of fluorine, the only other element which gives a significant yield of neutrons for polonium alpha particles. Because of the high yield of neutrons from beryllium, this element has been used almost exclusively as the target material in (α,n) radioactive neutron sources. The thin target yield of neutrons from beryllium bombarded by alpha particles has re-

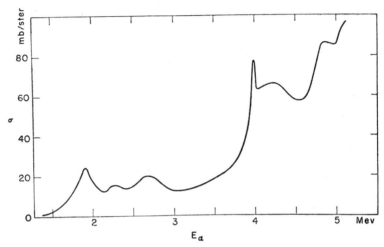

FIG. 7.1. *Neutron yield from alpha-particle bombardment of a thin beryllium target. The ordinates are cross sections in millibarns per steradian in the laboratory system.* E_α *is the energy of the alpha particles.*

cently been measured by Bonner and co-workers (1). Their excitation curve, obtained with an accelerator as the source of alpha particles, is shown in Fig. 7.1. The range of E_α, the energy of the alpha particles, in this curve extends approximately over that available from radioactive sources.

7.2. Polonium-Beryllium (α,n) Sources

The Po-Be neutron source has historical interest because it was used in the discovery of the neutron. This source emits gamma rays of very low intensity—a practical advantage possessed by few other radioactive neutron sources. On the other hand, Po-Be sources have a relatively rapid rate of decay. Po^{210}, used in these sources, has a half-life of approximately 140 days. The (α,n) reaction by which alpha particles release neutrons from beryllium can be represented by

$$_4Be^9 + {}_2He^4 \rightarrow {}_6C^{12} + {}_0n^1 + 5.7 \text{ Mev} \tag{7.1}$$

Hence the reaction is exoergic. The maximum energy of the Po^{210} alpha particles is about 5.3 Mev. Therefore the distribution of neutrons from the reaction of Eq. 7.1 according to energy would be expected to range from about 6.7 Mev to 10.9 Mev, depending on whether the neutron is emitted in the same direction as that of the incident alpha particle or in the opposite direction. Actually the energy of the neutron E_n in the laboratory system is given by the complicated relation (7.2)

$$E_n = \frac{2M_\alpha M_n}{(M_n + M_C)^2} E_\alpha \cos^2 \theta + \frac{M_C - M_\alpha}{M_n + M_C} + \frac{M_C}{M_n + M_C} Q$$

$$\pm \frac{2\sqrt{M_\alpha M_n E_\alpha}}{M_n + M_C} \cos \theta \sqrt{\frac{M_\alpha M_n}{(M_n + M_C)^2} E_\alpha \cos^2 \theta + \frac{M_C - M_\alpha}{M_n + M_C} E_\alpha + \frac{M_C Q}{M_n + M_C}}$$

In Eq. 7.2, derived from the conservation of energy and momentum in the reaction, θ is the angle between the direction of the incident alpha particle and that of the emergent neutron. M_n is the mass of the neutron, M_α the mass of the alpha particle, and M_C the mass of the carbon nucleus. In arriving at the estimate of the distribution of the neutron energies, the constant value of 5.3 Mev was used for E_α. Actually not all particles reach a beryllium nucleus with this energy because of energy losses in the thick target material. Also the C^{12} nucleus may be left in an excited state, thus subtracting the excitation energy from that of the neutron. Finally, the cross section for the (α,n) reaction changes with changes in the value of E_α which must also be taken into account in determining the numbers of neutrons emitted at a given energy.

Measurements have been made of the energy distribution of neutrons from Po-Be sources by a number of investigators. Fig. 7.2 shows the data obtained by Elliot, McGarry, and Faust (2). They used a neutron coincidence spectrometer to make these measurements. The spectrometer, in combination with a 20-channel pulse-height analyzer, permitted many more observations on each point in the spectrum than is possible, for example, by the emulsion method in which the lengths of proton recoil tracks are measured. In the latter method, the energy of the neutron is computed from the length of the proton track, measured with a microscope.

Po-Be sources have been made in a variety of forms. One common method of preparation has been to mix fine beryllium powder with a solution of polonium. After drying thoroughly, the mixture is compressed into a small pellet, which is usually sealed in some kind of container. From the standpoint of the health of the operator this is a hazardous operation. Polonium is relatively volatile above room temperatures. Even more dan-

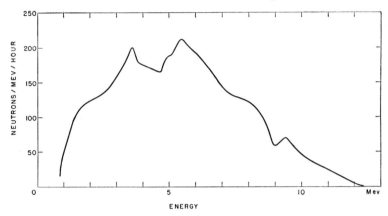

FIG. 7.2. *Relative numbers of neutrons according to energy from a* Po-Be (a,n) *source.*

gerous is the tendency for aggregates of polonium atoms to become detached from their support by recoil on the emission of alpha particles. The
result is that some of the polonium
becomes air-borne. The inhalation of
polonium is very dangerous. To reduce
these possibilities of injury and to permit the production of strong neutron
sources, Spinks and Graham (3) have
made a sandwich type of Po-Be
source. In their design, the polonium
is deposited electrolytically on one
side of a platinum foil and the foil in-
serted in a narrow slot between two
semicylinders of beryllium metal. The
details are represented in Fig. 7.3. A
maximum of 50 percent of the alpha
particles is available for production of
neutrons. Nevertheless appreciably
more intense sources than those customarily prepared can be made with a
minimum risk to the health of the
operator. The angular distribution of
fast neutrons about sources of this
design was measured by Spinks and
Graham. The experimental arrangement is sketched in Fig. 7.4. The boron
trifluoride counter tube, surrounded
by a paraffin moderator, remained

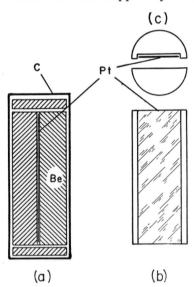

FIG. 7.3. *Diagram of a* Po-Be
(a,n) *source.* (a) *cross section of
assembled source,* (b) *elevation
of one beryllium semicylinder,* (c)
*top view of beryllium semicylin-
ders.* C—*metal capsule.* Pt—
*platinum foil coated with polo-
nium on one side.* Be—*beryllium
metal semicylinders.*

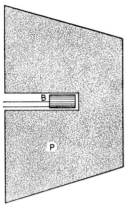
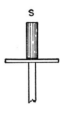

FIG. 7.4. *Arrangement used to measure the angular distribution of fast neutrons about a sandwich-type* Po-Be (a,n) *source.* B—BF$_3$ *proportional counter.* P—*paraffin block.* S—*neutron source.*

fixed. The source was turned about its central axis stepwise to obtain the data. The results of the measurements are plotted in polar coordinates in Fig. 7.5. Curve (a) is the distribution about the longitudinal axis of the cylindrical source and curve (b) the distribution about an axis perpendicular to the center of the longitudinal axis. The symmetry of curve (a) and the distortion of curve (b) are fairly typical of all cylindrical neutron sources. Consequently when spherical symmetry of the distribution of

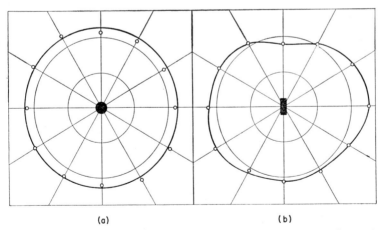

(a)   (b)

FIG. 7.5. *Angular distribution of fast neutrons for a cylindrical* Po-Be (a,n) *source,* (a) *around the longitudinal axis of the source and* (b) *around an axis perpendicular to the center of the longitudinal axis of the cylinder.*

neutrons from a source is desired, the source also must be as nearly spherical as possible. Table 7.1, giving the radium gamma ray equivalent of three
different sources made by the sandwich method, illustrates the low intensity of gamma rays from strong Po-Be neutron sources.

Table 7.1

GAMMA RADIATION FROM Po-Be NEUTRON SOURCES

	Source No. 1	Source No. 2	Source No. 3
Curies of polonium	2.1	3.2	3.5
Neutrons per sec	2.0×10^6	3.0×10^6	3.2×10^6
Radium gamma-ray equivalent (mg)	0.2	0.3	0.35

7.3. Radium-Beryllium (α,n) Sources

Numerous experiments, requiring moderate fluxes of neutrons, have been
performed using a mixture of fine beryllium powder and radium bromide
as a source of neutrons. Prior to the development and general availability
of accelerators and reactors, the Ra-Be (α,n) source was the most common
way to generate neutrons. Part of this popularity was based on the ease
with which large preparations of radium could be obtained and the long
half-life of radium. The half-life of about 1690 years insured that the rate
of emission of neutrons would be essentially constant with time. Ra-Be
sources have the disadvantage of emitting an intense and penetrating
gamma radiation. The gamma rays are a hazard to health and also produce
objectionable effects in some types of detectors of neutrons. For sources
containing more than a gram of radium bromide, the gamma rays are difficult to control by shielding. Furthermore, the radon generated in these
sources containing radium constitutes a constant threat of widespread
radioactive contamination of a laboratory. Part of the radon is liberated
as a free gas within the capsule containing the neutron source. To prevent
the escape of this radon requires the capsule to be and to remain absolutely gas-tight. It is problematical whether the radon gas of itself could
ever develop enough pressure to rupture a soldered metal capsule. However slight traces of water, which may be left in the constituents of the
source, are decomposed by the strong alpha radiation. The pressure developed by the decomposition of the water can cause and frequently has
caused the rupture of weak soldered seams with disastrous results to the
laboratory. Formerly it was the custom to enclose Ra-Be sources in brass
tubes closed by lead-tin soldered joints. This practice has been discontinued
because practically all such capsules eventually developed leakage of radon.

More recently, a strong corrosion-resistant alloy, such as Monel metal or stainless steel, has been used for containers. The seams are closed with a high-melting-point solder. With care this procedure produces a capsule with a reasonable probability of remaining tight.

Preparations of mixtures of radium bromide and beryllium powder have been made in a variety of ways. The volume can be reduced considerably by compressing the mixture to a density of about 1.75 g/cm³. The general features of a Ra-Be source are sketched in Fig. 7.6. Provision for temporarily attaching a long handle aids in reducing the gamma-ray exposure of the worker during handling. Anderson and Feld (4) state that a compressed Ra-Be source will have a yield of neutrons given approximately by

$$1.7 \times 10^7 \frac{M_{Be}}{M_{Be} + M_{RaBr_2}}$$

neutrons/sec/g of radium. Here M_{Be} is the mass of the beryllium and M_{RaBr_2} the mass of the radium bromide. The relative yields from various weights of beryllium powder mixed with salt containing 1 g of radium are plotted in Fig. 7.7. After the ratio of 10 g of beryllium to 1 g of radium has been reached, little additional gain in neutron emission is obtained from further additions of beryllium. Teucher (5) has determined the energy spectrum of the neutron from a Ra-Be (α,n) source, using the emulsion method. His data are represented by the curve in Fig. 7.8. As might be expected, there is some resemblance between this curve and the curve for the spectrum of Po-Be (α,n) neutrons shown in Fig. 7.2.

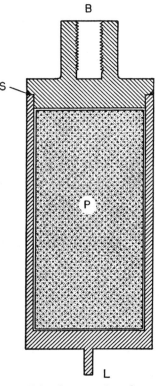

FIG. 7.6. *A typical radium-beryllium (α,n) source in cross section. B—threaded boss for attaching handle. S—hard-solder seal. P—compressed pellet of mixture of radium bromide and powdered beryllium. L—lug for holding capsule when attaching or removing handle.*

7.4. Plutonium-Beryllium (α,n) Sources

Plutonium forms an intermetallic compound with beryllium of the definite form $PuBe_{13}$ with a density of 3.7 g/cm³. The conveniently available plutonium isotope is Pu^{239}, which emits 5.1-Mev alpha particles. The half-

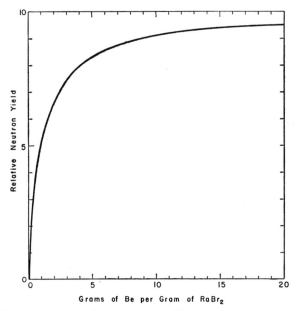

FIG. 7.7. *Variation of the neutron yield from a* Ra-Be (a,n) *compressed neutron source for increasing amounts of beryllium powder added to 1 gram of radium bromide.*

life is about 2.3×10^4 years. The gamma rays emitted in the radioactive decay of Pu^{239} are weak and of low energy. Therefore Pu-Be neutron sources offer the advantage of Ra-Be sources of long half-life and the favorable characteristic of Po-Be sources of a low intensity of gamma radiation. The neutron yield is somewhat lower for Pu-Be sources than from Ra-Be

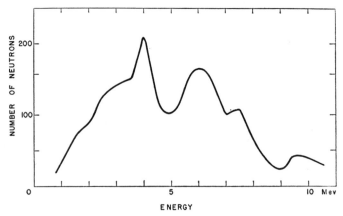

FIG. 7.8. *Energy spectrum of* Ra-Be (a,n) *neutron source.*

sources, but it is adequate for the purposes for which radioactive neutron sources are now used. A cylindrical source approximately 2 cm in diameter and 3 cm in height will yield about 10^6 neutrons per sec. Stewart (6) has measured the neutron spectrum and the absolute yield from a $PuBe_{13}$ preparation containing 13 g of plutonium and 7 g of beryllium. The neutron energies were determined by the emulsion method. The neutron yield was found to be 1.2×10^6 neutrons per sec. The distribution of the neutron energies is shown in Fig. 7.9. It seems quite likely that plutonium-beryl-

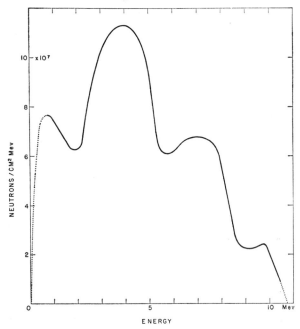

FIG. 7.9. *The distribution of energies for neutrons from a* $PuBe_{13}$ *(a,n) source.*

lium may replace other types of (α,n) radioactive neutron sources when plutonium becomes more readily available.

7.5. Americium-Beryllium (α,n) Sources

Americium also alloys with beryllium to form $AmBe_{13}$. Am^{241} has a half-life of about 470 years. Although this isotope decays by emitting alpha particles of about 5.4 Mev, these particles are followed by gamma rays in the 40 to 60 kev region in the majority of the disintegrations. This gamma-ray emission makes americium appear less satisfactory than plutonium for the preparation of neutron sources. Runnals and Boucher (7) have described the preparation of two AmBe alloys. One of these had a Be/Am atomic ratio of 263 : 1 and the other, identified as AmBe$_{13}$, had an atomic ratio of 14 : 1. The observed neutron yields are given in Table 7.2. Measured in a

Table 7.2

NEUTRON YIELDS FROM TWO
AMERICIUM-BERYLLIUM ALLOYS

	Source No. 1	Source No. 2
Be/atom ratio	263:1	14:1
Am α-activity disintegrations per sec	2.97×10^9	3.24×10^9
Yield in neutrons per sec	2.13×10^5	1.57×10^5
Neutrons per 10^6 α particles	71.7	48.5

similar manner, PuBe$_{13}$ sources yield about 40 neutrons per 10^6 alpha particles.

7.6. Radioactive (γ,n) Sources

There are only two nuclides which have thresholds for the (γ,n) reaction within the range of energies of gamma rays emitted by radioactive nuclei in their decay processes. They are H^2 and Be^9. Hence all radioactive (γ,n) neutron sources use either deuterium or beryllium as target material. The cross section in these nuclei for the (γ,n) reaction near the threshold energy is of the order of a millibarn. The approximate variation of σ_γ with the energy of the gamma rays E$_\gamma$ near the threshold is shown in Fig. 7.10 for both deuterium and beryllium. The solid curve for Be^9 is that deduced theoretically by Guth and Mullin (8). The curve gives a fairly close approximation to the experimental values. The dotted curve represents the trend of the experimental measurements for the (γ,n) cross section of the deuteron. From the standpoint of neutron sources, the most significant feature of these values of the cross sections is that they are small. A small cross section means that a photoneutron source using H^2 or Be^9 as a target will emit many times as many gamma rays as neutrons. Thus the undesirable effects of the gamma rays can be expected to be prominent in these photoneutron sources.

In principle, radioactive photoneutron sources offer the possibility of obtaining monoenergetic neutrons. If a radioactive nucleus emits only one gamma ray with energy above the threshold for the (γ,n) reaction in either beryllium or deuterium, the neutrons emitted should all be of the same energy, except for a small spread in energy resulting from the difference in direction between the gamma ray and the emitted neutron. Wattenberg (9)

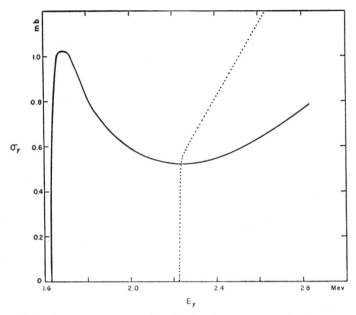

FIG. 7.10. *The cross section for the* (γ,n) *reaction in beryllium and deuterium at gamma-ray energies available from radioactive sources. The solid line is the theoretical curve for* Be *which agrees fairly well with experimental values. The dotted line is intended to indicate the trend of the experimental curve for the deuteron.*

has investigated the production of photoneutrons by radioactive sources. He gives the equation for the energy E_n of the emitted neutrons as

$$E_n = \frac{A-1}{A}\left[E_\gamma - E_T - \frac{E^2_\gamma}{1862(A-1)}\right] + \delta \qquad (7.3)$$

The relation in Eq. 7.3 is deduced from the conservation of energy and momentum in the interaction of the photon with the nucleus. A is the mass of the target nucleus, E_γ the energy of the gamma ray in Mev, and E_T the threshold energy in Mev for the (γ,n) reaction in the target nucleus. The correction term δ is given approximately by

$$\delta \approx E_\gamma \cos \theta \left[\frac{2(A-1)(E_\gamma - E_T)}{931A^3}\right]^{1/2} \qquad (7.4)$$

where θ is the angle between the path of the gamma ray and the direction of the emitted neutron. In practice, the neutrons have a much greater spread in energy than Eq. 7.3 would predict. A number of other factors enter into the determination of the energy with which the neutrons emerge from the target material. Neutrons are scattered in the target, suffering variable energy losses after release from the nuclei. Gamma rays are likewise scattered in the target and are no longer monochromatic on arrival at the nuclei. To obtain useful intensities of photoneutrons the target is thick. In thick targets the effect of these undesirable interactions is increased.

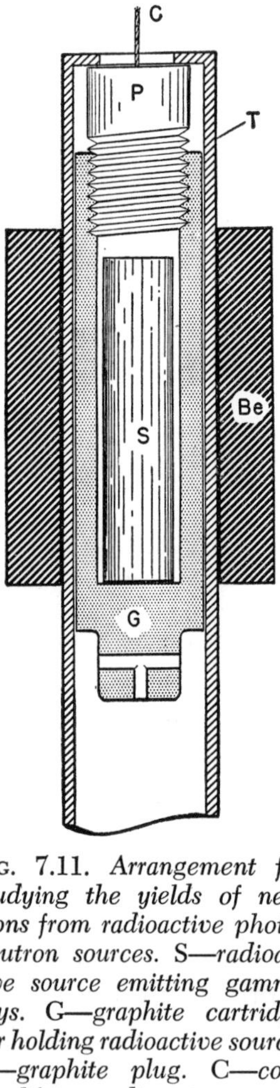

Russell and his co-workers (10) have measured the neutron yields from a few radioactive (γ,n) sources which might have practical use. Their measurements were made with the demountable neutron source shown in cross section in Fig. 7.11. A graphite cartridge G carrying the radioactive source S could be drawn up inside a beryllium or deuterium cylinder represented by Be while observations were in progress. At other times it could be lowered into a shielded vault to reduce gamma-ray exposures of workers in the vicinity. The detector of neutrons was an ionization chamber filled with boron trifluoride gas and surrounded by a cylinder of paraffin. This device detected neutrons of all energies with approximately the same efficiency. The observations on the rate of emission of neutrons were converted to correspond to that of a source of 1 curie of the radioisotope at a distance of 1 cm from 1 g of the target material. Table 7.3 contains data obtained in this way for several photoneutron sources using different nuclides as sources of gamma rays.

Snell, Barker, and Sternberg (11) have also measured the yields of photoneutrons from spheres of D_2O and of Be with Na^{24} and Ga^{72} sources of gamma rays inside a central cavity of the spheres. The arrangement is shown in cross section, both vertically and horizontally, in Fig. 7.12. The neutrons were detected by the activation of a foil F of indium mounted near the source of neutrons in a large block of paraffin as a moderator for the neutrons. To avoid the necessity of integrating the induced activity over the volume of the moderator, the in-

FIG. 7.11. *Arrangement for studying the yields of neutrons from radioactive photoneutron sources. S—radioactive source emitting gamma rays. G—graphite cartridge for holding radioactive source. P—graphite plug. C—cord for lifting radioactive source into position. T—brass tube. Be—cylinder of beryllium metal attached to tube T. For sources using deuterium an identically shaped thin-walled brass cylinder filled with heavy water replaced the beryllium metal.*

Table 7.3

YIELDS OF NEUTRONS FROM PHOTONEUTRON SOURCES

Source	$T_{1/2}$	E_γ (Mev)	E_n (Mev)	Yield (neutrons/sec)
$Na^{24} + D_2O$	14.8 hr	2.76	0.8	29×10^4
$Na^{24} + Be$	14.8 hr	2.76	0.2	14
$Mn^{56} + D_2O$	2.6 hr	2.7	0.2	0.3
$Mn^{56} + Be$	2.6 hr	1.8, 2.1, 2.7	0.15, 0.3	2.9
$Ga^{72} + D_2O$	14 hr	2.5	0.13	6.9
$Ga^{72} + Be$	14 hr	1.8, 2.2, 2.5	0.2	5.9
$In^{116} + Be$	54 min	1.8, 2.1	0.2	0.8
$Sb^{124} + Be$	60 days	1.67	0.02	19
$La^{140} + D_2O$	40 hr	2.5	0.15	0.7
$La^{140} + Be$	40 hr	2.5	0.6	0.2

dium foil was cut to a parabolic shape, as indicated in Fig. 7.12. Because an element of width of this parabolic foil has a length proportional to the square of the distance of this element from the center of the sphere, the activity of the element will also be proportional to r^2. Thus the activity measured in proportional to the quantity, r^2 times the activity, which would be used in the integration. The cadmium-covered foil responded to indium resonance neutrons and was about 15 cm long so that it covered the whole region of the indium resonance neutrons. To obtain the final data, the foil was calibrated by replacing the experimental photoneutron source by a calibrated source of similar dimensions. The results obtained from these measurements on neutron yields differed only slightly from the yields given in Table 7.3.

From this brief account of radioactive (γ,n) sources, it becomes apparent that they have limited usefulness. Indeed the same statement can be made of practically all radioactive sources, now that much more powerful and controllable sources of neutrons have come into existence. Radioactive sources will remain valuable as small laboratory reference sources and as calibrated standards. Wherever it is important to make absolute comparisons of measurements in different laboratories or under different experimental conditions, calibrated, portable neutron sources can be useful.

8.1. Accelerators as Sources on Neutrons

It is obvious that accelerators which can impart energies to beams of charged particles in excess of the threshold energy for release of neutrons in a target are adaptable as sources of neutrons. In those cases where the reaction in the target is exoergic, and no threshold exists, a particle beam of quite low energy can be used in the accelerator. As the control of the energy of the charged particles in the beams of accelerators has improved,

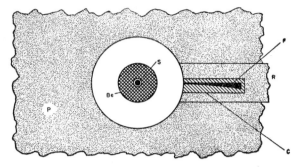

HORIZONTAL MID-SECTION

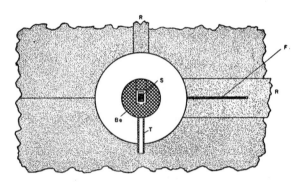

VERTICAL MID-SECTION

FIG. 7.12. *Arrangement used by Snell and co-workers in measuring the yield of neutrons from the (γ,n) reaction in deuterium and beryllium. P—paraffin. S—radioactive source. Be—beryllium sphere. F—parabolic indium foil. C—sheets of cadmium on each side of the foil F. R—removable paraffin plugs. T—aluminum tube supporting the beryllium sphere. A nearly identical sphere containing D_2O replaces the beryllium sphere for measurements with deuterium.*

along with methods of measuring the energy of the beam, it has become possible to generate neutrons with fairly well defined energies. Also as the energy to which charged particles can be accelerated has increased, the range of target nuclides has grown. The multiplicity of combinations which have been used for the generation of neutrons cannot be discussed in detail. However, some of the main features of the reactions more frequently used to produce neutrons will be outlined.

8.2. Neutrons from (α,n) and (α,2n) Reactions with Accelerators

Many accelerators of nuclear charged particles offer the opportunity to accelerate alpha particles to energies higher than those which can be obtained from radioactive sources. A few accelerators have been used to produce neutrons by the (α,n) reaction. When alpha particles with energies of the order of 20-Mev energy are available, the range of possible target nuclei for the (α,n) reaction covers the whole periodic table. Whereas cross sections for these (α,n) reactions are often small, of the order of millibarns, the high intensity of alpha-particle beams in accelerators tends to counteract this disadvantage. To illustrate the magnitude of the cross sections to be anticipated, the excitation curves for $Ag^{109}(\alpha,n)$ and $Ag^{109}(\alpha,2n)$ reac-

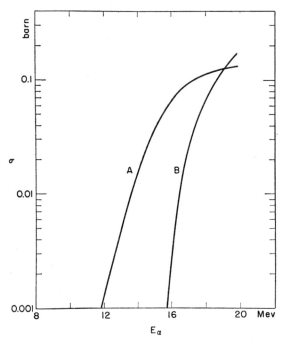

FIG. 8.1. *Cross sections for the* Ag^{109} (a,n) *reaction* (*curve* A) *and for the* Ag^{109} $(a,2n)$ *reaction* (*curve* B).

tions, as measured by Tendam and Bradt (12), are shown in Fig. 8.1. The curve for the (α,n) reaction which follows the variation of the cross section with E_α, the energy of the alpha particles, shows a steep rise soon after E_α passes the threshold energy for the release of a neutron. When the threshold for the $(\alpha,2n)$ reaction is reached, the cross section for this reaction follows a similar course. Both curves begin to level off at a cross section of about 10 millibarns. When E_α exceeds 20 Mev, reactions of the types $(\alpha,3n)$ and $(\alpha,4n)$ have been observed in some nuclei.

When the energy of the alpha particle beam is held constant and targets of increasing atomic number are introduced into the beam, the neutron yield decreases rapidly. The decrease in yield occurs even when the value of E_α is considerably above the thresholds of all the nuclei. The falling off of the neutron yield is illustrated by the measurements of Allen and co-workers (13) using a beam of 30-Mev alpha particles. Figure 8.2 represents the experimental curve which they obtained, using targets extending from beryllium to bismuth. In Fig. 8.2 the neutron flux ϕ is expressed in terms of the number of fast neutrons in the forward direction per second per steradian per microampere in the beam of the accelerator. For a combination of reasons the (α,n) reaction has not been found to be very useful as a source of neutrons in accelerators. The chief reason seems to be that the production of alpha-particle beams is difficult and the neutron yields are low. Hence accelerators with alpha-particle beams are mainly occupied with the investigation of nuclear levels which can be studied by means of the excitation curves.

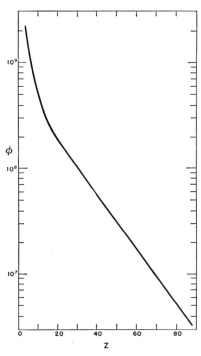

FIG. 8.2. *The variation of the fast neutron flux ϕ in the forward direction for elements from beryllium to bismuth, plotted according to atomic number Z, when bombarded by 30-Mev alpha particles. ϕ is expressed in neutrons per second per microampere beam current per steradian.*

8.3. The (p,n) Reaction as Sources of Neutrons

The $Li^7(p,n)Be^7$ reaction. As has been suggested by the preceding discussion, the (p,n) reaction has been much more popular than the (α,n) reaction as a source of neutrons in accelerators. The lower threshold energies and greater yields of neutrons have contributed to this popularity. A few values of E_T for the (p,n) reaction, taken mainly from Blosser and Handley (14), are given in Table 8.1.

Up to the present time the $Li^7(p,n)Be^7$ reaction has been most widely used as a source of neutrons with energies in the kilovolt region. The equation for the reaction is

$$Li^7 + H^1 \rightarrow Be^7 + n^1 - 1.63 \text{ Mev} \tag{8.1}$$

For energies below 80 kev for the neutrons, large proton currents are required on thin targets and the neutrons must be taken at angles greater

Table 8.1

THRESHOLDS E_T FOR THE (p,n) REACTION IN A FEW NUCLIDES

Nuclide	E_T (Mev)	Nuclide	E_T (Mev)
H^3	1.02	Ga^{69}	4.0
Li^7	1.88	Br^{79}	2.7
Sc^{45}	2.9	Rb^{87}	2.0
V^{51}	1.6	Y^{89}	3.6
Cr^{52}	5.4	Zr^{90}	7.0
Cu^{63}	4.2	Ru^{99}	2.4
Cu^{65}	2.2	Ru^{101}	1.4
Ni^{60}	6.8	Cd^{111}	1.6
Ni^{61}	2.8	Cd^{114}	3.0
Ni^{64}	2.4	Cs^{133}	1.0
Zn^{66}	5.9	Ce^{142}	3.5

than 90° to the direction of the proton beam. In spite of the complications which these requirements introduce, the large yield of neutrons and the low threshold energy of the reaction have made the method suitable for use in Van de Graaff accelerators. The large proton currents make it mandatory to use a rotating target to reduce evaporation of the thin lithium target by the heat developed by the beam. The lithium target must be evaporated in position in a vacuum and kept in the accelerator subsequently to avoid oxidation. Lampi (15) has described a device for preparing lithium targets which is shown in cross section in Fig. 8.3. The vacuum chamber may be detached from the accelerator and connected to a vacuum system for depositing the layer of lithium. With the valve closed, the chamber may be remounted on the accelerator, which is evacuated before the valve V is reopened. During bombardment by protons, the target is rotated on the ball bearings B by means of the worm gear at W.

The total cross section for the $Li^7(p,n)Be^7$ reaction as a function of the proton energy is shown in Fig. 8.4, representing the data of Hanson, Taschek, and Williams (16). Also from the same authors, the yields of neutrons in the forward direction from a thick target as a function of proton energy are shown in Fig. 8.5, curve N. The dotted curve E shows the corresponding values of the neutron energy E_n in terms of the right-hand ordinate scale. These neutron energies are in the Mev region. Yields and energies for E_n of the order of kilovolts are shown in Fig. 8.6 for a thin lithium target. The curves of Fig. 8.6 are for angles of 120° and 135° with respect to the proton beam. Further data on the energies of neutrons which can be obtained from the $Li^7(p,n)$ reaction are shown in curves C and D of Fig. 8.7, also from reference (16). The curves of Fig. 8.7 give the energy of the neutrons for protons with energies from 0 to 4 Mev. Curve C is for 0° with respect to the proton beam and curve D for 180°. For comparison,

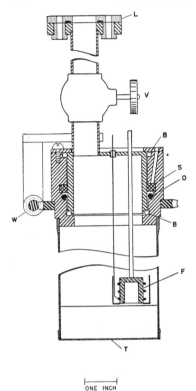

ONE INCH

FIG. 8.3. *A detachable rotating lithium target. L—Lucite insulators. V—shut-off valve. B—ball bearings. S—felt oil seal. O—vacuum o-ring seal. F—lithium furnace. W—worm and gear. T—tantalium cup 0.01 in. thick welded to tube.*

similar curves for the H³(d,n) reaction are shown at A and B, and for the H³(p,n) reaction at E and F.

8.4. Monoenergetic Neutrons

The description of the Li⁷(p,n) reaction suggests that accelerated charged particles present the possibility of obtaining nearly monoenergetic neutrons over a wide range of energies. In fact, the production of monoenergetic neutrons has been one of the most valuable functions of accelerators. Special precautions are required to confine the energies of the neutrons to a narrow band. Most important is the use of thin targets. Thin targets avoid serious losses of energy by the bombarding particles prior to their interaction with nuclei. Actually, it is usual to specify the thickness of a target in terms of the loss of energy suffered by the bombarding particles in passing through it. This designation of thickness in terms of energy comes about from the fact that the loss of energy for a specific particle and target may be defined, over a small range of energy, approximately by

$$-\frac{dE}{dx} \approx C$$

where C is a constant. Hence specifying $-dE$ for the target also specifies the thickness dx. Thus one may refer to a target as having a thickness of 2 kev for protons and this information is more pertinent than the actual thickness in more conventional units. Further, to secure approximately monochromatic neutrons, it is necessary to limit the solid angle over which they are accepted. The energy of the neutron, with other parameters constant, then depends on the angle between the direction of the neutron with respect to that of the beam of bombarding particles. Because the energy of the neutrons also depends on the energy of the proton beam, recent improvements in the control of the energy of the protons in accelerators have contributed to the sharpness with which the neutron energy can be defined.

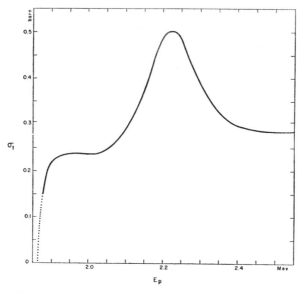

FIG. 8.4. *Cross section of the* $Li^7(p,n)Be^{17}$ *reaction as a function of the proton energy* E_p.

The relations between the kinetic energy of the neutron, the kinetic energy of the proton, and the angle of emission of the neutron may be made clearer by a review of the collision kinetics of the reaction. Fig. 8.8(a) is intended to represent the positions of a proton of mass M_p and a target nucleus of mass M_1 prior to a collision. The target nucleus is assumed at rest in the laboratory frame of reference and the proton has a velocity V_p. The diagram at Fig. 8.8(b) represents the relative positions immediately after a collision in which the proton has been captured in the target nucleus and a neutron of mass M_n and a velocity V_n has been emitted at an angle θ_n with respect to the initial direction of the proton. The product nucleus of mass M_2 proceeds with a velocity V_2 in the direction θ_2. Prior to the collision, the kinetic energy of the proton is $E_p = M_p V_p^2/2$ and its momentum is $M_p V_p = P_p$. The energy and momentum of M_1 are both zero. Further it is assumed that there is an absorption or release of energy of amount Q in the reaction. Applying conservation laws to the collision

$$E_n = E_p - E_2 + Q \qquad (8.2)$$

where $E_2 = M_2 V_2^2/2$ and Q may be either positive or negative. Similarly for the momentum

$$P_n = P_p - P_2 \qquad (8.3)$$

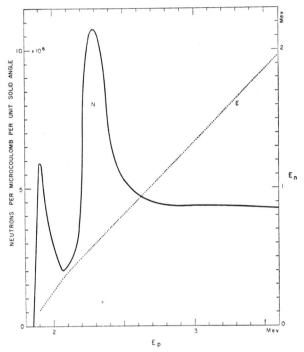

FIG. 8.5. *Yield and energy of neutrons in forward direction in the* Li(p,n) *reaction as a function of proton energy.*

which is a vectorial equation and can be represented by the vector diagram of Fig. 8.8(c). From this diagram

$$P_n^2 = P_2^2 - P_p^2 + 2P_p P_n \cos \theta_n \qquad (8.4)$$

Since $P^2 = 2ME$, Eq. 8.2 can be converted to the form

$$\frac{P_n}{2M_n} = \frac{P_p}{2M_p} - \frac{P_2}{2M_2} + Q \qquad (8.5)$$

To obtain a value for E_n, the quantity P_2 may be eliminated between Eq. 8.4 and Eq. 8.5 giving

$$E_n = \frac{P_n^2}{2M_n} = \frac{2M_p M_n}{(M_n + M_2)^2} E_p \cos^2 \theta_n + \frac{M_2 - M_p}{M_n + M_2} E_p + \frac{M_2}{M_n + M_2} Q$$

$$\pm 2 \frac{\sqrt{M_p M_n E_p}}{M_n + M_2} \cos \theta_n \sqrt{\frac{M_p M_n}{(M_n + M_2)^2} E_p \cos^2 \theta_n + \frac{M_2 - M_p}{M_n + M_2} + \frac{M_2 Q}{M_n + M_2}}$$

$$(8.6)$$

Eq. 8.6 is identical in form with Eq. 7.2 for production of neutrons by bom-

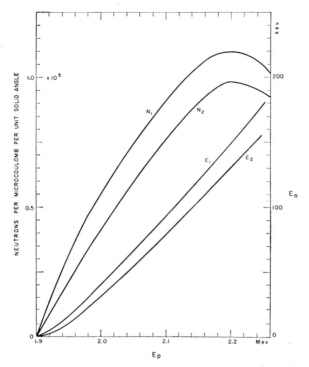

FIG. 8.6. *Yield and energy curves for neutrons from the* Li(p,n) *re-action at angles of 120° and 135°. Curves* N_1 *and* N_2 *are to be referred to the left-hand ordinates.* N_1 = *number of neutrons at 120°,* N_2 = *number of neutrons at 135°. Curves* E_1 *and* E_2 *are to be referred to the right-hand ordinates.*

$$E_1 = E_n \text{ at } 120°$$
$$E_2 = E_n \text{ at } 135°$$

bardment of a target with alpha particles. The equation is applicable to other charged-particle reactions by introducing corresponding masses. For a numerical example of the use of Eq. 8.6 we choose the $H^3(p,n)He^3$ reaction with the value of $Q = -0.735$ Mev. For simplicity we will use mass numbers in place of atomic mass units because the approximation will not differ greatly from the more accurate computation. We also select $\theta_n = 0$. Substituting in Eq. 8.6 the proper mass numbers, we have

$$E_n = \frac{E_p}{8} + \frac{E_p}{2} + \frac{3Q}{4} + \frac{\sqrt{E_p}}{2}\sqrt{\frac{E_p}{8} + \frac{E_p}{2} + \frac{3Q}{4}}$$

$$= \frac{5E_p}{8} + \frac{3Q}{4} + \frac{\sqrt{E_p}}{2}\sqrt{\frac{5E_p}{8} + \frac{3Q}{4}}$$

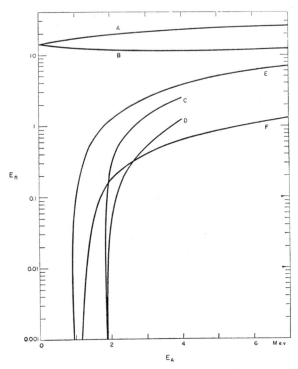

FIG. 8.7. *Neutron E_n as a function of the bombarding particle E_A at 0° and 180° for several reactions.*

Curve A—$H^3(dn)He^4$ at 0°   *Curve D—$Li^7(p,n)Be^7$ at 180°*
Curve B—$H^3(dn)He^4$ at 180°   *Curve E—$H^3(p,n)He^3$ at 0°*
Curve C—$Li^7(p,n)Be^7$ at 0°   *Curve F—$H^3(p,n)He^3$ at 180°*

Selecting 1 Mev for E_p we obtain

$$E_n = (\tfrac{5}{8} - 0.55) + \tfrac{1}{2}(\tfrac{5}{8} - 0.55)^{1/2} \text{ Mev}$$

$$= 0.0625 + 0.125 = 0.187 \text{ Mev}$$

From this numerical example it is clear that the positive sign is to be chosen for the term containing the radicals in Eq. 8.6.

McKibben (17) has constructed nomographs giving E_n as a function of E_p for values of θ_n from 0° to 180°. These nomographs are based on the relation between θ_n, the angle of emission of the neutron in the laboratory frame of reference and ϕ the angle of emission in the center-of-mass system. The construction of these diagrams turns out to be possible because E_n and E_2 are independent of the value of ϕ. In addition E_n may be considered to be made up of two parts, A_n^2 proportional to the velocity of the center of mass of M_n and M_2, and B_n^2 proportional to the velocity of M_n in the

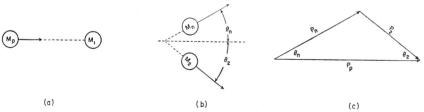

FIG. 8.8. *Vector diagram for collision of a proton with a nucleus of mass* M_1 *in the* (p,n) *reaction.*

$M_p = mass\ of\ proton.$
$M_1 = mass\ of\ target\ nucleus.$
$M_n = mass\ of\ neutron.$
$M_2 = mass\ of\ product\ nucleus.$
$\theta_n = angle\ of\ emission\ of\ the\ neutron\ in\ the\ laboratory\ system.$
$\theta_2 = direction\ of\ product\ nucleus\ in\ the\ laboratory\ system.$
$P_n = momentum\ of\ the\ neutron.$
$P_p = momentum\ of\ the\ proton.$
$P_2 = momentum\ of\ the\ product\ nucleus.$

Target nucleus is assumed to be at rest in the laboratory system. (a) *represents the situation before the impact,* (b) *after the impact, and* (c) *is a momentum diagram.*

center-of-mass system. The same mass is associated with A_n and B_n and they can be added vectorially to give $C_n = E_n$, as represented in Fig. 8.9. The nomograph is based on this addition of vectors. A schematic diagram of the general method of construction is given in Fig. 8.10. Radii at various values of θ_n are drawn from a common origin at 0 over a semicircle. Values of E_n on the diameter from 0 at distances corresponding to C_n in the diagram of Fig. 8.9. Semicircles with 0 as center are drawn through these points. The value of E_n has a constant value over the semicircles. With centers at a distance A_n from 0, a series of dotted semicircles with radii proportional to B_n are drawn for values of E_p. The angles in the system of dotted semicircles correspond to ϕ and the dotted radial lines for a constant ϕ are curved because of the shift of the center for each dotted semicircle. In the diagram of Fig. 8.10 quantities have been exaggerated to show the relation between the two systems of semicircles. A point on one set of semicircles in the nomograph is also a point in the other set. Therefore, referring to Fig. 8.10, if E_p is known to have the value E_b, the value of E_n for $\theta_n = 45°$ can be found by tracing the arc for E_b to the 45° radius. From this intersection, the solid circle is traced back to the scale for E_n. This procedure leads to the value $E_n = E_2$ on the diagram. Other possible uses for the nomograph can be recognized. A considerable number of these nomographs for different reactions have been constructed. When they are drawn in sufficiently fine detail to avoid extensive interpolation, they are difficult to

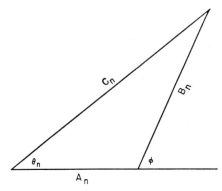

FIG. 8.9. *Vector diagram for neutron energy.*

$$E_n = A_n{}^2 + B_n{}^2 + 2A_nB_n \cos \phi = B_n{}^2 \left(\frac{\sin \phi}{\sin \theta_n}\right)^2$$

where ϕ is the angle of neutron emission in the center-of-mass system.

$$A_n = \frac{\sqrt{M_p + M_n}}{M_p + M_2} \sqrt{E_p}$$

$$B_n = \sqrt{\frac{M_1 M_2}{(M_p + M_1)M_n + M_2}} \sqrt{E_p - E_1}$$

$$E_1 = -\frac{M_p + M_1}{M_1} \qquad Q = \textit{threshold energy}$$

$$C_n = \sqrt{E_n}$$

read unless reproduced on a large scale. Since interpolations are over non-linear intervals, they lead to uncertainties. However, for approximate values in routine work the McKibben diagrams have been found useful. They are also convenient to display the main characteristics of a reaction in the generation of neutrons. In cases where one or two values of the neutron energy are to be determined accurately, computations, using Eq. 8.6, will often be found to be more convenient.

8.5. The $H^3(p,n)He^3$ Reaction

Now that tritium has become more abundant, it is frequently used to produce neutrons. One reaction in which tritium may be used to generate neutrons is the $H^3(p,n)He^3$ reaction. The reaction equation may be written

$$H^3 + H^1 \rightarrow He^3 + n^1 - 0.735 \text{ Mev} \tag{8.7}$$

Bombardment of tritium requires that it be in a form suitable as a target. The target must also be in a position to permit neutrons to be accepted at appropriate angles when monoenergetic neutrons of a specified energy are needed. A convenient gas target of tritium has been developed by Johnson

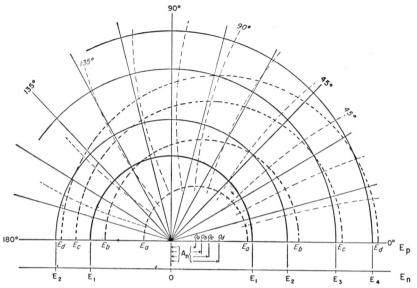

FIG. 8.10. *Schematic diagram of a McKibben nomograph for a* (p,n) *reaction.* E_p—*energy of bombarding proton.* E_n—*energy of emitted neutron.*

and Banta (18). A cross sectional diagram of their source is shown in Fig. 8.11. The tritium is confined in the cylindrical volume at the extreme end of the tubular housing by the reentrant tube H closed by a nickel-foil window at N. The tritium is introduced through the filling tube F and along the annular space between the tube H and the tubular housing. The tritium target, of course, may be bombarded by any of the charged particles avail-

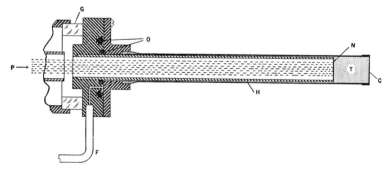

FIG. 8.11. *Tritium gas target. The gas cell at* T *is filled through the tube* F *and the annular space around the foil-holder tube* H. C— *platinum cap.* N—*nickel foil.* O—*o-ring seals.* G—*glass insulator. Protons from accelerator enter at* P.

able from accelerators. Thin solid targets of tritium may also be made. A number of metals absorb and retain large volumes of hydrogen isotopes when the hydrogen is introduced at high temperatures. Prominent among these metals is zirconium. Consequently tritium targets have been prepared by depositing a thin layer of zirconium on a backing of a metal of high melting point which is impervious to hydrogen, like tungsten. The zirconium layer is then impregnated with tritium at an elevated temperature. The impregnation process yields an essentially solid target of tritium

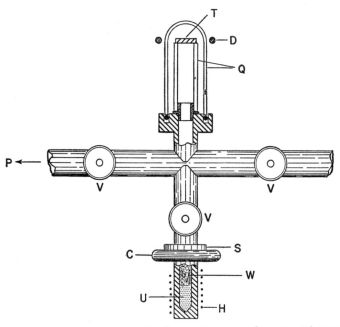

FIG. 8.12. *Vacuum system for loading a zirconium deposit with tritium to produce a solid target. V—UT compounds. S—stainless steel trap. W—glass wool. C—cooling coil. V—valves. P—to pump. Q—quartz tubes. D—induction heating coil. T—target material. H—heating coil.*

in which the number of tritium atoms per unit volume equals or exceeds the number of atoms of zirconium. A device for loading a zirconium target with tritium is described by Lillie and Conner (19). A sketch of the assembly is shown in Fig. 8.12. Of all-metal construction, except for the quartz tubes Q, the device is provided with valves so that connections may be made to vacuum pumps, to a tritium generator, or to flushing gas alternately. The tritium is released from the compound UT_3 contained in the lower extremity of the vertical tube. This compound releases tritium on heating and the tritium recombines with the uranium on cooling. The prepared blank target is placed at T and heated by induction currents from

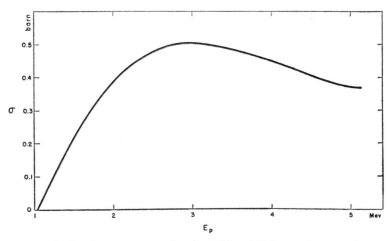

FIG. 8.13. *Total cross section for the* H³(p,n)He³ *reaction as a function of proton energy.*

the coil D during impregnation. The total cross section for the H³(p,n)He³ reaction, as measured by Willard, Bair, and Kington (20), is shown in Fig. 8.13. The curve showing the cross section as a function of E_p extends from the threshold at 1.02 Mev up to 5 Mev. The yield of neutrons near the threshold is substantial. The absence of excited states in He³ in the region covered by the curve of Fig. 8.13 indicates that the neutrons from this reaction should be monoenergetic. The general characteristics of the emission of neutrons from the H³(p,n) reaction are conveniently illustrated by the McKibben diagram in Fig. 8.14.

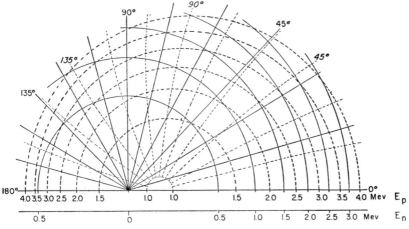

FIG. 8.14. *McKibben diagram for the* H³(p,n)He³ *reaction.*

8.6. The (p,n) Reaction in Targets of Higher Atomic Number

Although targets of low atomic number have been more popular in the past for the generation of neutrons, Brugger, Bonner, and Marion (21) have called attention to the reactions $Sc^{45}(p,n)Ti^{45}$ and $Cu^{63}(p,n)Zn^{63}$ for the production of monoenergetic neutrons in the kilovolt region of energies. In addition to the obvious advantages of these elements in the preparation of targets, the nuclear reactions have characteristics which make them useful in the production of monoenergetic neutrons. For example, when the proton energy exceeds the threshold by 4 kev in scandium, the neutron

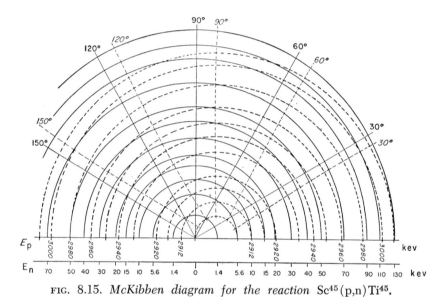

FIG. 8.15. *McKibben diagram for the reaction* $Sc^{45}(p,n)Ti^{45}$.

energy reaches 10 kev. If the spread of energy in the proton beam is 1 kev, the resultant spread in the neutron energy is 2 kev. When the neutron energy reaches 20 kev, the spread of energy of the neutrons equals that of the proton beam. Also when 20-kev neutrons are emitted at $\theta_n = 0$, the neutron energy is still 19.5 kev at $\theta_n = 15°$. This comparative uniformity of the neutron energy over a large angle is useful when large samples must be used in measuring scattering or absorption of neutrons. Another advantage of these heavier targets is the reduction of the doppler broadening of the neutron energy. A McKibben diagram for the reaction $Sc^{45}(p,n)Ti^{45}$ is shown in Fig. 8.15. For the $Cu^{63}(p,n)Zn^{63}$ reaction, protons in the energy range 4.2 to 4.4 Mev will yield neutrons with energies corresponding to the neutron energy scale of Fig. 8.15.

Gibbons, Macklin, and Schmitt (22) have proposed the use of the resonance emission of neutrons in the reaction $V^{51}(p,n)Cr^{51}$ as a source of monochromatic neutrons of energies from 5 to 120 kev. The emission spectrum of these neutrons in the forward direction consists of very sharp peaks as shown in Fig. 8.16. The curve in Fig. 8.16 covers the range of proton energies from the threshold at 1.566 Mev up to 1.67 Mev. The natural widths of the resonances added to the spread of energy in the proton beam appear

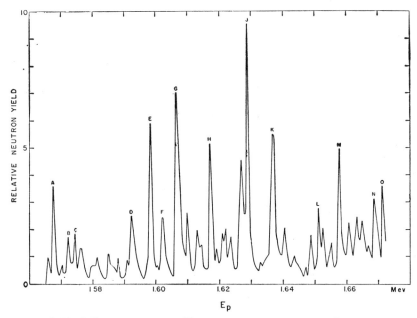

FIG. 8.16. *Relative neutron yield in counts per microcoulomb as a function of the bombarding proton energy for the reaction,* $V^{51}(p,n)Cr^{51}$. *The target was 1 kev thick and the neutrons were accepted in a forward cone with a half-angle of 45°.*

to be less than 1 kev, the thickness of the vanadium target. The neutron energies for the selected lettered peaks of Fig. 8.16 are given in Table 8.2.

8.7. Neutrons from the (p,n) Reaction at Higher Energies

Accelerators which can produce beams of protons with energies of the order of 400 Mev may be used to generate neutrons of approximately equal energy. For example, Goodell and co-workers (23) have investigated the distribution of the energy of neutrons when targets of beryllium, lithium, and carbon were bombarded by protons of 375 Mev. The results were similar for each target. Comparative curves are shown in Fig. 8.17. In the

Table 8.2

ENERGIES OF NEUTRONS FROM RESONANCE PEAKS
IN THE REACTION $V^{51}(p,n)Cr^{51}$

Peak	E_p (Mev)	E_n (kev)
A	1.568	4.8
B	1.573	11.3
C	1.575	13.6
D	1.592	34
E	1.598	40
F	1.603	45
G	1.607	50
H	1.617	61
J	1.629	74
K	1.637	82
L	1.651	97
M	1.658	104
N	1.669	116
O	1.672	119

measurements from which these curves were plotted, the proton beam was monitored by a bismuth fission chamber. The chamber gave the "monitor counts" used in specifying the ordinates of the graph in Fig. 8.17. The energies of the neutrons were determined by measuring the range of recoil protons scattered at 45° by a sheet of polyethylene.

Fireman and Rowland (24) have irradiated water and liquid ammonia with 2.2-Bev protons to investigate the neutrons produced at this very high energy. To evaluate the results, they determined the relative yields

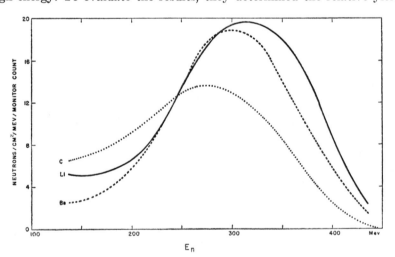

FIG. 8.17. *Comparison of the neutron energy distribution from the proton bombardment of carbon, lithium, and beryllium at 375 Mev.*

of neutrons from oxygen and from nitrogen in comparison with the neutrons from a Ra-Be neutron source. The neutrons were detected by imbedding cadmium-covered indium foils at various depths in a paraffin block near the target material. The activation of the indium by neutrons with energies corresponding to the resonance level in indium was taken as a measure of the neutrons. The relative counting rates of the indium foils as a function

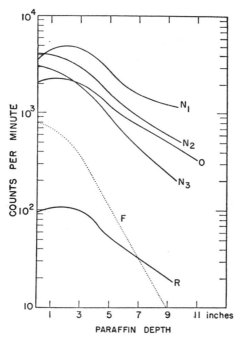

FIG. 8.18. *Activities produced in cadmium-covered indium foils imbedded in a paraffin block by neutrons generated by 2.2-Bev protons on nitrogen and oxygen compared with fission neutrons and those from a standard Ra-Be source. Curve N_1—neutrons from irradiated NH_3 at 60°. Curve N_2— neutrons from irradiated NH_3 at 90°. Curve N_3—neutrons from irradiated NH_3 at 120°. Curve F—neutrons from U^{235} fission. Curve R—neutrons from Ra-Be source. Counts per minute are relative to the standard Ra-Be source for cadmium-covered indium foils at various depths in the paraffin.*

of the depth of the foil in the paraffin block are plotted in Fig. 8.18 at several angles from the target. For comparison, the curves for the fission neutrons from U^{235} and for the neutrons from the Ra-Be source were measured in the same geometry and the results plotted as curve F and curve R, respectively. The cross section for neutron production by 2.2-Bev protons in nitrogen was estimated as about 1 barn, and in oxygen as about 0.65 barn, from these measurements.

8.8. The (d,n) Reaction as a Source of Neutrons

Nearly all of the (d,n) reactions which have been used in the generation of neutrons are strongly exoergic. Hence the reactions have no thresholds and neutrons are released at deuteron energies approaching zero. An exception is the reaction $C^{12}(d,n)N^{13}$, which is endoergic with $Q = -0.28$ Mev and a threshold energy $E_T = 0.33$ Mev. Otherwise devices which can accelerate deuterons to an energy of a few kilovolts are usable as sources of neutrons. The low energy required for the deuteron beam largely accounts for the numerous installations using deuterons to obtain neutrons in the early days of accelerators. Although the number of (d,n) reactions is considerable, only a few have proved valuable as sources of monoenergetic neutrons. In fact, only two are well suited to this use. They are the $H^2(d,n)He^3$ and the $H^3(d,n)He^4$ reactions. Other (d,n) reactions, such as $Li^7(d,n)Be^8$ with a high Q-value of 15 Mev, and $Be^9(d,n)B^{10}$, while giving high neutron yields, do not give simple neutron spectra.

8.9. The $H^2(d,n)He^3$ Reaction as a Source of Neutrons

This reaction has been widely used in the production of monoenergetic neutrons. One of the convenient characteristics of the $H^2(d,n)He^3$ reaction is a high yield of neutrons at deuteron energies below 1 Mev. The reaction equation is

$$H^2 + H^2 \rightarrow He^3 + n^1 + 3.3 \text{ Mev} \qquad (8.8)$$

A popular method for preparing targets for use in an accelerator for the (d,n) reaction on deuterons has been to freeze heavy water on a refrigerated metal support. The total neutron yield, for energies of the bombarding deuterons below 1 Mev, from a thick target of D_2O ice is shown in Fig. 8.19. A composite curve for the total cross section for neutron production is reproduced in Fig. 8.20. The curve is taken from Hunter and Richards (25) who made an extensive study of the yield of neutrons from the $H^2(d,n)He^3$ reaction. Their data were taken with a gas target 2 cm in length corresponding to 50 to 150 kev thickness for deuterons. The competing reaction, $H^2(d,p)H^3$ always occurs along with the (d,n) reaction when deuterons are bombarded by deuterons. Actually the (d,p) cross section is approximately equal to the (d,n) cross section in this reaction. Experimental values of the ratio σ_n/σ_p, as plotted by McNeill (26), using data from various observers, are shown in Fig. 8.21 for deuteron energies up to 0.3 Mev. More precise measurements of the ratio of the (d,n) cross section to the (d,p) cross section for the deuteron have been made by Arnold and co-workers (27) in the region up to $E_d = 120$ kev. Their work yielded the data given in Table 8.3. The fact that protons are emitted in numbers nearly equal to those for the neutrons from the bombardment of deuterons by deuterons has been used

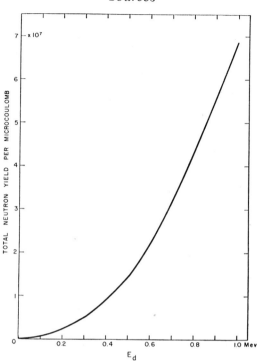

FIG. 8.19. *Variation of total neutron yield for thick target of* D_2O *ice with the energy of the deuterons.*

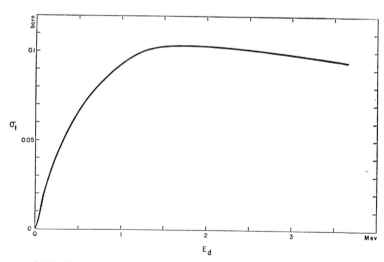

FIG. 8.20. *Total cross section of the reaction* $H^2(d,n)He^3$ *as a function of the energy of the deuteron.*

Table 8.3

CROSS SECTIONS FOR THE H²(d,p)H³ AND H²(d,n)He³
REACTIONS AND THE RATIOS σ_n/σ_p FOR VALUES
OF E_d UP TO 120 KEV

Observations were made at $\theta = 90°$

E_d (kev)	σ_p (mb)	σ_n (mb)	σ_n/σ_p
19	0.213	0.200	0.904
22	0.391	0.367	0.913
25	0.629	0.592	0.941
30	1.14	1.08	0.947
33	1.54	1.46	0.948
36	1.98	1.88	0.949
40	2.56	2.43	0.949
46	3.58	3.42	0.956
53	4.98	4.78	0.960
60	6.50	6.25	0.961
67	8.14	7.86	0.965
73	9.59	9.30	0.969
80	11.2	10.9	0.973
93	13.9	13.6	0.978
100	15.4	15.2	0.987
107	16.5	16.6	1.006
110	17.1	17.0	0.994
120	17.5	17.4	0.994

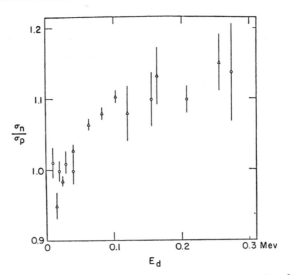

FIG. 8.21. *Variation of the ratio of the cross section,* σ_n, *for the reaction* H²(d,n)He³ *to* σ_p *for the reaction* H²(d,p)H³ *with the energy of the bombarding deuteron.*

to monitor the yield of neutrons from the bombardment. The protons can be conveniently detected and counted, of course. The estimation of the neutron production from the measurement of the protons is advantageous at low bombarding energies. For higher values of energy of the bombarding deuterons, the recoiling He³ particles are used. A simplified McKibben diagram for the H²(d,n)He³ reaction is reproduced in Fig. 8.22.

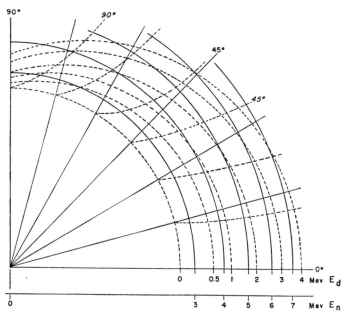

FIG. 8.22. *Nomograph for the reaction* H²(d,n)He³.

8.10. The H³(d,n)He⁴ Reaction as a Source of Neutrons

The H³(d,n) reaction is outstanding, among the (d,n) reactions which have been used for generating monoenergetic neutrons, for its high positive value of Q. The equation of the reaction is

$$H^3 + H^2 \rightarrow He^4 + n^1 + 17.6 \text{ Mev} \tag{8.9}$$

This reaction is characterized by an intense production of neutrons of high energy for bombarding energies of the order of $E_d = 100$ kev. The variation of the cross section with E_d is shown in Fig. 8.23. The solid curve represents the computations made by Conner, Bonner, and Smith (28), using the Breit-Wigner one-level formula in the form

$$\sigma = \frac{2J + 1}{2s + 1} \frac{\pi}{(2i + 1)k^2} \frac{\Gamma_d \Gamma_n}{(E_\lambda + \Delta_\lambda - E)^2 + \frac{1}{4}(\Gamma_d + \Gamma_n)^2} \tag{8.10}$$

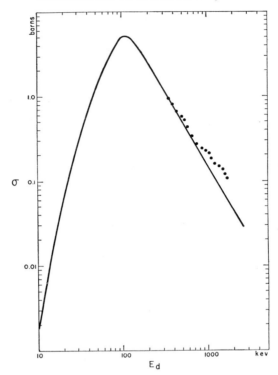

FIG. 8.23. *Variation of the cross section for the reaction* $H^3(d,n)He^4$ *with the energy of the deuteron.*

where J is the angular momentum of the compound nucleus, s and i are the spins of the incident particle and the target nucleus, respectively, and k is the wave number of the relative motion. Γ_d and Γ_n are deuteron and neutron level widths, respectively, E_λ is a constant and Δ_λ the level shift. E is the center-of-mass energy. The cross section was also measured over the range of bombarding energies represented by the scale for E_d in Fig. 8.23. The agreement of the observations with the theoretical curve is excellent, except at the upper end of the curve where deviations of the experimental observations are shown by a series of dots. Therefore it can be concluded that the curve represents an isolated resonance peak with a maximum at approximately 100 kev. The existence of the resonance accounts for the large yield of neutrons at 100 kev. In the production of neutrons by the (d,n) reaction on tritons, either the tritons may be accelerated to strike a deuterium target or, for example, the deuterons may be accelerated into a gas target of H^3. Fig. 8.24 shows the nomograph for this reaction.

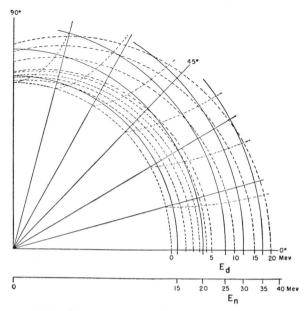

FIG. 8.24. *Nomograph for the reaction* $H^3(d,n)He^4$.

8.11. Deuteron Stripping Reactions in the Generation of Neutrons

We have seen that the deuteron can be considered as a combination of a neutron and a proton. There is considerable evidence to support the view that this structure is not bound together very firmly. It seems very probable that the neutron and the proton are outside the range of their mutual nuclear forces for a large part of the time. It is not surprising, therefore, that a deuteron traveling at high speed through a target may have its proton captured in a nucleus while the neutron continues on its way. Such a process has been repeatedly observed with the neutron retaining its proportional fraction of the original energy of the deuteron, roughly one-half. The interaction has naturally come to be known as the *stripping of the deuteron.* Although the converse interaction in which the neutron is captured, releasing a proton, also occurs, it is of interest in the present discussion only as a competing reaction which may reduce the number of neutrons released. The neutrons from deuteron stripping can be identified by the fact that the maximum of their distribution of energy is at an energy equal to one-half the energy of the incident deuteron, as indicated in Fig. 8.26. A more important characteristic of the stripping reaction is the concentration of the neutrons in a very narrow cone about the forward direction of the deuteron. The existence of this cone distinguishes the stripped neutrons quite definitely from those neutrons produced by direct reaction with nuclei, as in the usual (d,n) reactions.

Serber (29) has developed a function giving the angular distribution of the numbers of the neutrons about the direction of the bombarding deuterons. A number of measurements have been made of the distribution for neutrons resulting from the stripping of deuterons of about 190-Mev energy. A recent example is the data obtained by Schecter and his co-workers (30). The data are plotted in Fig. 8.25 which shows the relative intensity of the neutrons as a function of the angle of the

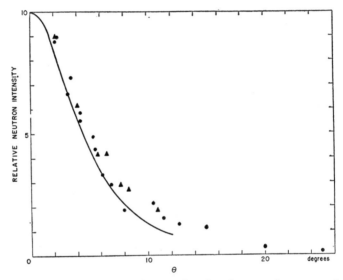

FIG. 8.25. *Observations on the angular distribution of neutrons from stripping 190-Mev deuterons in carbon. Triangles represent the vertical, circles the horizontal distribution. The curve is that computed by Serber* (29).

forward cone. The circles give the horizontal and the triangles the vertical distribution. These neutrons were produced by stripping 190-Mev neutrons in a carbon target. The curve drawn in Fig. 8.25 shows the distribution computed from the formula developed by Serber. The good agreement between observation and theory has been interpreted as a confirmation of the validity of the theory.

An unfortunate characteristic of stripped neutrons, when the stripping reaction is to be used as a source of neutrons of high energy, is the wide spread in the distribution of the energies of the neutrons. In the stripping of 190-Mev deuterons the spread of energy may be of the order of 20 Mev for a beam of neutrons having their maximum energy at about 85 Mev.

This energy distribution has also been computed by Serber and his curve is shown in Fig. 8.26. Measurements by Hadley and his co-workers (31) of the energy distribution of the primary neutrons obtained by stripping 190-Mev deuterons on beryllium are also in agreement with the curve of Fig. 8.26 within experimental errors. The broad distribution of the neutron energies complicates the use of these neutrons for nuclear investigations, such as the measurement of cross sections. Averages only, over a fairly large region of energies, are obtainable from measurements made with neu-

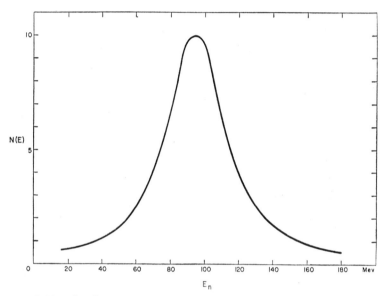

FIG. 8.26. *The theoretical distribution of the energy of neutrons from stripping 190-Mev deuterons for a nucleus transparent to neutrons.*

trons produced by stripping. The data would fail to show rapid changes in the dependence of measured quantities on the energy of the neutrons.

8.12. Production of Neutrons by the (γ,n) Reaction by Accelerators

When bremsstrahlung from betatrons with energies exceeding 20 Mev became available, it also became possible to generate neutrons by the (γ,n) reaction in any of the elements. The threshold energy for the (γ,n) reaction ranges from around 10 Mev for nuclei with high mass number up to about 19 Mev for $A = 12$. Below $A = 12$, the threshold energies decrease again. Some values of the thresholds for the (γ,n) reaction are given in Table 8.4.

The energy E_m of the photons at which the cross section for the (γ,n) reaction has the maximum value σ_m varies slowly from about 13.5 Mev

Table 8.4

THRESHOLD ENERGIES E_T IN MEV
FOR THE (γ,n) REACTION IN SEVERAL NUCLIDES

Nuclide	E_T	Nuclide	E_T
C^{12}	18.7	Ca^{40}	15.8
N^{14}	10.8	Ca^{44}	11.4
O^{16}	15.6	Sc^{45}	12.0
F^{19}	10.7	Ti^{46}	13.3
Mg^{24}	16.6	Fe^{54}	13.8
Mg^{25}	7.2	Co^{59}	10.2
Mg^{26}	11.1	Ni^{58}	11.7
Al^{27}	12.7	Ni^{60}	11.6
Si^{28}	16.9	Cu^{63}	10.9
Si^{29}	8.5	Cu^{65}	10.2
Si^{30}	10.6	Zn^{64}	11.6
P^{31}	12.4	Br^{81}	10.2
S^{32}	15.0	Rb^{87}	9.0
K^{39}	13.5	Mo^{92}	13.3
A^{40}	9.8	Nh^{93}	8.7

for $A = 200$ to about 22.5 Mev in the region around $A = 20$. Table 8.5 contains some approximate values from various authors of σ_m for the (γ,n) reaction. At photon energies of 20 Mev and higher, a whole series of nuclear reactions are possible. The situation can be illustrated by reference to Fig. 8.27, which shows the variation of the (γ,n) cross section in Mg^{24} with the photon energy E_γ, as measured by Nathans and Yergin (32). This curve has a pronounced maximum to which it rises rapidly from the threshold energy. The value of σ then sharply decreases with increasing E_γ. This behavior of the cross section curve is characteristic of the (γ,n) reaction. On the x-axis in Fig. 8.27 the threshold energies for the (γ,p), $(\gamma,2p)$, and (γ,pn) reactions are indicated by arrows. Depending on the value of E_γ, this whole complex of reactions may be occurring simultaneously and with varying intensities. Supplementing Table 8.5, we give in Fig. 8.28 the curve for σ_m as a function of the mass number of the target, as plotted by Nathans and Halpern (33). The curve indicates the σ_m varies as $A^{3/2}$ in the region covered by the graph. To show the order of the yields of neutrons in the (γ,n) reaction, their curve for the neutron yield for rhodium is reproduced in Fig. 8.29. It becomes evident from this curve that the photoproduction of neutrons with accelerators under present conditions suffers from the disadvantage noted in connection with radioactive photoneutron sources. The intensity of the gamma rays far exceeds that of the neutrons. In the region of much higher photon energies here encountered this disadvantage is aggravated. The high intensity of the gamma radiation accounts in part for the infrequent use of the (γ,n) reaction as a source of neutrons in accelerators.

The photoneutron reaction, however, has proved valuable in the study of nuclear structure. It may, in this connection, be of interest to investigate the distribution of the energy of the photoneutrons. Price (34) has measured the energy spectrum of photoneutrons from several heavy nuclei when

Table 8.5

MAXIMUM (γ,n) CROSS SECTIONS, σ_m, WITH POSITION OF THE PEAK E_m

Target	σ_m (barn)	E_m (Mev)
Li	0.004	17.5
C^{12}	0.0083	22.5
O^{16}	0.0114	24.2
N^{14}	0.0028	24.2
Mg^{24}	0.0085	20
Mg^{25}	0.016	20
Si^{29}	0.023	15
P^{31}	0.0166	19
Cl	0.033	19
A^{40}	0.038	20
Ca^{40}	0.015	19.5
V^{51}	0.100	17.7
Cr	0.105	19.7
Ni	0.050	16.5
Br	0.175	16.0
Sr^{86}	0.155	16.0
Sr^{88}	0.200	16.8
Y^{89}	0.190	16.3
Zr^{90}	0.180	16.4
Zr^{91}	0.200	16.3
Ta	0.63	15
Pb	0.81	13.7
Bi	0.92	14.2

irradiated by 22-Mev bremsstrahlung from a betatron. His observations on bismuth are represented by the circles in Fig. 8.30. The curve is the theoretical distribution, on the basis of a statistical nuclear model, of the neutron energies to be expected if the energy level density ω_R in bismuth were given by

$$\omega_R = ce^{\sqrt{a\epsilon}} \tag{8.11}$$

where c is a constant, $\epsilon = E_n$, the neutron energy, and $a = 1.6(A - 40)^{1/2}$ with A the atomic mass number. This representative curve for the energy distribution of neutrons resulting from the action of photons on heavy nuclei does not exhibit characteristics which would make this reaction a useful

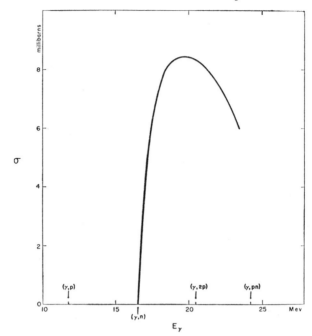

FIG. 8.27. *The* (γ,n) *cross section for the reaction* $Mg^{24}(\gamma,n)Mg^{23}$. *Arrows indicate the location of thresholds for various photonuclear reactions in* Mg^{24}.

source of neutrons for most purposes. Considering that other means of generating neutrons in the same region of energy have been discussed in preceding sections, and that these methods offer possibilities of preselecting the range of energy of the neutrons, photoneutron sources appear in a still more unfavorable light.

9.1. The Nuclear Reactor as a Neutron Source

The unusually large cross section of U^{235} for thermal neutrons is responsible for its use as the active ingredient of the fuel elements of most reactors which have been constructed to date. The high energies with which neutrons are released in the fission process also accounts for the extensive neutron moderator which is a basic feature of reactors using U^{235} for fuel. The moderator serves to reduce the energies of the fission neutrons to thermal energies with a minimum of loss by neutron capture or by escape from the moderator. Therefore a thermal neutron reactor can be used as a source of neutrons over a considerable range of energies. The useful range is not, however, as great as might be thought at first glance, as will appear from

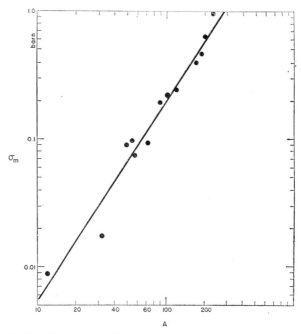

FIG. 8.28. *Log-log plot of the maximum cross section* σ_m *against* A *the mass number. The straight line indicates that* σ_m *is proportional to* $A^{3/2}$.

the following brief discussion of the characteristics of a reactor as a neutron source. It is not the aim to enter into a detailed discussion of the reactor because other excellent sources of this information are listed in the bibliography at the end of this book. Some of the principles which are fundamental to the operation of reactors will, however, be outlined later in dealing with the interactions of neutron with matter. An elementary description of a few of the principal research reactors now in use for generation of neutrons for experimental use will be introduced here to aid in visualizing methods of using reactors as neutron sources. Thermal reactors have been divided into two general types, depending on whether the fuel is distributed uniformly throughout the moderator or is arranged as a lattice of concentrated elements in some definite pattern in the moderator. When the fuel is mixed with the moderating medium, the reactor is called homogeneous, and when the fuel elements are distributed in a lattice the reactor is said to be heterogeneous. A considerable differentiation in design is also introduced when enriched U^{235} is used in the fuel elements as compared with the design of a reactor for using purified natural uranium as a fuel in which the ratio of U^{238} to U^{235} is approximately 139.

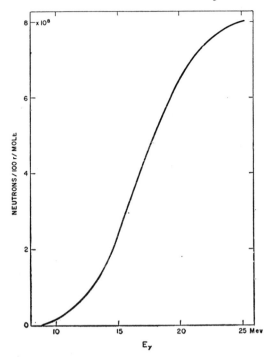

FIG. 8.29. *Yield of neutrons per mole per 100 roentgens for the* (γ,n)
reaction in rhodium as a function of the gamma-ray energy.

9.2. Heterogeneous Natural Uranium Thermal Reactors

The low concentration of U^{235} in natural uranium demands a specially designed moderator for the fission chain reaction to be self-sustaining. One requirement is that the moderator be of considerable size, particularly if graphite is used as the moderating material. The moderator must also capture very few neutrons, that is have a low capture cross section for thermal neutrons. Two materials have been found satisfactory for the construction of moderators for use with natural uranium. These substances are highly purified graphite and heavy water. Fig. 9.1 is a schematic diagram of a cross section of a heterogeneous thermal reactor using natural uranium with graphite as a moderator. The natural uranium metal rods are distributed in a lattice in a cube of graphite at least 20 feet on an edge. The thermal column is a feature of practically all reactors for the generation of neutrons for experimental use. The thermal column is, as indicated in the various figures illustrating the construction of reactors, a column of graphite of rectangular cross section. The column is of the order of 6 to 7 feet on an

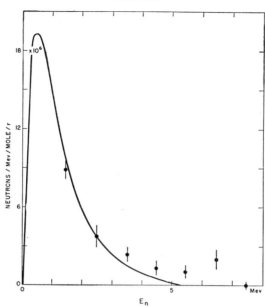

FIG. 8.30. *Observed energy spectrum of photoneutrons emitted from bismuth irradiated by 22-Mev bremsstrahlung. The curve shows the theoretical distribution for a level density* ω_R *given by* $\omega_R = Ce\sqrt{a\epsilon}$.

edge and extends from the moderator of the reactor into the reactor shield. No sources of neutrons exist within the thermal column. Neutrons entering from the moderator gradually approach a thermal distribution of energies as they diffuse through the column. The significance of the thermal column will be further outlined in discussing the distribution of the energies of the neutrons in a reactor. Fig. 9.2 represents a thermal reactor using natural uranium which has heavy water as the moderator. The reactor using heavy water as a moderator can be somewhat smaller than one using graphite because neutrons lose energy more rapidly in a given path length in heavy water. Most of the bulk of a completed heavy-water reactor is in the radiation shield. This shield, which has practically the same thickness for all reactors, is usually the equivalent of about 7 feet of high-density concrete. Because the principal purpose of the radiation shield is to protect workers in the vicinity from radiation, it is also sometimes called the biological shield.

9.3. Heterogeneous Reactors with Enriched U[235]

When U[235] in more concentrated form than that existing in natural uranium became plentiful it was possible to reduce drastically the size of the

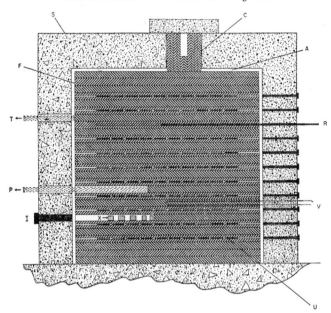

FIG. 9.1. *A graphite-moderated heterogeneous reactor using natural uranium. C—thermal column. A—duct for cooling air. S—shield. F—reflector. T—thermal neutrons. P—pile neutrons. I—irradiation chamber. X—samples for irradiation. R—control rod. U—uranium lattice. V—pneumatic tube for short irradiations.*

thermal reactor core containing the fuel elements. In addition, ordinary water could then be used as a moderator and also as the main part of the radiation shield. Fig. 9.3 indicates some of the basic features of a thermal reactor using enriched U^{235} and ordinary water as a moderator. The graphite reflector, which aids in preventing the escape of thermal neutrons from the reactor, and the thermal column are usually retained in the different specific designs of reactors with enriched U^{235} and ordinary water.

9.4. Homogeneous Reactors

Many designs of homogeneous thermal reactors have been proposed. A few of these designs have been constructed as sources of neutrons. The most familiar is the "water boiler" sketched in Fig. 9.4. Here the enriched uranium is dissolved in normal water. The solution of a uranium salt enriched in U^{235} is contained in a stainless steel sphere about a foot in diameter. The details of the original model constructed at the Los Alamos Scientific Laboratory will be found in reference (35).

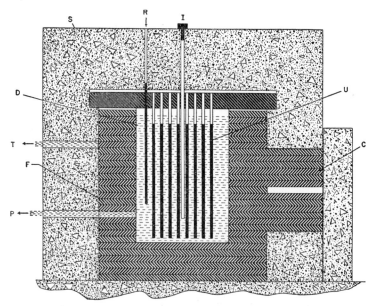

FIG. 9.2. *A heavy water moderated heterogeneous reactor using natural uranium. U—uranium rods. D—heavy water. F—graphite reflector. S—shield. C—thermal column. I—irradiation chamber. R—control rod.*

9.5. The Distribution of the Energy of Neutrons in a Reactor

Regarded as a source of neutrons, a reactor will contain neutrons of all energies from the maximum energy in the fission spectrum down to the thermal distribution of energies. The fission spectrum of U^{235} is represented empirically in Fig. 9.5 by the curve given by the equation $n(E) = 1765\sqrt{E}\ e^{-0.775E}$. This curve agrees within experimental errors with the measurements of Cranberg and co-workers (36). The extrapolation of the curve toward higher energy indicates the existence of a small but significant number of neutrons with energies as high as 15 Mev. Neutrons of this energy have been observed in a reactor. Because the moderation of the neutrons is essential to the operation of the reactor, the fission spectrum is released in a medium which begins immediately to slow the neutrons down to thermal velocities. Hence, in addition to the fission spectrum of fast neutrons, there exist in the reactor groups of neutrons which are in the process of being slowed down. One characteristic of the moderating process is that the number of neutrons with an energy E is proportional to $1/E$. Thus there are many more neutrons in the process of being slowed down than

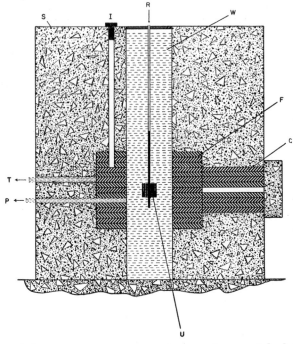

FIG. 9.3. *A heterogeneous reactor using uranium enriched in* U²³⁵ *with ordinary water as moderator. R—control rod. S—shield. W— ordinary water. F—graphite reflector. C—thermal column. U—uranium fuel elements enriched in* U²³⁵. *T—thermal neutrons. I—irradiation chamber.*

there are in the fission spectrum. The presence of the fission spectrum in a reactor is almost completely hidden by the larger numbers of slower neutrons. The flux of the fission neutrons is about equal to that of the thermal neutrons in the region of a reactor where the uranium is situated. The approximate equality comes about because each thermal neutron on absorption in the uranium will release about 1.4 fission neutrons in the moderator. However, the intensity of the fission spectrum decreases exponentially with distance from the uranium. These few facts regarding the fission spectrum in a reactor are sufficient to demonstrate that the reactor itself is not a suitable source of fission neutrons. As has been suggested, it is difficult even to observe the fission spectrum in a reactor. However, a thermal neutron beam from a reactor can be used to produce fission neutrons. The fission source is obtained by placing a target of fissile material in the thermal beam which converts this target into a convenient and intense source of fission neutrons.

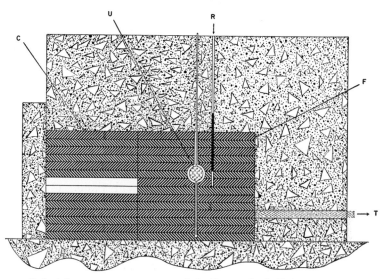

FIG. 9.4. *A homogeneous reactor of the "water boiler" type. R—control rod. U—solution of uranium enriched in* U^{235} *in water. F—graphite reflector. C—thermal column. T—thermal neutrons.*

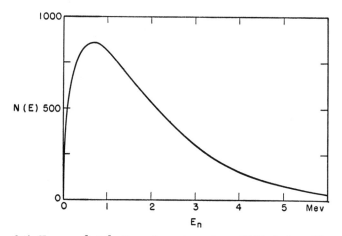

FIG. 9.5. *Energy distribution of neutrons from* U^{235} *fission. The empirical equation of the curve is*

$$N(E) = 1765\sqrt{E}\, e^{-0.775E}$$

and the observed points fell on this curve within experimental error. The extrapolation of the curve indicates the presence of a small number of neutrons with energies of the order of 15 Mev.

9.6. Resonance Neutrons

On the other hand, the neutrons that are in the process of being slowed down in the reactor, frequently called resonance neutrons, are very useful. These neutrons acquired the name of resonance neutrons because of their ability to excite neutron resonance levels in nuclei in the region of energies extending from thermal up to about 1 Mev. They are present in small numbers, in comparison with the thermal neutrons, in the pile neutrons taken directly from the moderator of a reactor. The spectrum of these pile neutrons has been measured by Borst and Sailor (37) for the Brookhaven reactor. Their observations are plotted in Fig. 9.6, taken with a crystal spectrometer. The ordinates of their graph represent the relative intensities of the flux at various energies at the detector of the spectrometer. Although their curve shows the flux to be proportional to $E^{-1.92}$, whereas the theory of the slowing down process requires a flux distribution proportional to E^{-1}, this departure is introduced by the reflectivity of the crystal of the spectrometer. Because the reflectivity of the crystal is also known to be proportional to E^{-1}, the data actually indicate that the observed flux distribution is proportional to $E^{-0.92}$, within reasonable agreement with expectation.

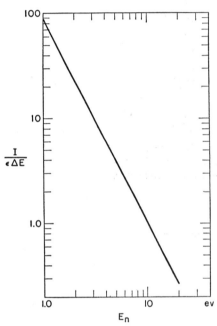

FIG. 9.6. *The spectrum of resonance neutrons as observed with a crystal spectrometer outside the Brookhaven reactor.*

9.7. The Cadmium Ratio

The presence of resonance neutrons in a reactor interferes with measurements where it is desired to observe the effects of thermal neutrons only. One means of determining the ratio of the intensity of the thermal neutrons to that of the resonance neutrons is by measurement of the cadmium ratio. The reason for the use of cadmium for excluding the effects of resonance neutrons becomes apparent from the curve in Fig. 9.7. The curve shows the total absorption cross section of cadmium as a function of the neutron energy in the range of energies from 0.01 to 10 ev. The curve reveals that cadmium is practically opaque to thermal neutrons, but transparent to neutrons having energies greater than about 0.4 ev. The cadmium ratio is defined as the ratio between the observed neutron intensity as revealed by a particular detector to the intensity observed with the same detector surrounded by a layer of cadmium. In the first measurement the detector responds to the sum of the thermal plus the resonance neutrons. In the second measurement the detector responds only to the resonance neutrons. If ϕ_{th} is the thermal neutron flux and ϕ_r the resonance flux, using a detector of unknown sensitivity, the measurement of the cadmium ratio is made in terms of

$$R_c = \frac{C_1\phi_{th} + C_2\phi_r}{C_2\phi_r} = 1 + \frac{C_1\phi_{th}}{C_2\phi_r} \quad (9.1)$$

where R_c is the cadmium ratio, and C_1 and C_2 are sensitivity constants. If $C_1 = C_2$ for the particular detector used then

$$\frac{\phi_{th}}{\phi_r} = R_c - 1 \quad (9.2)$$

Eq. 9.2 does not give the absolute values of the fluxes but only their ratio, unless the sensitivity constants for the detector are known.

Turning to a $1/v$ detector for the measurement of the cadmium ratio, where the sensitivity of the detector is inversely proportional to the neutron velocity, hence inversely proportional to $E_n^{1/2}$, we may write

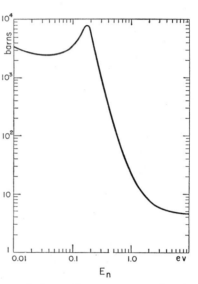

FIG. 9.7. *Total cross section of cadmium as a function of neutron energy.*

$$R_c - 1 = \frac{\phi_{th}\, \sigma_{\text{act th}}}{\phi_r \displaystyle\int_{0.4\,\text{ev}}^{\infty} \sigma_{\text{act}} \frac{dE}{E}} \quad (9.3)$$

in which account is taken of the dE/E distribution of the energies of the resonance neutrons. On introducing the dependence of the cross sections on the neutron energy, Eq. 9.3 becomes

$$R_c - 1 = \frac{\phi_{th} \dfrac{1}{\sqrt{0.025}}}{\phi_r \displaystyle\int_{0.4\,\text{ev}}^{\infty} \dfrac{dE}{E^{3/2}}} = \frac{2\phi_{th}}{\phi_r} \quad (9.4)$$

The computation in Eq. 9.4 assumes that the $1/v$ dependence of the sensitivity of the detector extends over the range of the energies of the resonance neutrons.

9.8. The Thermal Column

The need for neutrons which have been brought as nearly into thermal equilibrium with the temperature of the medium as can conveniently be done is responsible for the thermal column. We have seen that the thermal column is a part of practically all research reactors. Because the reactor is a source of intense gamma radiation, the thermal column often is separated from the reactor proper by a screen of bismuth several inches thick. Bismuth is used because it has a high absorption coefficient for gamma rays and an exceptionally low capture cross section for thermal neutrons. The size of the column, about 7 feet on an edge, is selected to reduce the leakage of neutrons through the sides. From measurements of the cadmium ratio in a thermal column its advantage as a method of isolating thermal neutrons becomes apparent. The curves in Fig. 9.8 follow, approximately, unpublished data taken by Seren in the thermal column of the first heavy-water reactor constructed at the Argonne National Laboratory. Curve A represents the activities induced in indium foil covered by cadmium at various distances from the outside face of the column. Curve B represents the corresponding measurements with bare indium foil. Therefore the cadmium ratios R_c are obtained by dividing the ordinates of curve B by the corresponding ordinates of curve A. These ratios are plotted in Fig. 9.9. Just inside the thermal column R_c has a value of about 7×10^4 and rises to a value of about 1.5×10^5 where it remains for several centimeters in a direction toward the reactor. It then falls until it has reached about 10^3 at the graphite reflector of the reactor. This decline in the value of R_c would continue if measurements were made at increasing distances into the reflector. Each thermal column will have a different distribution of the cadmium ratio, depending on the geometrical arrangement of the components of the reactor. R_c may also change in a given column with changes in the fuel loading or changes of the distribution of neutron absorbers in the reactor. Where it is important to know the values of cadmium ratios, they are usually measured for each observation in a series of measurements. Because cadmium ratios have very low values near the center of a reactor, where the thermal flux has its greatest value, this high-flux region cannot be used for many types of experiments with thermal neutrons. As has been suggested, experiments requiring a nearly pure thermal flux must be performed with neutrons from the thermal column. An example of an experiment requiring a high cadmium ratio for the flux is the measurement of thermal neutron cross sections by determining the transmission of a neutron beam. The sacrifice in the value of the flux of thermal neutrons obtainable from

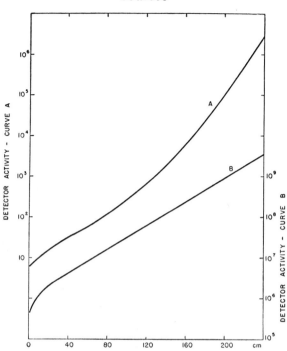

FIG. 9.8. *Activities induced in indium foil exposed at various positions in a thermal column. Curve* A, *to be referred to the left-hand ordinates, is for indium foil covered with cadmium. Curve* B, *to be referred to the right-hand ordinates, is for bare indium foil.*

a thermal column is the price which must be paid for the removal of the epithermal neutrons. It is usual to take graphite stringers out of a thermal column to form an open channel for the escape of the flux to the outside of the reactor shield where the experiments can be performed. The distance to which this channel penetrates the column is determined by the permissible lower limit to the cadmium ratio for the experiment in hand. If this distance is d and the cross-sectional area of the channel is A, then a flux of neutrons per cm² per sec equal to ϕ emerging through the inner face of the channel will produce a flux ϕ_x at the outer face of the column given by

$$\frac{\phi A}{4\pi d^2} = \phi_x \tag{9.5}$$

As the distance d is made shorter the value of ϕ_x relative to ϕ increases. However ϕ simultaneously decreases almost to the same extent. Hence the chief net gain is in the cadmium ratio as d decreases up to the point where the cadmium ratio begins to fall off near the exterior face of the column.

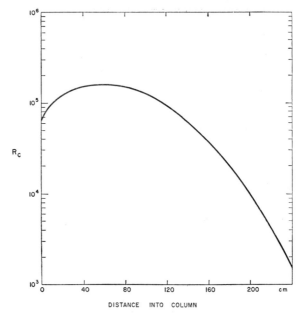

DISTANCE INTO COLUMN

FIG. 9.9. *Values of the cadmium ratio* R_c *computed from the observations of Fig. 9.8.*

This decrease in the cadmium ratio near the outer face of the column is caused by epithermal neutrons which have escaped from other parts of the reactor and entered the column from the outside. Therefore the distribution of the cadmium ratio near the outer face of the column is determined by the details of the design of the reactor.

As an example of the use of Eq. 9.5, assume that a channel 2.5 meters deep and 20 cm square extends into a thermal column. The flux entering the inner face of this channel is 5×10^{10} neutrons per cm² per sec. Then the flux at the outer face of the channel is

$$\phi_x = \frac{(5 \times 10^{10})\ 400}{4\pi(62500)} = 2.54 \times 10^7 \text{ neutrons per cm}^2 \text{ per sec}$$

9.9. Thermal Neutrons

The kinetics of neutrons in thermal equilibrium with the medium in which they exist is completely described by the well-known kinetic theory of gases. The number of neutrons per unit volume in the velocity interval dv is given by

$$\frac{dn}{dv} = \frac{4n}{v_0{}^3\sqrt{\pi}}\,v^2 e^{-v^2/v_0{}^2} \tag{9.6}$$

where $v_0 = 2kT/M_n$ is the most probable velocity for an absolute temperature T and n is the total number of neutrons per unit volume. This velocity v_0 therefore corresponds to the maximum density of neutrons in the distribution curve showing the relative densities of thermal neutrons at various velocities. In the definition of v_0, the constant k is the Boltzmann constant of kinetic theory. For a temperature of 20°C or 293°K, we may compute v_0 as

$$v_0 = \frac{2(1.38 \times 10^{-16})293}{1.675 \times 10^{-24}} = 2205 \text{ meters per sec}$$

The distribution described by Eq. 9.6 is plotted as curve A in Fig. 9.10 with $n(v_0)$ normalized at unity for $T = 293°K$. For many purposes it is more useful to consider the distribution of the flux density of thermal neutrons. Because neutron flux is obtained by multiplying the number of neutrons of a given velocity by this velocity, and is expressed as nv, the flux distribution is obtained by multiplying Eq. 9.6 by v which gives

$$\frac{d(nv)}{dv} = \frac{4n}{v_0^3 \sqrt{\pi}} v^3 e^{-v^2/v_0^2} \tag{9.7}$$

The flux distribution, with the most probable flux again normalized to unity, is plotted as curve B in Fig. 9.10. The maximum flux occurs, not at v_0, but at $(\sqrt{3/2})v_0$, as indicated by the displacement of curve B relative

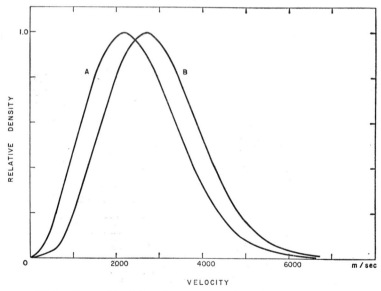

FIG. 9.10. *Maxwellian distribution for thermal neutrons at 20°C. Curve A gives the neutron density as a function of velocity. Curve B gives the density of the neutron flux as a function of velocity. Each curve is normalized for a maximum ordinate of unity.*

to curve A. Table 9.1 gives a few definitions of quantities used with reference to Maxwellian distributions for thermal neutrons.

Table 9.1

DEFINITIONS FOR MAXWELLIAN DISTRIBUTION
OF THERMAL NEUTRONS

Quantity	*Definition*
Normalized velocity distribution, $n(v)$	$\dfrac{4}{\sqrt{\pi}}\left(\dfrac{M_n}{2k_T}\right)^{3/2} v^2 e^{-M_n v^2/v_0 kT}$
Most probable velocity, v_0	$\sqrt{\dfrac{2k_T}{M_n}}$
Average velocity	$\dfrac{2v_0}{\sqrt{\pi}}$
Root mean square velocity	$(3/2)v_0$
Normalized energy distribution, $n(E)$	$\dfrac{2}{\sqrt{\pi k^3 T^3}}\sqrt{E}e^{-E/kT}$
Most probable energy	$kT/2$
Energy at which the flux is a maximum	kT
Average energy	$3kT/2$

It is obvious that neutrons from any source may be slowed down to a thermal distribution of velocities. In the early days of experimentation with neutrons many types of sources were used in this way. Now that nuclear reactors are becoming more numerous they are the most widely used sources of thermal neutrons. The high fluxes which these reactors provide make experiments with thermal neutrons far more convenient and rapid than formerly. In fact the reactor can provide beams of thermal neutrons of much higher intensity than is available from any other source now known. Practically all reactors which have been constructed thus far for experimental purposes have an average flux of at least 5×10^{11} neutrons per cm² per sec. The MTR reactor completed at Arco, Idaho, in 1952 has an average flux of 2×10^{14} thermal neutrons with a maximum accessible flux in the reflector near the core of 4.5×10^{14} neutrons per cm² per sec. It is true that these fluxes may be reduced by a factor of a thousand or more by the time they reach a completely thermalized beam outside the reactor. Even so, they still are the most intense beams of thermal neutrons now available.

SYMBOLS FOR CHAPTER III

A	nuclear mass number
E	kinetic energy of a particle
E_p	kinetic energy of a proton
E_n	kinetic energy of a neutron
E_α	kinetic energy of an alpha particle
$E_\gamma = h\nu$	energy of a photon
E_T	threshold energy in a nuclear reaction
i	spin of a target nucleus in a nuclear reaction
J	angular momentum quantum number of a compound nucleus
k	Boltzmann's constant
P	momentum of a particle
P_n	momentum of a neutron
P_p	momentum of a proton
R_c	cadmium ratio
s	spin of an incident particle in a nuclear reaction
T	absolute temperature in degrees K
v	velocity of a particle
v_0	most probable velocity of thermal neutrons in a Maxwellian distribution.
α	alpha particle
γ	gamma ray
Γ_d	nuclear level width for a deuteron
Γ_n	nuclear level width for a neutron
θ	angle in laboratory system of coordinates between the direction of an incident particle and the direction of a product particle
θ_n	angle in the laboratory system between the direction of an incident particle and the direction of a neutron released in a nuclear reaction
λ	wavelength of a neutron
σ_act	neutron activation cross section
$\sigma_\mathrm{act\ th}$	thermal neutron activation cross section
σ_m	maximum value of σ
ϕ	angle between the direction of an incident particle and the direction of the product particles in the center-of-mass system
ϕ	neutron flux
ϕ_th	thermal neutron flux

ϕ_r resonance neutron flux
ω_R nuclear energy level density

PROBLEMS FOR CHAPTER III

1. Compute the most probable velocity for thermal neutrons at a temperature of 35°C. To what energy in electron volts does this velocity correspond?

2. Compute the maximum energy of neutrons released by a (γ,n) reaction from a phosphorus target by 17-Mev gamma rays.

3. Compute the energy of neutrons obtained from the $Li^7(p,n)$ reaction at an angle of 80° with respect to the proton beam when $E_p = 2.9$ Mev.

4. An indium foil exposed to saturation activity in a thermal column yields 3.34×10^6 counts per minute when extrapolated back to the time of removal from the column. When exposed in the same place but completely shielded by cadmium the same foil gives a saturated activity of 450 counts per minute. Compute the cadmium ratio.

5. Compute the energy of neutrons released at $\theta_n = 30°$ in the $Sc^{45}(p,n)$ reaction with $E_p = 3.2$ Mev.

6. Derive the expression for the relation between E_n and E_p, the energy acquired by a proton at rest when struck by a neutron of energy E_n when the proton recoils at an angle θ with respect to the direction of the neutron.

REFERENCES FOR CHAPTER III

1. T. W. Bonner, A. A. Kraus, Jr., J. B. Marion, and J. P. Schiffer. *Phys. Rev.* **102,** 1348 (1956).
2. J. O. Elliot, W. I. McGarry, and W. R. Faust. *Phys. Rev.* **93,** 1348 (1954).
3. J. W. T. Spinks and G. A. R. Graham. *Can J. Res.* **28A,** 60 (1950).
4. H. L. Anderson and B. T. Feld. *Rev. Sci. Inst.* **18,** 186 (1947).
5. M. Teucher. *Z. Phys.* **126,** 410 (1949).
6. Leona Stewart. *Phys. Rev.* **98,** 740 (1955).
7. O. J. C. Runnalls and R. R. Boucher. *Nature* **176,** 1019 (1955).
8. E. Guth and C. J. Mullin. *Phys. Rev.* **76,** 234 (1949).
9. A. Wattenberg. *Phys. Rev.* **71,** 497 (1947).
10. I. B. Russell, D. Sachs, A. Wattenberg, and R. Fields. *Phys. Rev.* **73,** 545 (1948).
11. A. H. Snell, E. C. Barker, and R. L. Sternberg. *Phys. Rev.* **80,** 637 (1950).
12. D. J. Tendam and H. L. Bradt. *Phys. Rev.* **72,** 1118 (1947).
13. A. J. Allen, J. F. Nechaj, K. H. Sun, and B. Jennings. *Phys. Rev.* **81,** 536 (1951).
14. H. G. Blosser and T. H. Handley. *Phys. Rev.* **100,** 1342 (1955).
15. E. Lampi. *Rev. Sci. Inst.* **22,** 429 (1951).
16. A. O. Hanson, R. F. Taschek, and J. H. Williams. *Rev. Mod. Phys.* **21,** 635 (1949).
17. J. L. McKibben. *Phys. Rev.* **70,** 101A (1946).
18. C. H. Johnson and H. E. Banta. *Rev. Sci. Inst.* **27,** 132 (1956).
19. A. B. Lillie and J. P. Conner. *Rev. Sci. Inst.* **22,** 210 (1951).
20. H. B. Willard, J. K. Bair, and J. D. Kington. *Phys. Rev.* **90,** 865 (1953).
21. R. M. Brugger, T. W. Bonner, and J. B. Marion. *Phys. Rev.* **100,** 84 (1955).
22. J. H. Gibbons, R. L. Macklin, and H. W. Schmitt. *Phys. Rev.* **100,** 167 (1955).
23. W. F. Goodell, Jr., H. H. Loar, R. P. Durbin, and W. W. Havens, Jr. *Phys. Rev.* **89,** 724 (1953).

24. E. L. Fireman and F. S. Rowland. *Phys. Rev.* **97,** 780 (1955).
25. G. T. Hunter and H. T. Richards. *Phys. Rev.* **76,** 1445 (1949).
26. K. G. McNeill. *Phil. Mag.* **46,** 800 (1955).
27. W. R. Arnold, J. A. Phillips, G. A. Sawyer, E. J. Stovall, Jr., and J. L. Tuck. *Phys. Rev.* **93,** 483 (1954).
28. J. P. Conner, T. W. Bonner, and J. R. Smith. *Phys. Rev.* **88,** 468 (1952).
29. R. Serber. *Phys. Rev.* **72,** 1008 (1947).
30. L. Schecter, W. E. Crandall, G. P. Millburn, and J. Ise, Jr. *Phys. Rev.* **97,** 184 (1955).
31. J. Hadley, E. Kelly, C. Leith, E. Segrè, C. Wiegand, and H. York. *Phys. Rev.* **75,** 351 (1949).
32. R. Nathans and P. F. Yergin. *Phys. Rev.* **98,** 1296 (1955).
33. R. Nathans and J. Halpern. *Phys. Rev.* **93,** 437 (1954).
34. G. A. Price. *Phys. Rev.* **93,** 1279 (1954).
35. Los Alamos Scientific Laboratory. *Rev. Sci. Inst.* **22,** 489 (1952).
36. L. Cranberg, G. Frye, N. Nereson, and L. Rosen. *Phys. Rev.* **103,** 662 (1956).
37. L. B. Borst and V. L. Sailor. *Rev. Sci. Inst.* **24,** 141 (1953).

Chapter IV

DETECTION OF NEUTRONS

10.1. Principles of Neutron Detection

In common with all neutral particles, neutrons can be detected only by means of secondary charged particles which they release in passing through matter, or by other secondary processes which produce ionizing radiations. For reasons of practical efficiency, the secondary particles must be generated at energies which can produce ionization conveniently detectable by devices which respond to the effects of ionization. The secondary charged particles may be protons released by collisions of neutrons with hydrogen nuclei; they may be the direct result of nuclear disintegration produced by neutrons, like the alpha particles from the reaction $B^{10} + n^1 \rightarrow Li^7 + \alpha$; or they may be the radioactive radiations from product nuclei which become radioactive as the result of neutron capture. The usefulness of each of the various approaches to the problem of detecting neutrons is controlled by the requirement that measurable ionization effects be produced. For example, slow neutrons on collision with hydrogen nuclei will not produce protons which satisfy the requirement of being able to produce a conveniently detectable ionization. Equally, fast neutrons often do not have sufficiently high capture cross sections to produce conveniently measurable radioactivity in target nuclei. Consequently detection can be classified to a large extent in terms of the energy of the neutrons to be detected. The application of the basic principles of neutron detection has produced numerous devices for measurement of neutrons in various categories of energy. Some typical examples will be described in this chapter.

10.2. Detection of Slow Neutrons: Foil Activation Method

A number of elements have a large activation cross section for the (n,γ) reaction. The elements of this class which also yield a radioactive product with a convenient half-life can be used as detectors of slow neutrons. Because the detectors must be used as thin foils and need not be more than 3 or 4 cm² in area, they can determine the values of neutron fluxes in small localized regions. Gamma radiation with energies less than 6 Mev does not affect them. Another desirable requirement for these detectors is the absence of resonances with unusually large capture cross sections for neutrons with energies in the vicinity of the slow neutron region. We shall also see that a $1/v$ dependence of the activation cross section is an advantage. Table 10.1 lists a few of the nuclides which have been used in the detection of slow neutrons. The percentage isotopic abundance in the natural element, the activation cross section σ_{act} for thermal neutrons, and the mean life τ of the radioactive product are given for each nuclide. Some prominent resonances from the point of view of capture cross sections for slow neutrons are also listed.

Table 10.1

NUCLIDES WHICH HAVE BEEN USED IN THE FOIL
ACTIVATION METHOD OF DETECTING SLOW NEUTRONS

Target	Abundance (%)	σ_{act} (barns)	τ	Resonances (ev)
Mn^{55}	100	13.4 ± 0.3	3.72 hr	310
				2900
				8200
Rh^{103}	100	12 ± 2	6.5 min	1.25
		140 ± 30	63.5 sec	
Ag^{107}	51.35	44 ± 9	3.3 min	
Ag^{109}	48.65	2.8 ± 0.5	389 days	
		110 ± 20	34.9 sec	
In^{113}	4.23	56 ± 12	70.7 days	
		2.0 ± 0.6	103 sec	
In^{115}	95.77	145 ± 15	78.1 min	1.46
		52 ± 6	18.7 sec	3.9
				9.1
Au^{197}	100	96 ± 10	3.9 days	4.9
$Au^{198}(2.7\ d)$		$35,000 \pm 10,000$	4.6 days	

To determine the neutron flux $\phi = nv$ to be measured in the activation method we note from the definition of σ_{act} that a foil having an area of 1 cm^2, a density of N nuclei per cm^3, and a thickness x, will capture neutrons at a rate R per sec given by

$$nv\sigma_{act}Nx = R \qquad (10.1)$$

$$\text{or} \qquad \phi = \frac{R}{\sigma_{act}Nx} \text{ neutrons per cm}^2 \text{ per sec} \qquad (10.2)$$

The radioactive product will be characterized by a half-life $T_{1/2}$ from which the disintegration constant λ is obtained by the relation $\lambda = \ln 2/T_{1/2}$. The average life τ is equal to $1/\lambda$. In practice it is convenient to count the radioactive disintegrations with an over-all efficiency ϵ. We define C_0 as the counting rate which would be observed for a period of irradiation such that no further increase in radioactivity is produced by prolonging the exposure to neutrons. This is known as irradiation to saturation. Then

$$R = \frac{C_0}{\epsilon} \tag{10.3}$$

The counting rate C for any irradiation time less than that required for saturation, from the laws of radioactive transformations, is given by

$$C = C_0(1 - e^{-t/\tau}) \tag{10.4}$$

where t is the length of the irradiation. It is usual to count the number of emitted particles from the radioactive target in an interval of time beginning at time t_1 subsequent to the interruption of the irradiation and stopping at a time t_2 measured from the same reference time, the cessation of irradiation. If I is the number of counts observed in the interval $t_2 - t_1$ per cm² of the foil then

$$C_0 = \frac{I}{\tau(e^{-t_1/\tau} - e^{-t_2/\tau})(1 - e^{-t/\tau})} \tag{10.5}$$

With the value of C_0 determined from Eq. 10.5, ϕ can be ascertained by use of Eq. 10.3 and Eq. 10.2. For a numerical example illustrating the use of these equations we may select an indium foil with an area of 4 cm², $\sigma_{act} = 145$ barns, and $Nx = 3.8 \times 10^{20}$ atoms per cm². The mean life for In¹¹⁶ is 78.1 min. We assume the time of irradiation is 100 min and counting is started 20 min after interruption of irradiation and continued for 10 min. A total count of $I = 164000$ was observed with $\epsilon = 0.95$. Then we have

$$C_0 = \frac{41000}{78.1(e^{-20/78.1} - e^{-30/78.1})(1 - e^{-100/78.1})}$$

$$= 6850 \text{ counts per min}$$

$$R = \frac{6850}{0.95} = 7100 \text{ counts per min} = 118 \text{ counts per sec}$$

$$\phi = \frac{118}{145 \times 10^{-24}(3.8 \times 10^{20})} = 2140 \text{ neutrons per cm}^2 \text{ per sec}$$

In actual measurements, several precautions and corrections are required in the use of the simple outline just given for the determination of ϕ. The nature of these procedures can be illustrated by referring to indium detectors. Details will vary with each target material but the principles remain the same. Indium is selected as an example because it has been used more frequently as a detector and some of the corrections are better known. Indium has also been found particularly useful in the measurement of slow neutrons which do not have a thermal distribution of velocities, using the method of the cadmium difference. The term cadmium difference refers to the familiar procedure of measuring the activity induced in bare indium foil and repeating the observation with the indium surrounded by cadmium, as in the determination of the cadmium ratio previously described. In the use of indium for measuring neutron flux, perhaps the first consideration need be given to the thickness of the foil to be selected for the measurement. It might be anticipated that increasing the thickness of the foil would increase the sensitivity of detection because the rate of neutron absorption is proportional to the number of nuclei present in the target. However, this anticipated increase in sensitivity is obtained only up to an optimum thickness, as shown in the experimental curve of Fig. 10.1. The curve shows

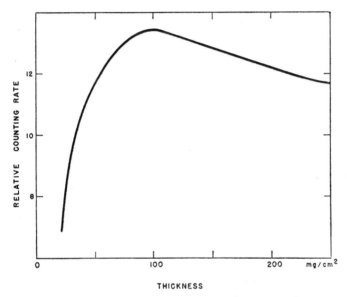

FIG. 10.1. *Variation of counting rate with thickness of indium foil exposed to the same flux of thermal neutrons.*

the variation of the observed counting rate from indium foils of the same area activated in the same flux for increasing thickness of the foils, as reported by Tittle (1) (2). After reaching a thickness of about 100 mg/cm², the counting rate begins to fall off. This decrease of sensitivity with increasing thickness of the foil is caused by the sum of two effects. As the thickness of the foil increases, a point is reached where part of the beta particles emitted from nuclei in the foil are completely absorbed in the foil. To the effect of the absorption of beta particles is added the effect of the presence of the indium, which strongly absorbs neutrons and reduces the neutron flux about it in a moderating medium below the value existing before the indium was introduced into the flux. Fortunately this difficulty is not present in experiments with neutron beams. This reduction in flux also increases with increasing thickness of the indium. Because it is sometimes difficult to determine the correction for internal absorption of the beta radiation in the detector, it is usual to choose detectors thin enough that the effect of the absorption on the counting rate is negligible.

The correction for the depression of the neutron density by the presence of the foil may be made by a method suggested by Bothe (3). In analyzing the problem of estimating the depression of neutron density, Bothe assumed that a circular foil of radius R would be equivalent in effect on the neutron density to a spherical shell of a radius $2R/3$. The spherical shell was introduced to simplify the analysis. It has been found from comparison with experimental data that the results of the analysis are in better agreement with observations if the radius of the shell is taken as equal to the radius of the circular foil. The basis for this analysis will be clearer in the light of the discussion of the diffusion of neutrons in a subsequent chapter. The formulas will be given here without explanation of the origin of the new quantities which they introduce. Bothe computes a factor F by which the thermal neutron counting rate is to be multiplied to correspond to the true neutron density. The general formula is

$$F = 1 + \frac{\alpha}{2}\left[\frac{3R}{2\lambda_{\mathrm{tr}}}\frac{L}{R+L} - 1\right] \tag{10.6}$$

When $L \gg R \gg \lambda_{\mathrm{tr}}$, the case for a nonabsorbing medium, Eq. 10.6 becomes simply

$$F = 1 + \frac{3\alpha R}{4\lambda_{\mathrm{tr}}} \tag{10.7}$$

In Eq. 10.6, λ_{tr}, the transport mean free path, has been substituted for the scattering mean free path λ_s used by Bothe. L is the diffusion length of neutrons in the moderating medium and α is given by

$$\alpha = 1 - e^{-\mu x}(1 - \mu x) + \mu^2 x^2 Ei(-\mu x) \tag{10.8}$$

in which μ is the neutron absorption coefficient in the detector, x is the thickness of the detector, and $Ei(-\mu x)$ is the exponential integral function taken from tables (4). α represents the average probability of the absorption of a neutron in an isotropic flux in a layer of material of thickness x and having a neutron absorption coefficient μ. Fig. 10.2 is a graph of Eq. 10.8. Some currently accepted values for λ_{tr} and L are given in Table 10.2.

Another important correction must be applied to the observed resonance activity because resonance neutrons are absorbed by the layer of cadmium covering the detector in the second stage of the measurement. The resonance correction will vary with the thickness of the indium detector as well as with the thickness of the cadmium covering. The correction factor F_{Cd} is determined most reliably by activation measurements in the same

Table 10.2

VALUES FOR THE NEUTRON DIFFUSION LENGTH L
AND THE TRANSPORT MEAN FREE PATH λ_{tr}
IN CENTIMETERS FOR COMMON MODERATORS

Moderator	L	λ_{tr}
Water	2.76	0.425
D_2O	178	2.52
Graphite	50.2	2.7
Paraffin	2.42	0.39
Beryllium	31	2.6

flux with different thicknesses of cadmium foil around the detector. Extrapolation of these observations to zero thickness of cadmium reveals the magnitude of the correction. When this procedure is also carried out for indium detectors of various thicknesses, curves similar to those shown in Fig. 10.3 are obtained. The curves show the values of F_{Cd} as a function of the thickness of the indium detector for three different thicknesses of the cadmium cover.

One other precaution characteristic of activated foils as neutron detectors is illustrated by indium. When In^{115} is exposed to thermal neutrons, two activities are induced in the indium. One has a half-life of 54.1 min and

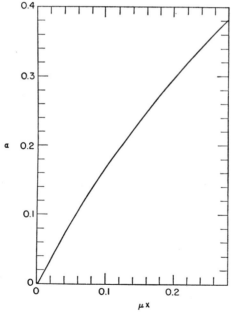

FIG. 10.2. *Curve showing the value of a as a function of μx.*

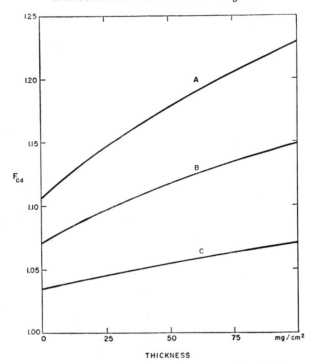

THICKNESS

FIG. 10.3. *Curves showing* F_{cd} *as a function of the thickness of the indium foil for three different thicknesses of cadmium, A—0.060 in., B—0.040 in., and C—0.020 in.*

an activation cross section of 145 ± 15 barns. This is the activity which is used in the measurement of neutrons. The other activity has a half-life of 13 sec and an activation cross section of 52 ± 6 barns. The 13-sec activity decays too rapidly to be useful. Its effect on the measurement of the 54.1-min activity can be eliminated by waiting 7 or 8 half-lives of the fast-decaying activity, about 3 min, before beginning the counting operation.

10.3. Thermal Neutron Detectors Obeying the 1/v Law

An important consequence of the use of a detector of thermal neutrons in which the activation cross section is inversely proportional to the velocity of the neutrons is that the total neutron density ρ, rather than the neutron flux, is measured. This fact can be easily demonstrated by substituting $\sigma = \sigma_0 v_0 / v$ where v_0 is defined in Table 9.1 and σ_0 is the corresponding activation cross section, into Eq. 10.1, and introducing $\rho = \int n(v) dv$

for n. Then we have

$$Nx\rho\sigma_0 v_0 = R \tag{10.9}$$

with σ_0, v_0, N, and x all constants so that R is proportional to ρ, independent of the neutron velocity in the region of velocities for which the $1/v$ law is valid. In the case of thermal neutrons with a Maxwellian distribution of velocities, a knowledge of the neutron density is equivalent to knowing the flux density.

10.4. Measurement of the Intensity of Neutron Beams by the Activated Foil Method

When the foil method is used to measure the neutron flux in thermal neutron beams, it is usual to place the foil with its plane perpendicular to the direction of the neutrons. Then the rate of production R of radioactive nuclei per unit area of the foil is given by

$$R = \int_0^\infty \phi(E)dE(1 - e^{-N\sigma t}) \tag{10.10}$$

where σ is the activation cross section, N the number of target nuclei per cm³, and t the thickness of the foil. In the case where $N\sigma t$ is very large in comparison with unity, the absorber is called "black" and the rate of production of radioactive nuclei for a foil of area A is

$$R = A \int_0^\infty \phi(E)dE \tag{10.11}$$

and the activation measures the total flux directly. When the foil is relatively transparent to neutrons, corresponding to a small activation cross section or a very thin detector, the expression for r becomes

$$R = NtA \int_0^\infty \phi(E)\sigma(E)dE \tag{10.12}$$

where $\sigma(E)$ expresses the variation of the activation cross section with the energy of the neutrons. Because the variation of the cross section is large for slow neutrons, conditions are encountered ranging all the way from those represented by Eq. 10.11 to those represented by Eq. 10.12.

10.5. The Szilard-Chalmers Reaction in Relation to the Activation Method of Measuring Neutrons

When the activation cross section is large, or the flux to be measured is strong, the activity induced by the (n,γ) reaction will yield a radioactive source which can be measured conveniently. When these favorable conditions do not exist, the activity may be too weak for reliable measurements. Because the radioactive product in the (n,γ) reaction is isotopic with the target, no chemical concentration to develop a source of higher specific activity is possible ordinarily. An exception to this rule is provided by the Szilard-Chalmers reaction. In this reaction the radioactive product may be separated from the inactive isotope chemically. At least three conditions must be met to make a Szilard-Chalmers reaction successful. First the radioactive atoms must be separated from the molecules to which they belong. Hence the target must be a chemical compound. Secondly the radioactive atoms must not recombine with the parent molecules and thermal exchange with other inactive molecules must be slow. Finally, a chemical method must be found for removing the radioactive atoms in their new chemical form. The first condition is rather easily met. The gamma rays emitted from product atoms in the (n,γ) reaction can provide recoil energy sufficient to break the chemical bond between the radioactive atoms and the molecules to which they belong. The chemical bond energies range from 1 to 5 ev in the majority of cases. The recoil energy E_r in ev from the emission of a gamma ray of energy E_γ in Mev is given by the relation

$$E_r = \frac{537 E_\gamma^2}{A} \tag{10.13}$$

where A is the mass number of the recoiling atom. Table 10.3 contains some values of E_r calculated from Eq. 10.13. Energies as high as $E_\gamma = 8.6$

Table 10.3

VALUES OF E_r FOR SELECTED VALUES OF E_γ AND A

E_γ / A	1 Mev	2 Mev	4 Mev	8 Mev
20	27 ev	108 ev	432 ev	1728 ev
40	14	54	216	864
80	7	27	108	432
160	3.5	14	54	216
200	2.7	11	43	171

Mev have been measured for the (n,γ) reaction. The gamma-ray spectra in (n,γ) reactions are complex, containing many lines. Hence angular relations between successive gamma rays might partially cancel momentum components in the direction of the chemical bond. However, experiments have proved that recoil energies in the (n,γ) reactions are sufficient in many cases to rupture chemical bonds which hold the radioactive atoms in their molecules. The second requirement of absence of chemical exchange of radioactive atoms with similar inactive atoms in other molecules is undoubtedly most difficult to meet. Therefore it seems probable that the exchange rate provides the chief limitation on the efficiency of the Szilard-Chalmers reaction. Even so, in specific instances, efficiencies of nearly 100 percent have been observed, particularly with halogen compounds. Thus radioactive products represented by Cl^{38}, Br^{80}, Br^{82}, and I^{128} have been obtained, using readily available chemical techniques, in high concentrations.

The third requirement of a convenient chemical method for separating the radioactive atoms from their inactive isotopes is met in various ways, depending upon the chemical properties of the radioactive atoms. In the case of halogen compounds, extraction with water often gives efficient yields. Separations based on differences in the oxidation state before and after neutron capture have also been successful. A large fraction of the Mn^{56} activity can be removed from neutron-irradiated neutral or acid permanganate solution as MnO_2. Because of the state of ionization of the radioactive atoms, if the material to be separated is in the form of a gas, the active atoms may be collected on charged electrodes, both positive and negative electrodes picking up radioactive atoms. Obviously the Szilard-Chalmers reaction is of greatest interest in relation to the measurement of neutrons in situations where the fluxes are very weak, such as the neutrons generated by cosmic radiation.

10.6. Ion Chambers and Counter Tubes for Detection of Slow Neutrons

Proportional counters and pulse ionization chambers, using boron trifluoride enriched in B^{10} as a filling gas, are the most commonly used devices in the electrical detection of slow neutrons. The detection process is based on the (n,α) reaction in B^{10}, which has the large thermal cross section of 4010 barns. The particles released, alpha particles and Li^{7*} nuclei, produce high specific ionization in gases. Therefore these particles are readily detected in the presence of other more weakly ionizing particles, such as the secondary electrons from gamma rays. By use of circuits which discriminate against pulse heights below some selected level, the gamma ray background can usually be eliminated almost completely in the recording circuit. However, when an intense gamma ray background is present, an amplifying circuit with a poor time resolution may record several closely adjacent gamma ray pulses as a single large pulse. The reaction energies for the two products of the $B^{10}(n,\alpha)$ reaction are 1.473 Mev for the alpha particles and 0.841 Mev for the excited lithium nuclei. These energies should give a ratio of the ionization per particle, I_α and I_{Li}, as $I_\alpha/I_{Li} = 1.75$. Most measured values of this ratio have been somewhat higher, about 1.85. However observations by De Juren and Rosenwasser (5), under carefully controlled conditions, gave values as low as 1.78 for the ratio of the heights of the ionization pulses. Fig. 10.4 is a sectional diagram of a proportional counter tube suitable for use with boron trifluoride as a detector of slow neutrons. Many designs of proportional counter tubes have been proposed. The sketch here is intended to illustrate the essential features of a design suggested by Cockroft and Curran (6). The novelty of their design is the introduction of the field tubes, labeled F in Fig. 10.4. These tubes, insulated electrically from all other parts, are maintained at a potential approximately one-third the full potential difference between the center wire and the external metal cylinder. Operated in this way, the field tubes limit the sensitive volume V, indicated by the shading, to a definite cylindrical volume with ends at some distance from the ends of the tube. Also within this volume there is very little distortion of the electric field. Therefore the distribution of the heights of the pulses is that characteristic of the normal counter action, undisturbed by the considerable number of pulses of reduced heights which can occur in the end regions of the counter tube in the absence of the field tubes.

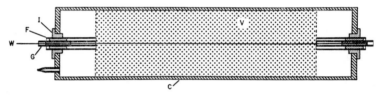

FIG. 10.4. *Proportional counter tube with field tubes to define the sensitive volume. F—field tube. V—sensitive volume. W—center wire. G—guard tube. I—insulation.*

Frequently it is desirable to screen a detector tube from neutrons originating from other sources than the one under study. Screening can be accomplished by the shield illustrated in Fig. 10.5. The detector is covered by a layer of material having a strong absorption coefficient for slow neutrons, such as a compound of boron or a layer of cadmium, except for the front end where the slow neutrons to be measured are admitted. This absorbing layer is in turn covered by a layer of paraffin, thick enough to reduce the velocities of any fast neutrons incident upon it to velocities near the thermal region by the time these neutrons reach the absorbing layer.

The analysis of the detection process for an ionization chamber or proportional counter follows the same general lines as in the case of activated foils. To illustrate the use of a slightly different approach, we will assume the filling gas to be BF_3 enriched in B^{10} so that the reaction rate will follow the $1/v$ law for neutron energies up to 10 kev. We can then write, following Eq. 10.9

$$R = NV \int n(v) v \sigma(v) dv \qquad (10.14)$$

with $\sigma(v) = \sigma_0 v_0 / v$. As before, we can replace $\int n(v)\, dv$ by ρ the density of the neutrons of all energies per cm^3 and obtain

$$R = NV\rho\sigma_0 v_0 \qquad (10.15)$$

where R is the counts per second, N the number of B^{10} atoms per cm^3 and V the sensitive volume of the ion chamber or counter tube in cm^3. Eq. 10.15 is identical in form with Eq. 10.9 for activated foils. No mention has yet been made of the efficiency factor, which plays an important role in the foil activation method, for ion chambers and counters. Filled with BF_3 gas, the efficiency of detection of a neutron-induced disintegration in chambers and counters approaches 100 percent. The wall effect, that is the loss

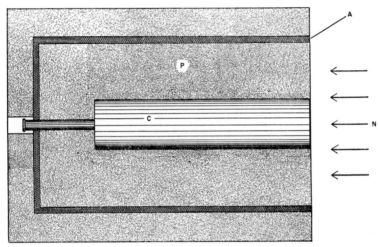

FIG. 10.5. *A long neutron counter. N—neutron beam. P—paraffin shield. C—counter tube. A—slow neutron absorber.*

of a count because the ionizing particles enter the wall by too short a path to produce detectable ionization, is usually very small. In proportional counters the wall effect may often be neglected. An estimate of the sensitivity for the production of disintegrations can be made by considering the neutron absorption coefficient, $\mu = N\sigma$, of the boron trifluoride gas. Here σ is the cross section for the (n,α) reaction in boron. At a pressure of 1 atmosphere for $B^{10}F_3$, $\mu = 0.103(0.025/E)^{1/2}$ cm^{-1}, where E is the energy of the neutron in electron volts. Thus a counter tube about 20 cm in length would vary from black to transparent in the range of energies of thermal neutrons. Put in another way, at a neutron energy of 0.025 ev there would be about 0.91 disintegrations per incident neutron.

The pulses from both ion chambers and proportional counters have heights proportional to the primary ionization. However proportional counters have a gas amplification factor. The gas amplification factor can be of the order of 100 or more with BF_3 proportional counter tubes, as indicated in Fig. 10.6, taken from Rossi and Staub (7). This means that less electronic amplification is required to record the pulses. Also the rise time of the pulses is shorter in the proportional counter than in the ion chamber. This faster rise of the pulse gives proportional counters an important ad-

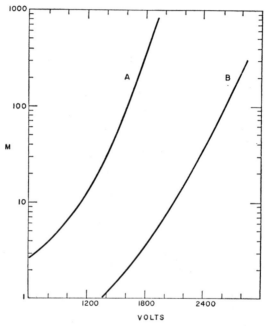

FIG. 10.6. *The gas multiplication M as a function of the voltage across the counter tube for a BF_3 proportional neutron counter. Curve A, center wire diameter 10 mils, tube diameter 1.5 inches, pressure of BF_3 gas 10 cm Hg. Curve B, center wire diameter 1 mil, tube diameter 1.56 inches, BF_3 pressure 80.4 cm Hg.*

vantage over the ion chambers. Clipping circuits can be used in the amplifier for the proportional counter, allowing faster counting rates without having the adjacent pulses pile up in the amplifying circuit. Pile-up is used to describe the result of two or more successive pulses being unresolved and recorded as a single pulse. Another advantage of the proportional counter over the ion chamber is that in the counter the size of the pulse is, for a given number of primary ions, almost independent of the location within the sensitive volume of the ionizing event which triggered the pulse. When neutrons of thermal energies enter a BF_3 proportional counter tube

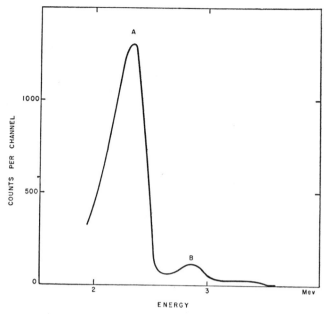

FIG. 10.7. *Distribution of pulse-heights from a BF$_3$ proportional counter tube in a thermal neutron flux.*

the distribution of pulse heights is similar to that shown in Fig. 10.7, according to measurements by James and co-workers (8). The greater number of pulses, at peak labeled A, is the result of the B^{10}(n,α)Li^{7*} reaction. The smaller peak at B contains the pulses resulting from the B^{10}(n,α)Li^7 reaction.

10.7. The Long Counter

The BF$_3$ proportional counter tube has been modified by Hanson and McKibben (9) to make it sensitive to fast neutrons. Because the neutrons to be detected travel parallel to the cylindrical axis of the counter tube, this modification has been called the long counter. In the diagram of the long counter shown in Fig. 10.5; the conventional proportional counter tube C is embedded in a cylinder of paraffin P. Around this paraffin is a layer A of an absorber for slow neutrons which, in turn, is covered with an outer layer of paraffin. As was explained above in connection with the shielding of counter tubes from extraneous neutrons, the last two layers serve to exclude neutrons from detection which have been scattered towards the counter tube by material in its vicinity. Neutrons enter the long counter in the direction of the arrows at N. Assuming that these neutrons have energies extending from thermal energies up to several Mev, it is clear that only those neutrons in the $1/v$ region for absorption in boron will be detected with a practical efficiency. However, as the faster neutrons travel through the layer of paraffin immediately surrounding the counter tube, they will be slowed down to velocities which are within the $1/v$ range for absorption. On diffusing into the counter tube, these neutrons which have been slowed down sufficiently will be detected. If the counter and paraffin mantle are long enough to slow down the neutrons of the highest energies in the incident beam to the slow neutron region before the escape through the back end of the tube, there is a possibility of detecting the

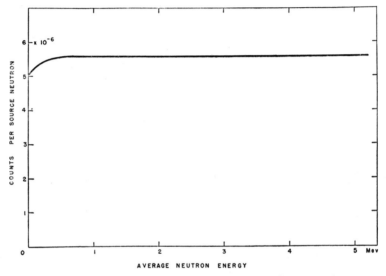

FIG. 10.8. *Efficiency of a long neutron counter as a function of neutron energy in terms of counts per neutron emitted from a source 41.5 inches from the front face of the counter tube.*

neutrons throughout the range of the incident energies. In fact, neutrons incident at an energy of about 100 kev have a slightly better chance of detection than those at lower energy. The faster neutrons are slowed down at greater depths in the paraffin and have less chance of escaping from the front face of the counter assembly before detection. Experimental tests have verified the expectation that the long counter has an efficiency for the detection of neutrons which is practically constant over a considerable range of neutron energies. This is clearly shown by the curve plotted in Fig. 10.8 which represents data obtained by Nobles and co-workers (10). To obtain these data, several sources of neutrons, each having a wide spread of energies about a different average, were mounted successively 41.5 inches from the front face of a long counter. The relative source strengths were known to ± 1 percent and the absolute yields less accurately, possibly within 5 percent. The curve in Fig. 10.8 shows that the efficiency, in terms of counts per neutron emitted by the source, is constant within limits of error from 5 Mev down to a few hundred kev. Even at 25 kev the curve has dropped by only 10 percent.

10.8. Scintillators as Slow Neutron Detectors

Considerable work has been done by various investigators to develop scintillation counters for slow neutrons. The success of these efforts would make available to neutron measurements the technical developments in scintillation counting which have made rapid progress in the measurement of beta and gamma radiation. One attractive feature of scintillation counting is the rapid rise of the light pulses in crystal phosphors. The photomultiplier tube used with the phosphor permits full advantage to be taken of the rapid rise in the luminous response of crystals. The transit time of a photoelectron across a photomultiplier is about 5×10^{-8} sec. The light from a phosphor comes to a maximum after the application of the stimulus in a time of the same order of magnitude. These figures represent a speed of response nearly 100 times faster than that usually obtained with proportional counter tubes. The rapidity of response makes possible very short resolving times which, as we have seen in the discussion of proportional counters, is very desirable when counting neutrons in the presence of a strong gamma-ray background.

Because neutrons cannot produce scintillations directly, for the detection of slow neutrons it is necessary to incorporate some material into the phosphor which will produce ionizing radiation on the passage of neutrons through the mixture. One of the early methods of solving this problem involved the preparation of alternate thin layers of a boron compound and of zinc sulfide. The alpha particles released by the neutrons from the boron were detected by the well-known ability of activated zinc sulfide to scintillate under the action of alpha particles. Whereas this sandwich was relatively insensitive to gamma rays, it did not have a very satisfactory efficiency for the detection of neutrons. Not all ionizing particles from the disintegration of the boron succeeded in producing scintillations and only a fraction of the light from the scintillations reached the photomultiplier, much of the light being lost by reflection in the discontinuities of the sandwich. Both these difficulties can be corrected to some extent by fusing the zinc sulfide in a glassy layer of boric anhydride. The resulting wafer is applied directly to the window of the photomultiplier tube, as indicated in Fig. 10.9. Gunst, Connor, and Bayard (11), for example, report that scintillators of the wafer type have a useful neutron efficiency in the presence of strong gamma rays. Defining efficiency as the counting rate per unit thermal neutron flux at a discriminator setting which records only 0.01

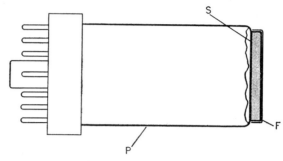

FIG. 10.9. *A photomultiplier tube and scintillator for detection of thermal neutrons. F—aluminum cover and reflector. P—photomultiplier tube. S—scintillator composed of boric anhydride and zinc sulfide crystals.*

gamma ray photon per sec, one of these scintillating wafers 0.005 inch in thickness has an efficiency of 0.12 for neutrons in the presence of a gamma ray intensity of 70 roentgens per hour. Increasing the thickness of the wafer to 0.029 inch increases the neutron efficiency to 0.18. The pulse-height curves obtained by Gunst and his co-workers are shown in Fig. 10.10.

One of the main advantages of scintillation detectors for slow neutrons is the high efficiency per unit volume of the phosphor. When the scintillating crystalline compound of the phosphor itself contains an element sensitive to neutrons, the efficiency of a crystal may approach 100 percent. This high efficiency is illustrated by the results of an investigation by Nicholson and Snelling (12) of lithium iodide phosphors activated with europium. Neutrons are detected in the crystals by scintillations arising from the products of the reaction $Li^6(n,\alpha)H^3$. The reaction energy of 4.79 Mev is shared between the alpha particle and the triton. The thermal neutron efficiency curve which the authors calculate for the crystals as a function of the thickness of the crystals in centimeters is shown in Fig. 10.11. There is an important drawback to the use of LiI(Eu) crystals to detect neutrons in the presence of gamma rays. The lithium iodide crystal has the same efficiency for detecting gamma rays as a NaI(Tl) crystal of equal weight. This situation is illustrated by the pulse-height curves in Fig. 10.12 for a LiI(Eu) crystal detector. The dotted curve marked γ shows the response of the Li crystal to an unshielded radium source delivering a gamma-ray dose of 10 mr/hr. The peak marked n shows the response to a Po-Be neutron source which produces a total neutron count in the crystal of 10 per sec. Under these conditions there is no significant pile up of gamma-ray pulses. With increasing intensity of the gamma rays, a point would be reached where coincident gamma-ray pulses would mask the neutron peak completely. Reducing the clipping time of the pulses in the amplifier cir-

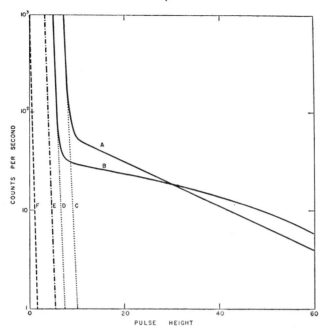

FIG. 10.10. *Integral bias curves for two thicknesses of a scintillator composed of a mixture of ZnS and B_2O_3 in a thermal flux of about 250 neutrons per cm^2 per sec and a gamma-ray intensity of about 70 roentgens per hour. Curve A—neutrons plus gamma rays for a scintillator 0.029 in. thick. Curve B—neutrons plus gamma rays for a scintillator 0.005 in. thick. Curve C—gamma rays only for a scintillator 0.029 in. thick. Curve D—gamma rays only for a scintillator 0.005 in. thick. Curve E—no scintillator. Curve F—noise.*

cuit will be helpful only down to clipping times of the order of the decay time of the luminosity in the phosphor. Any further shortening of the clipping time also reduces the sizes of the neutron pulses. For gamma radiation of energy less than 2 or 3 Mev, an intensity of about 20 mr/hr is the most that can be tolerated if the neutron count is about 10 per sec. At higher gamma-ray energies there is direct interference between neutron and photon pulses and the ratio of gamma rays to neutrons must be quite small.

10.9. Fission Chambers for Detection of Thermal Neutrons

The relatively high cross sections for fission by thermal neutrons of U^{235}, Np^{237}, and Pu^{239}, as familiar examples, has led to the development of thermal neutron detectors in which the fission fragments produce the primary ioni-

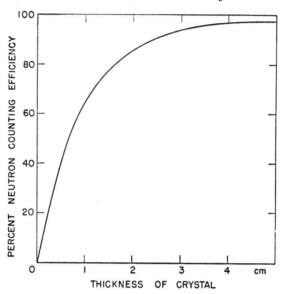

FIG. 10.11. *Calculated slow-neutron efficiency of LiI (Eu) crystal as a function of the thickness of the crystal.*

zation in a pulse ionization chamber or a proportional counter tube. There are several limitations on the design of fission counters. One is imposed by strong alpha-particle background always present in fission chambers. Another involves the short range of the fission fragments, of the order of 2 cm in air. One consequence of these factors is that the sensitive layer of fissionable material introduced into the counting chamber must be quite thin, of the order of 100 micrograms per cm², to insure that the pulses produced by the fission fragments are much larger than the pulses from the alpha particles. Also the resolution of the recording system must be high to reduce the effect of approximately coincident alpha-particle pulses on the recorded counting rate. These restrictions make the use of fission chambers for the detection of thermal neutrons most attractive when detectors of small volume are required. An example is described by Nobles and Smith (13) and is sketched in Fig. 10.13. The central collecting electrode C consists of a small metal plate, 0.7 inch square, on which the layer of fissionable material is deposited. The chamber is filled with spectroscopically pure argon at a pressure of 4 atmospheres. The chamber is sealed after filling by pinching off the copper tube used for filling the chamber at S. The use of a high pressure of the filling gas insures almost complete absorption of the fission fragments in the gas of the chamber, whereas the alpha particles, in the short distance available, will yield only a small fraction of their energy in ionization before striking the walls of the chamber. The differential

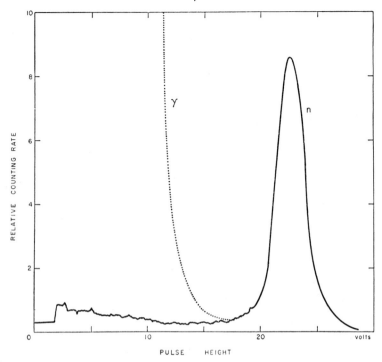

FIG. 10.12. *Pulse-height curve showing response of LiI (Eu) crystal to thermal neutrons in the presence of gamma rays.* γ—*response to gamma rays.* n—*response to neutrons.*

pulse-height curve for the chamber of Fig. 10.13 when exposed to thermal neutrons is shown in the graph of Fig. 10.14. The alpha particle and noise background appears in the region of pulses of low energy at A. The low-energy pulses are followed by a region where the number of pulses has a minimum at B which serves as a natural bias point for the discriminator of an electronic counting system. The pulses of the fission fragments appear in two peaks, at C and D, characteristic of thermal fission. One of the chief advantages of a fission chamber as a detector is its high sensitivity to thermal neutrons. A fission chamber can be used to make measurements of thermal fluxes too weak to permit reliable measurements by the activated foil method.

10.10. Detectors for Neutrons in the Intermediate Range of Energies

Very few satisfactory detectors for neutrons with energies in the range from 10 ev up to 10^5 ev have been found. Cross sections in this range of neutron energies are generally so low that thick layers of the sensitive ele-

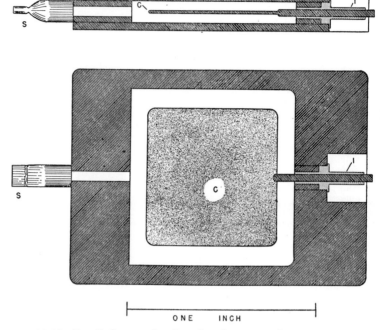

FIG. 10.13. *Small fission chamber for detecting slow neutrons.* I—
insulator. C—*plate on which fissioning material is deposited.* S—
seal.

ment are required to yield adequate intensities of ionizing radiations. If
these radiations consist of alpha or beta rays, self-absorption of the radiation in the detecting element precludes the use of thick layers. Sensitive
elements which emit gamma rays are not subject to the same limitation.
Rae and Bowey (14) have designed a detector which utilizes the soft gamma
rays from the reaction

$$B^{10}(n,\alpha)Li^{7*} \rightarrow Li^7 + \gamma \ (480 \text{ kev}) \tag{10.16}$$

for measuring neutrons of intermediate energies. Layers of B^{10} which are
opaque to neutrons with energies up to about 1 kev may then be used as
the detector. The detector efficiency then depends chiefly on the efficiency
with which the gamma rays may be detected. By using a NaI phosphor
with a rapid rate of rise of the luminous response in a single-channel scintillation spectrometer, the disturbing background from other radioactive
sources and the cosmic radiation was materially reduced. In addition a
thorough system of lead screening and neutron shields were provided. The
arrangement is sketched in Fig. 10.15. Two photomultipliers, each with a
sodium iodide phosphor C, faced the boron detector B from opposite sides.

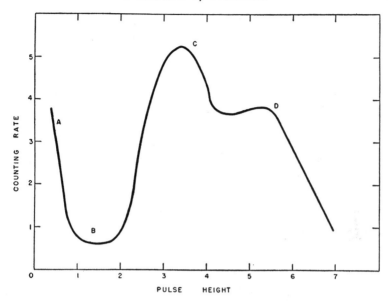

FIG. 10.14. *Differential pulse-height curve for the fission chamber of Fig. 10.13.*

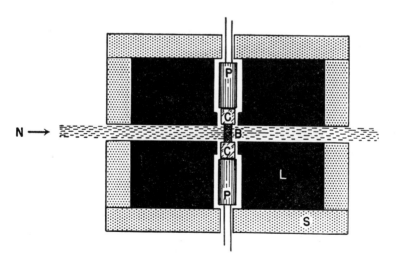

FIG. 10.15. *Scintillation detector for neutrons of intermediate energy utilizing the gamma rays from the reaction* $B^{10}(n,a)Li^{7*} \rightarrow Li^7 + \gamma$ *(480 kev). C,C—sodium iodide crystals. P,P—photomultiplier tubes. L—lead shield. S—boric acid glass shield. B—thin-walled aluminum cylinder filled with amorphous B^{10}. N—neutron beam.*

The boron detector consisted of a thin-walled aluminum cylinder, 3 inches in diameter and 1.25 inches high, filled with amorphous B^{10}. The beam of neutrons N traversed this cylinder in a direction perpendicular to its axis and the axes of the photomultipliers. With the single-channel pulse analyzer set to count the total-energy peak of the Li^{7*} gamma radiation, an efficiency of about 2.6 percent for the detection of the neutrons was obtained. This efficiency was practically constant up to neutron energies of about 1 kev. Because the amount of boron used was no longer opaque to neutrons above this energy, a drop of about 15 percent in the efficiency could be expected at 5 kev and the efficiency would drop to about 1 percent at 50 kev. Hence this method of detection, as described, should be useful only in the range of neutron energies from 10 ev up to 10^4 or 10^5 ev. It would be difficult to operate in the presence of gamma radiation.

10.11. Detection of Fast Neutrons

The activation cross sections of most nuclides are quite small for neutrons with energies greater than 1 Mev. The order of magnitude of the cross sections are illustrated by a few examples in Table 10.4 containing data taken

Table 10.4

ACTIVATION CROSS SECTIONS OF A FEW NUCLIDES
FOR 14-Mev NEUTRONS

Reaction	Half-life	σ (isotopic)
$Al^{27}(n,p)Mg^{27}$	9.6 min	0.079 barn
$Al^{27}(n,\alpha)Na^{24}$	15.0 hr	0.135
$P^{31}(n,p)Si^{31}$	170 min	0.091
$Fe^{56}(n,p)Mn^{56}$	2.6 hr	0.124
$Cu^{63}(n,2n)Cu^{62}$	9.9 min	0.510
$Cu^{65}(n,2n)Cu^{64}$	12.8 hr	0.97
$Cu^{65}(n,p)Ni^{65}$	2.6 hr	0.019
$Ag^{107}(n,2n)Ag^{106}$	24.5 min	0.56
$Ag^{109}(n,2n)Ag^{108}$	2.3 min	1.0

from Forbes (15). These low activation cross sections for the production of radionuclides practically rule out the activation principle as a convenient method for detecting fast neutrons.

On the other hand, the observation of recoiling protons from the neutron-proton scattering interaction offers not only larger cross sections but also the opportunity to use much thicker targets from which to eject the protons. For neutrons of 1-Mev energy the scattering cross section of hydrogen is about 4 barns and at 10 Mev it is still of the order of 1 barn. The magnitude of the yield of protons from a paraffin radiator bombarded by neutrons has been studied by Rhody and Hopkins (16). If the range-energy relation for protons in paraffin is known, it is possible to calculate the variation in the yield of protons from a paraffin radiator as a function of the energy of the neutrons. Hirschfelder and Magee (17) have computed the range-energy curves for protons in a number of materials, including paraffin. Their curve for paraffin is reproduced in Fig. 10.16. The data for the curve are obtained by computations using values of stopping powers for

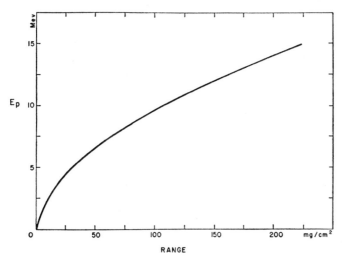

FIG. 10.16. *Calculated range-energy curve for protons in paraffin.*

carbon, hydrogen, and nitrogen, by means of the well-known formula of Bethe (18). Bethe's formula is usually written in the form

$$-\frac{dE}{dx} = \frac{4\pi e^4 z^2 Z N}{mv^2}\left[\ln \frac{2mv^2}{I\,(1-\beta^2)} - \beta^2\right] - C_K \qquad (10.17)$$

where e is the charge on an electron, m is the mass of an electron, N is the number of atoms per cm³, z the charge on the moving particle, Z the atomic number of the absorbing atoms, v the velocity of the particle, $\beta = v/c$, with c the velocity of light, I is the average ionization potential of the absorbing atoms, and C_K is a correction factor for the effect of the K electrons.

The curves which Rhody and Hopkins obtained for the numbers of protons from paraffin radiators of five different thicknesses as a function of the neutron energy E_n are shown in Fig. 10.17. We will now outline the steps by which the numerical values for the curves were obtained. The computations are of the usual form, starting with the equation for the energy of the recoiling proton. In the elastic scattering process, the application of the principles of the conservation of energy and momentum reveals

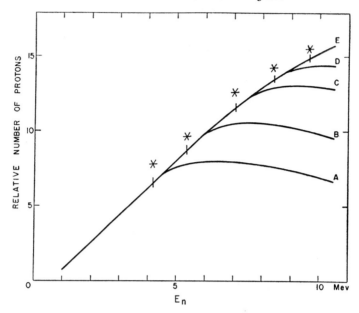

FIG. 10.17. *The counting rate as a function of neutron energy for five thicknesses of paraffin radiator. A—25, B—42, C—68, D—80, E— 115 mg/cm². Asterisks indicate the value of E′ for each radiator.*

that the energy E_p acquired by the proton in collision with a neutron in which the proton is at rest is given by

$$E_p = E_n \cos^2\theta \qquad (10.18)$$

where E_n is the energy of the incident neutron and θ is the scattering angle of the proton in the laboratory system, as indicated in the diagram of Fig. 10.18. In the center-of-mass system Eq. 10.18 becomes

$$E_p = \frac{E_n}{2}(1 - \cos\phi) \qquad (10.19)$$

where ϕ is the common scattering angle for both the neutron and the proton. The probability that a proton acquires an energy between E and $E + dE$ is

$$P(E)dE = \frac{\sigma(\phi)d\omega}{\sigma_s} = \frac{\sigma(\phi)}{\sigma_s} 2\pi \sin\phi d\phi \qquad (10.20)$$

where $\sigma(\phi)$ is the differential scattering cross section and σ_s is the integral scattering cross section. Differentiating Eq. 10.19 and combining the result with Eq. 10.20 gives

$$P(E) = \frac{\sigma(\phi)}{\sigma_s} \frac{4\pi}{E_n} \qquad (10.21)$$

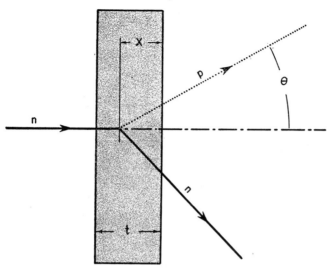

FIG. 10.18. *Geometry used in the analysis of the recoil protons from a paraffin radiator.*

From the known spherical symmetry of scattering in the center-of-mass system, $\sigma(\phi)/\sigma_s$ is equal to $1/4\pi$. Hence

$$P(E) = \frac{1}{E_n} \qquad E \leqq E_n \qquad (10.22)$$

$$P(E) = 0 \qquad E > E_n \qquad (10.23)$$

From the point of view of detection, the residual energy of the proton after escaping from the radiator is of direct interest. This emergent energy will be represented by U and the differential distribution function $f(U)$ will be normalized to represent the number of proton recoils in unit energy interval divided by the total number of recoils. Similarly, the integral distribution $F(U)$ will represent the fraction of the total number of recoils with energy greater than any specified value. Therefore, when normalized in this way, the value of the integral energy distribution corresponding to a given value of U will give the detection efficiency when U is chosen equal to M, if M represents the minimum value of the residual energy of the proton to which a detector corresponds. It is further convenient to deal with the ratio of the residual recoil energy to the neutron energy, $f(U/E_n)$ and $F(U/E_n)$.

The proton recoil energy is a function only of the neutron energy. In a gas

$$f\left(\frac{U}{E_n}\right) = P(E)E_n \frac{dE}{dU} \qquad (10.24)$$

and

$$F\left(\frac{U}{E_n}\right) = \int_{\frac{U'}{E_n}}^{1} f\left(\frac{U}{E_n}\right) d\left(\frac{U}{E_n}\right) \tag{10.25}$$

where U' is any value of U. The efficiency of a radiator can be defined as the average number of recoils produced per neutron incident on the radiator and becomes

$$\epsilon(E_n) = tQ\sigma_s(E_n) \tag{10.26}$$

where t is the thickness of the radiator in mg/cm^2, Q is the number of hydrogen atoms per unit mass, and $\sigma_s(E_n)$ is the scattering cross section. For monoenergetic neutrons in a collimated beam perpendicular to the surface of the radiator, the counting rate of a detector becomes

$$N = \epsilon(E_n) F\left(\frac{M}{E_n}\right) = tQ\sigma_s(E_n) F\left(\frac{M}{E_n}\right) \tag{10.27}$$

In a gas where the residual recoil energy is equal to the total recoil energy, $E = U$, we have

$$f\left(\frac{U}{E_n}\right) = 1 \qquad E \leqq E_n \tag{10.28}$$

and

$$f\left(\frac{U}{E_n}\right) = 0 \qquad E > E_n \tag{10.29}$$

Also

$$F\left(\frac{U}{E_n}\right) = \int_{\frac{U'}{E_n}}^{1} d\left(\frac{U}{E_n}\right) = 1 - \frac{U'}{E_n} \tag{10.30}$$

The counting rate, neglecting wall corrections, in a counter tube becomes

$$N = tQ\sigma_s(E_n)\left(1 - \frac{M}{E_n}\right) \tag{10.31}$$

In the case of a thin radiator, from which all recoil protons escape (though they lose some of their energy in doing so) the amount of energy loss depends on the depth of the point at which the proton originated and the angle of recoil. Let $R(E)$ represent the range of protons of energy E in the radiator, $X/\cos \phi$ their path length in the radiator, and $R(U)$ the residual range outside the radiator, so that

$$R(E) = \frac{X}{\cos \phi} + R(U) \tag{10.32}$$

Substituting the value of $\cos \phi$ from Eq. 10.18, we have

$$R(E) = X \sqrt{\frac{E_n}{E}} + R(U) \tag{10.33}$$

and the fraction of the total number of recoils with energy greater than U becomes

$$F(U) = \frac{1}{tE_n} \int_U^{E_n} X dE \qquad (10.34)$$

In order to correlate Eq. 10.34 with published range-energy data, assume

$$R(E) = kE^m \qquad (10.35)$$

so that appropriate values may be assigned to k and m to give agreement with published curves. Eq. 10.35 is adequate for our purpose for the fast neutrons which we have under consideration. If $R_0(E_n)$ is the range of a proton with energy equal to the energy of the neutron E_n, we find that Eq. 10.33 gives

$$X = R_0 \sqrt{\frac{E}{E_n}} \left[\left(\frac{E}{E_n} \right)^m - \left(\frac{U}{E_n} \right)^m \right] \qquad (10.36)$$

so that Eq. 10.34 becomes

$$F\left(\frac{U}{E_n} \right) = \frac{1}{t} \int_{\frac{U'}{E_n}}^{1} X \left(\frac{E}{E_n} \right), \left(\frac{U}{E_n} \right) d \left(\frac{E}{E_n} \right) \qquad (10.37)$$

For the thin radiator under consideration, there is some proton energy E' at which X may become equal to t, that is the proton recoil energy is sufficient for the proton to traverse the total thickness of the radiator and be detected. When $X = t$

$$t = R_0 \sqrt{\frac{E'}{E_n}} \left[\left(\frac{E'}{E_n} \right)^m - \left(\frac{U}{E_n} \right)^m \right] \qquad (10.38)$$

If E' is less than E_n there are two terms in the integration and Eq. 10.37 becomes

$$F = \frac{1}{t} \int_{\frac{U}{E_n}}^{\frac{E'}{E_n}} X d \left(\frac{E}{E_n} \right) + \frac{1}{t} \int_{\frac{E'}{E_n}}^{1} t \, d \left(\frac{E}{E_n} \right) \qquad (10.39)$$

Substituting the value for X in Eq. 10.36 and integrating gives

$$F = \frac{R_0}{t} \left[\frac{4m}{6m+9} \left(\frac{U}{E_n} \right)^{m+3/2} + \frac{2}{2m+3} \left(\frac{E'}{E_n} \right)^{m+3/2} \right.$$
$$\left. - \frac{2}{3} \left(\frac{U}{E_n} \right)^m \left(\frac{E'}{E_n} \right)^{3/2} + \frac{t}{R_0} \left(1 - \frac{E'}{E_n} \right) \right] \qquad (10.40)$$

When X is always less than t, the case of a thick radiator, Eq. 10.37 has only one term and yields on integration

$$F = \frac{R_0}{t} \left\{ \frac{4m}{6m+9} \left(\frac{U}{E_n} \right)^{m+3/2} + \frac{2}{6m+9} \left[3 - (2m+1) \left(\frac{U}{E_n} \right)^m \right] \right\}$$

(10.41)

The counting rate N is now given by Eq. 10.31 for the two conditions

$$N(E_n \geqq E') = Qk\sigma_s(E_n) \left[\frac{4m}{6m+9} M^m \left(\frac{M}{E_n} \right)^{3/2} \right.$$

$$\left. + \left(\frac{2}{2m+3} E'^m - \frac{2}{3} M^m \right) \left(\frac{E'}{E_n} \right)^{3/2} + \frac{t}{k} \left(1 - \frac{E'}{E_n} \right) \right]$$

(10.42)

$$N(E_n \leqq E') = Qk\sigma_s(E_n) \left\{ \frac{2}{2m+3} E_n^m + M^m \left[\frac{4m}{6m+9} \left(\frac{M}{E_n} \right)^{3/2} - \frac{2}{3} \right] \right\}$$

(10.43)

The curves for $M = 0.5$ Mev are plotted in Fig. 10.17, using Eq. 10.42 and Eq. 10.43 with values of k and m which fit the range-energy curve of Fig. 10.16. These values turned out to be $m = 1.72$ and $k = 1.9$ where R is in mg/cm^2 and E is in Mev in Eq. 10.35. It is to be noted from the curves in Fig. 10.17 that the counting rate continues to rise after the neutron energy exceeds E' and later falls off. Also for thick targets the counting rate is nearly linear with the neutron energy up to E'.

To test the correctness of the foregoing computations, Rhody and Hopkins measured the distribution of lengths of proton recoil tracks from a paraffin radiator in a Wilson cloud chamber. They found the integral range distribution to agree well with the calculated distribution. The differential distribution, although somewhat more scattered, also agreed within the statistics of the observations.

Currently, the proton-recoil method for detection of fast neutrons is used chiefly with two types of radiators. One type of radiator is the filling gas containing hydrogenous molecules of a proportional counter tube. The other type is polyethylene, used in thin sheets with several different detectors of protons.

10.12. Proportional Counters for Detection of Fast Neutrons by Recoil Protons

For neutrons with energies of the order of 1 Mev, proportional counter tubes, filled with special gases, of the general form shown in Fig. 10.4, are frequently used. Methane is mixed with the filling gas to provide the hydrogenous radiator. A commonly used mixture for the filling gas is 20 percent methane and 80 percent krypton. To increase the sensitivity, the pressure of the gas in the counter tube is of the order of 5 or 6 atmospheres. It is desirable, for satisfactory operation of the counter tube, that the gases be pure. Often it is not sufficient merely to fill the counter tube initially with pure gases. Some means for maintaining the purity is also required. A magnesium ribbon heated to about 160°C has been found satisfactory for purification. To maintain the purity of the counter gases, they are circulated continuously through a purifying chamber, containing the heated magnesium ribbon, connected permanently to the counter tube.

Neutrons of energies greater than 1 Mev can be detected by the gas-type recoil counters by increasing the volume of the counter. The larger volume

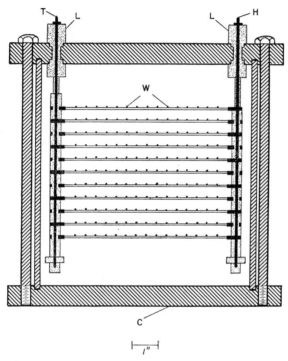

FIG. 10.19. *Multiple-wire proportional counter for fast-neutron detection. The cross section shows the arrangement of grids. C—cylindrical metal chamber. W—wire grids. L—Lucite insulators. T—terminal for collecting electrodes. H—terminal for high-voltage electrodes.*

is most conveniently obtained by introducing a system of wire grids into the chamber, with collecting electrodes interleaved between high-voltage electrodes. The grids lower the voltage required for operation, as compared with a single-wire chamber of the same size, and tend to maintain all the desirable features of single-wire counter tubes of smaller dimensions. Fig. 10.19 is a cross section of a multiple-wire proportional counting chamber designed by Sun and Richardson (19). As constructed, this chamber contained 1.2 atmospheres of methane and operated at 3400 volts. This chamber was found to have the desirable characteristics possessed by most proportional counters which give them advantages over pulse ion chambers. Among these are more rapid rise of pulse than in ion chambers, allowing the use of short clipping times to improve resolution and thus discriminate against the piling up of gamma-ray pulses. Further, the size of the pulse is relatively independent of the point of origin of the primary ionization in the chamber. In addition, this design of multiple-wire chamber has been found to be almost completely insensitive to gamma radiation when operated at an over-all efficiency of 0.17 percent for detecting neutrons of energies ranging from 0.3 to 10 Mev.

10.13. Scintillation Detectors for Fast Neutrons

By molding a scintillating phosphor which is sensitive to recoiling protons, such as ZnS, into a plastic serving as a fairly dense radiator, it has been possible to design scintillators which are effective detectors of fast neutrons. A scintillator of this kind has been described by Hornyak (20). The low sensitivity of zinc sulfide to energetic electrons permits a detector using this compound as a scintillator to operate with moderate efficiency for fast neutrons in the presence of a much stronger flux of high-energy gamma rays. Fig. 10.20 shows the variation of the efficiency of one of these scintillators for neutrons from a Po-Be source with increasing concentration of ZnS in Lucite. Another important factor relating to the discrimination between neutrons and gamma rays is the grain size of the phosphor. Preferably the diameter of a phosphor grain should be less than the average range of the recoiling protons. For neutrons of an energy of about 4 Mev this range is estimated as 35 microns in the phosphor. Most commercial samples of ZnS have grains of smaller diameter and are suitable for use without further preparation. The final design of the neutron-sensitive button con-

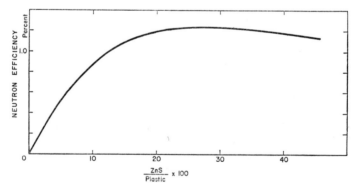

FIG. 10.20. *Percentage neutron efficiency of a fast-neutron scintillation detector as a function of the ratio of zinc sulfide to plastic for neutrons from a Po-Be source.*

tained 1.5 g of ZnS dispersed in 10 g of Lucite, making a cylinder 1 inch in diameter and 5/8 of an inch thick. The separate contributions to the integral spectrum of noise, of 17.6-Mev gamma rays, and of neutrons in the forward direction from a thick target of lithium bombarded by 2.35-Mev protons are shown in Fig. 10.21. Plastic scintillators are more efficient for the detection of fast neutrons than the usual proton recoil counter tubes. The efficiency of the plastic scintillators also increases with the energy of

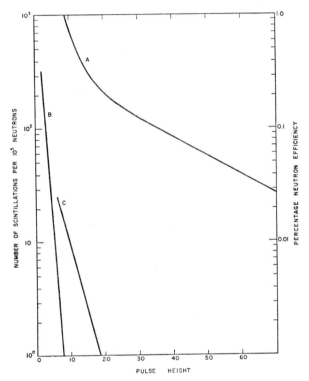

FIG. 10.21. *Integral bias curves for a scintillation detector composed of zinc sulfide crystals in plastic. A—0.5-Mev neutrons. B—tube noise. C—17.6-Mev gamma rays.*

the neutrons in the range of energies covered by the curve in Fig. 10.22. This graph shows the integral pulse height spectrum and efficiency for three different energies of neutrons.

Another approach to the problem of detecting fast neutrons by scintillators has been suggested by McCrary, Taylor, and Bonner (21). They have found that isolated spheres of anthracene will yield brighter scintillations from recoil protons than from the electrons released by gamma rays if the diameter of the anthracene spheres is in the range from 3 to 8

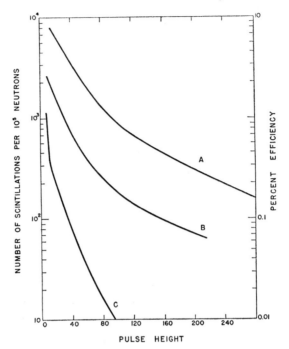

FIG. 10.22. *Integral pulse-height curves for a plastic scintillator and efficiency as a function of discriminator bias. A—14.2-Mev neutrons. B—Po-Be neutrons. C—0.5-Mev neutrons.*

mm. Furthermore, the same secondary electron from a gamma ray with energy of the order of 5 Mev can be prevented from exciting more than one anthracene sphere if several millimeters of glass or quartz separate the individual spheres. Fig. 10.23 is a diagram of an arrangement to isolate the anthracene spheres in which each sphere has a direct view of the photomultiplier tube, obstructed by no other sphere. This arrangement practically insures that the height of each pulse will be approximately the same for protons of the same energy. When the anthracene spheres are isolated as shown in Fig. 10.23, most of the gamma-ray background is contributed by secondary electrons of less than 1 Mev energy which may be completely absorbed in a single sphere. An electron of this energy could yield a pulse equal to that of a 2.5-Mev neutron.

10.14. The Detection of Ultra-High-Energy Neutrons

The efficiencies of detectors of neutrons with energies greater than 50 Mev are usually low. Proton recoils from a thin hydrogenous target may

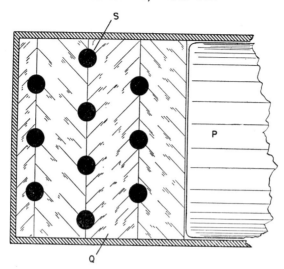

FIG. 10.23. *Scintillation, neutron-sensitive spheres S mounted between quartz plates Q to reduce gamma-ray background. P—photomultiplier tube.*

be measured with a telescope consisting of three proportional counter tubes in line by observing coincidences in the response of the counter tubes. An example is the apparatus used by Hadley and collaborators (22) which is sketched in Fig. 10.24. In this example, the target was a sheet of polyethylene with a thickness of 150 mg/cm², which is quite translucent to neutrons of the energies used in the experiment. The telescope can be made insensitive to protons generated by neutrons of energies lower than some arbitrary value by introducing suitable absorbers at A in Fig. 10.24. One

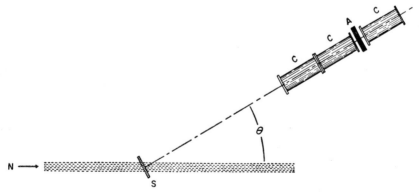

FIG. 10.24. *Counter telescope for detecting proton recoils from a radiator exposed to fast neutrons.*

advantage of this telescope is that the total range of the recoil protons can be measured and the energy of the neutrons deduced from this measurement. The use of a thin radiator also makes possible a good resolution of the neutron spectrum. However, the efficiency is sacrificed by the use of a thin radiator and may be of the order of 10^{-5} or less.

Because neutrons of energies greater than 50 Mev can induce fission in some of the heavy stable elements, fission chambers made with such elements as electrodes may be used to detect these ultra-high-energy neutrons. Bismuth has a larger cross section for fission than any of its neighbors in the periodic table, so this element was selected by Wiegand (23) for use in the fission chamber, sketched in Fig. 10.25, which he designed. Half of the

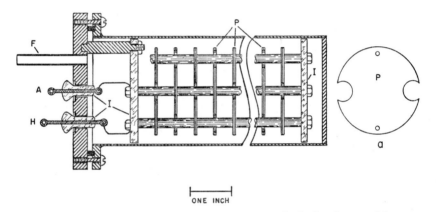

ONE INCH

FIG. 10.25. *High-energy neutron detector in which the fission of bismuth produces the ionizing particles. F—filling tube. A—terminal for collector electrodes. H—terminal for high-voltage electrodes. I—insulators. P—electrode plates. An outline of a typical plate is shown at* a.

thin aluminum plates serving as electrodes were coated on both sides with a thin layer of bismuth by evaporation. In the model described, a total of 28 plates was used, connected alternately to two separate systems of insulated metal supporting rods, as indicated in Fig. 10.25. The set of plates without bismuth coating was connected to an amplifier through the terminal A. The coated set was connected through the terminal H to −800 volts. An outline of one of the plates is shown at the right at *a*, indicating the notches through which the supporting rods of the opposite system of electrodes passed. The chamber was filled to a pressure of 1 atmosphere with a mixture of gases consisting of 96 percent argon and 4 percent carbon dioxide. If the gases are pure, this mixture yields pulses with a rapid rise time, about 4 microseconds, characteristic of electron collection on the electrodes connected to the amplifier. A measurement of the efficiency of this fission chamber detector indicated that the efficiency was of the order of 10^{-6}. Therefore the detector is mainly useful in strong beams of neutrons.

Recently the properties of liquid scintillators for the detection of ultra-high-energy neutrons have been investigated. As an example, we refer to the liquid scintillators developed by Christie and his co-workers (24). For scintillation counters in experiments where angular resolution is important, a cylindrical container of Lucite for the scintillating liquid is mounted on the end of a single photomultiplier tube, as shown in cross section in Fig. 10.26. The scintillating liquid consisted of a mixture of 3 g of p-terphenyl per liter of phenylcyclohexane. It is desirable to add a substance to this mixture which shifts the wavelength of the scintillations to a region where the photomultiplier is most sensitive. A much larger detector, using nine photomultipliers, was constructed in the form of a metal drum in the shape

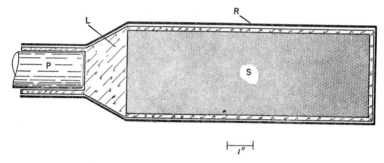

FIG. 10.26. *Liquid scintillator as a high-energy neutron detector. P—photomultiplier tube. L—Lucite container. R—reflector. S—scintillating liquid.*

of a truncated cone, sketched in Fig. 10.27. High efficiencies were obtained with this large detector for neutrons of energies of the order of 100 Mev. Below 15 Mev, the proton recoils come from hydrogen alone. A negligible fraction of these protons have ranges sufficient to reach the walls of the container. Hence for neutron energies below 15 Mev, a $\Delta E/E$ distribution of recoil protons is produced by neutrons with energy E. For neutrons with energies of 100 Mev, on the other hand, protons are released also from carbon in the liquid and the ranges of the protons are large enough for wall effects to become apparent. In addition, the height of pulses from an organic scintillator is not proportional to the energy absorbed by the scintillator. These complications at the higher neutron energies cause the fraction of the observed recoils to depend strongly on the setting of the discriminator in the electronic circuit connected to the photomultiplier. The order of the efficiency obtained, and its dependence on the bias setting, are illustrated by the experimental curve of Fig. 10.28 for neutrons of 129 Mev.

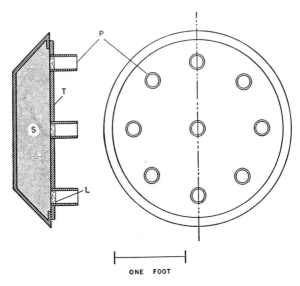

ONE FOOT

FIG. 10.27. *Large liquid scintillator consisting of a steel drum* T *filled with a scintillating liquid* S. P—*receptacles for photomultiplier tubes.* L—*Lucite window.*

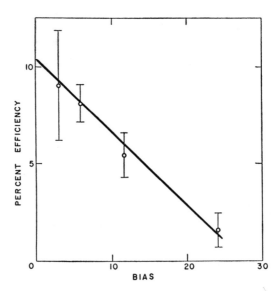

FIG. 10.28. *Efficiency of the large scintillation counter of Fig. 10.27 as a function of bias for 129-Mev neutrons.*

10.15. Threshold Detectors

Numerous reactions of neutrons with nuclei have definite thresholds for the energies of the neutrons below which the reactions do not occur. These thresholds extend from a few tenths of 1 Mev up to 20 Mev and higher and, in the higher energy range, involve either (n,2n) or charged-particle reactions. When the product is radioactive with properties which permit accurate measurement of the induced activity it is possible by the activation method to determine approximately the spectral distribution of neutrons from a source by the use of several detectors with thresholds at different energies. An example of a threshold for a neutron reaction is shown in Fig. 10.29. The graph shows the excitation curve for the reaction $Si^{28}(n,p)Al^{28}$

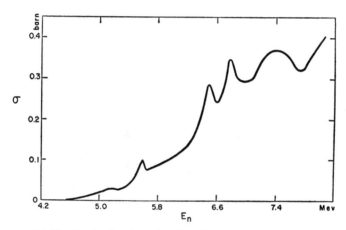

FIG. 10.29. *Excitation function for the reaction* $Si^{28}(n,p)Al^{28}$.

as determined by Marion, Brugger, and Chapman (25). The curve shows the characteristic rapid rise of the cross section for the reaction just above the threshold energy with the subsequent appearance of resonance peaks at various intervals. The cross sections are low, compared with many thermal neutron activation cross sections, but many charged particle reactions initiated by neutrons have much lower cross sections. A threshold detector responds to the neutrons of all energies above the threshold energy. However, the neutron cross section naturally changes with the neutron energy. This variation of the cross section requires the determination of an average value of the cross section, $\bar{\sigma}$, for convenience in using threshold detectors in estimating neutron fluxes. The value of $\bar{\sigma}$ may be obtained by measuring the radioactivity induced in the detector by a known flux with the same distribution of neutron energies as the flux to be measured. At best, the threshold detector does not give a very accurate determination of fluxes but its simplicity, compared with more accurate methods, offers much to recommend it where the accuracy is not too important.

As an example of the procedure which may be followed in the use of a threshold detector, we may consider the reaction $S^{32}(n,p)P^{32}$ which yields a radioactive product well suited for measurement by the counting of beta particles. The threshold of this reaction is at 1 Mev but the effective threshold is somewhat higher, about 2.5 Mev. A sample of sulfur having a thickness greater than the range of the beta particles from P^{32} will, in a given flux, acquire a saturation activity dependent only on its area. For calibration, a sample of phosphorus of similar dimensions can be irradiated in a known flux of thermal neutrons producing a known number of P^{32} atoms in a reaction having a cross section of 0.23 barn. From the ratio of the counting rate from the phosphorus to that in the sulfur in the unknown flux, and the value $\bar{\sigma} = 0.03$ barn for the reaction $S^{32}(n,p)P^{32}$, the flux of neutrons above the threshold of the $S^{32}(n,p)$ reaction incident on the sulfur sample can be computed. It is obvious that the use of threshold detectors will yield best results in strong fluxes having the same spectral distribution, in a fission spectrum for example.

As a numerical example to illustrate the use of sulfur and phosphorus as described in the preceding paragraph, we will assume that the cross section for the $P^{31}(n,\gamma)$ reaction, equal to 0.23 barn and the average cross section $\bar{\sigma}$ for the $S^{32}(n,p)$ reaction, equal to 0.03 barn, have been ascertained from tables or supplementary experiments. The targets of sulfur and of phosphorus are assumed each to have an area of 1 cm² and, for simplicity, to contain 10^{22} atoms. The phosphorus target is exposed to a thermal neutron flux of 10^6 neutrons per cm² per sec. The disintegration rate at saturation will be $10^6(0.23 \times 10^{-24})10^{22} = 2300$ disintegrations per sec. This disintegration rate would give a counting rate of 2300ϵ in a counter with an over-all efficiency of ϵ. However, we use the same counter for measurement of the sulfur target and the efficiency factor cancels out. We now irradiate the sulfur target in the unknown flux and determine the saturated disintegration rate to be 1200 disintegrations per sec. The unknown flux of neutrons ϕ above the threshold for the $S^{32}(n,p)$ reaction is given by

$$\phi = \frac{1200}{10^{22}(0.03 \times 10^{-24})} = 4 \times 10^6 \text{ neutrons per cm}^2 \text{ per sec.}$$

In each case only the beta rays emerging from the surface of the thick target are counted but this factor is included in the over-all efficiency of the counting arrangement. Because the targets are very nearly the same thickness the self-absorption factor for the irradiated targets will be nearly the same.

Table 10.5, taken from Cohen (26), contains a list of nuclides suitable for use as threshold detectors by the activation method.

Table 10.5

THRESHOLD DETECTORS FOR NEUTRONS

Target nucleus	Threshold Mev	Half-life of activity	Convenient material
		(n,2n)	
C^{12}	20.2	20.5 min	Graphite
N^{14}	10.6	10.1 min	Urea
O^{16}	16.5	2.1 min	Cellophane
F^{19}	10.4	112 min	LiF
P^{31}	12.3	2.6 min	$(NH_4)H_2PO_4$
Cr^{50}	13.4	42 min	Cr_2O_3
Ni^{58}	11.7	36 hr	Ni metal
As^{75}	10.3	16 day	As_2O_3
Ag^{107}	9.6	24.5 min	Ag metal
Sb^{121}	9.3	16 min	Sb_2O_3
I^{127}	9.5	13 day	NH_4I
Pr^{141}	9.4	3.5 min	Pr_6O_{11}
		(n,p)	
Mg^{24}	2.1	14.8 hr	Mg metal
Al^{27}	2.1	10.2 min	Al metal
P^{31}	1.1	170 min	$(NH_4)H_2PO_4$
S^{32}	1.0	14.3 day	S powder
Ti^{49}	1.1	57 min	Ti metal
Cr^{52}	2.8	3.9 min	Cr_2O_3
Fe^{56}	2.1	2.6 hr	Fe metal

10.16. Photographic Emulsions as Detectors of Neutrons

The nuclear track emulsion is an excellent detector for the protons which recoil from neutrons in the neutron-proton-scattering process when the neutron energy exceeds about 2 Mev. The proton tracks are easy to identify and the emulsion offers, in principle, a simple and direct means of measuring both the intensity and the energy of the neutrons. Also, by visual discrimination, it is possible to eliminate entirely from the measurements the effects of other disturbing radiations, such as gamma rays. One basic requirement for the use of emulsions in the measurement of neutrons is a knowledge of the range-energy curve for protons in the emulsion. Much work has been done on the range-energy relation for protons, and reliable curves, similar to the one prepared by Bradner and co-workers (27) reproduced in Fig. 10.30, can be found in the literature for ascertaining the energy of a proton from the length of its track in the emulsion. The measurement of the track lengths is accomplished with a microscope having a

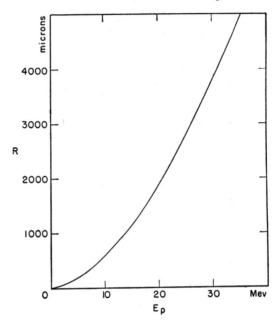

FIG. 10.30. *Range-energy curve for protons in a nuclear emulsion.*

carefully constructed micrometer stage. This scanning of the nuclear plates represents the one serious disadvantage of the emulsion method. The scanning is a time-consuming operation which can also become fatiguing to the eyes.

A detailed description of the measurement of neutron energy spectra by the emulsion technique has been prepared by Rosen (28). The radiator from which the protons are expelled may be external to the nuclear plate, which then serves only to record the proton tracks. The external radiator requires a strong flux to provide a sufficient number of proton tracks for measurement. For example, at 14 Mev a time-integrated neutron flux of the order of 10^8 neutrons per cm^2 is needed to produce 25 tracks per mm^2 in an emulsion 200 microns thick. This estimate assumes that the protons are projected in a cone with a half-angle of 10° and that the tracks start and stop in the emulsion. The sacrifice in sensitivity introduced by the external radiator is compensated by the accuracy which can be attained and by the flexibility of the components. Thus the external radiator permits the measurement of the angular distribution of proton recoils by the introduction of a system of slits between the radiator and the photographic plate. About a 15-fold increase in sensitivity results when the nuclear emulsion also serves as the radiator. The emulsion then records the protons expelled from the hydrogen nuclei in the emulsion.

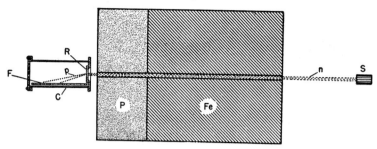

FIG. 10.31. *Collimator for use with an external radiator to record re-coiling protons in a nuclear emulsion. F—photographic plate. C—evacuated chamber. p—proton beam. R—radiator. P—paraffin. Fe—iron block. n—neutron beam. S—source of neutrons.*

Collimation of the neutron beam is desirable when an external radiator is used. Collimation allows the nuclear plate to be shielded from the neutron beam, greatly reducing the number of protons projected in the emulsion by extraneous neutrons. Without adequate neutron shielding, the background of unwanted proton tracks could obscure the tracks of protons originating in the radiator. The arrangement suggested by Rosen for this collimation and shielding is shown in Fig. 10.31. After leaving the source, the neutrons pass through a channel in a thick shield and enter the evacuated chamber containing the radiator and the photographic plate. The shield consists principally of iron because of its large cross section for the scattering of high-energy neutrons. This scattering process reduces the energies of the neutrons below the level at which they can project protons which will generate measurable tracks in the emulsion. The thick paraffin block between the iron shield and the evacuated chamber further reduces the energy of the neutrons. Thus neutrons outside the collimating channel are effectively prevented from initiating recoils in the radiator. The geometry of Fig. 10.32 is convenient for the analysis of the measurements. In the notation of the

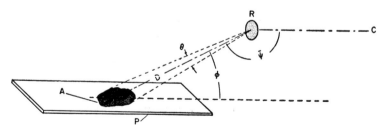

FIG. 10.32. *Geometry used in the analysis of proton tracks from an external radiator. P—photographic plate. A—area scanned in the emulsion. R—external radiator. C—axis of the collimator for neutrons. D—distance from center of A to center of R.*

figure, θ is the solid angle in the laboratory coordinate system subtended by the area scanned, A, at the radiator. Hence $\theta = A \sin \phi / D^2$. Then the solid angle subtended by A at the radiator in the center-of-mass system, designated by Ω, is given by $\Omega = (4 \cos \bar{\psi})\theta$ where $\bar{\psi}$ is the average angle between the neutron and proton beams. The neutron distribution may then be computed from the relation

$$N(E_p)dE_p = F(E_n)dE_n n_0 \frac{\sigma(E_n)}{4\pi} \Omega \qquad (10.44)$$

where n_0 is the number of hydrogen atoms in the radiator exposed to neutrons, $\sigma(E_n)$ is the n-p-scattering cross section, and $E_p = E_n \cos^2 \bar{\psi}$. The straightforward computation would use the proton recoil energy distribution to obtain $N(E_p)$ and then solve Eq. 10.44 for $F(E_n)$ = the number of neutrons of energy E_n per cm² per Mev incident on the radiator. It is more conveTient, however, to determine the numbers of protons corresponding in range to pre-selected intervals of neutron energy by calculating for the end points of each interval of neutron energy the corresponding ranges for the protons in the emulsion. The number of proton tracks in each interval may then be multiplied by the factor

$$\frac{\pi D^2}{n_0 \sigma(E_n) A \sin \phi \cos \bar{\psi}}$$

to give the number of neutrons per cm² per energy interval as a function of the neutron energy. In this factor only $\sigma(E_n)$ varies with the neutron energy.

The use of the nuclear emulsion itself also as a radiator is not only more sensitive than the external radiator but it also permits measurements at lower neutron energies. The arrangement for exposing the plate when the emulsion serves as a radiator is very simple, as indicated in Fig. 10.33. Interference by neutrons which have not proceeded directly from the source to the plate is reduced by suspending the plate in a position remote from dense objects which can scatter the neutrons. The analysis of the measurements in this case can be made in terms of the solid angle θ selected for the acceptance of tracks in the emulsion. The flux $F(E_n)$ for an interval of neutron energy E_n then is given by

$$F(E_n) = \frac{4\pi}{n_0 t A \theta 4 \cos \bar{\psi}} \frac{N_p(E_p) P_c(E_p) T_c(E_n)}{\sigma(E_n)} \qquad (10.45)$$

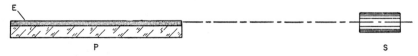

FIG. 10.33. *Arrangement for exposure of a nuclear emulsion to neutrons when the emulsion also serves as a radiator. E—emulsion. P— photographic plate. S—source of neutrons.*

where t is the thickness of the emulsion in cm $P_c(E_p)$ the probability correction for tracks which leave the emulsion, and $T_c(E_n)$ an attenuation factor for neutrons traversing an average distance in the emulsion or in the emulsion and the glass of the plate.

An external radiator which emits charged particles other than recoil protons may be used to study neutron spectra and the reactions induced by neutrons. The use of a photographic emulsion in such cases is illustrated by the work of Allred and co-workers (29) with the detector shown in Fig. 10.34. The evacuated chamber C containing the photographic plate P is mounted in front of an open channel in the thermal column of a reactor.

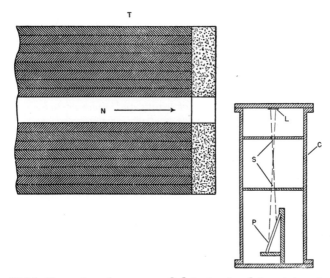

FIG. 10.34. *Geometry of source and detector for determining the energy spectra of charged particles from nuclear reactions with thermal neutrons. T—thermal column of reactor. N—neutron beam. L—lithium foil. S—slits. C—evacuated chamber. P—photographic plate.*

The chamber thus exposed to thermal neutrons contains a radiator which is a thin film of Li_2CO_3 on a platinum foil, mounted at L. The alpha particles and tritons from the exothermic reaction $Li^6(n,\alpha)H^3$ pass through the system of slits and are incident on the photographic plate. Very good resolution is obtained by this procedure, as indicated in Fig. 10.35, which is the distribution of track lengths for the alpha particles and tritons. Converting these track lengths to energy by the appropriate range-energy relation, yields a Q for the reaction of 4.67 ± 0.21 Mev compared with a value of about 4.9 Mev obtained by others using different methods. The ordinates of the curve in Fig. 10.35 give the actual numbers of observed tracks. The maxima of the curve have a statistical standard deviation of

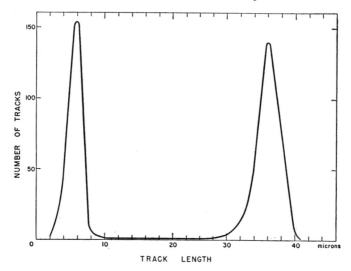

FIG. 10.35. *Range distribution of tritons and alpha particles from the* Li⁶ (n,α) H³ *reaction for thermal neutrons as measured in a nuclear emulsion.*

about ±10 percent. The small number of individual observations which can be conveniently made constitutes one of the handicaps of the emulsion method. Measuring track lengths is so laborious that it is difficult to extend observations to a sufficient number of tracks to give much better statistics than those represented by the curve of Fig. 10.35.

10.17. The Cloud Chamber as a Neutron Detector

The tracks produced by protons recoiling from collisions of neutrons with hydrogen in a cloud chamber provide another method for measuring fast neutrons. These tracks in the cloud chamber are strictly analogous to the proton tracks in nuclear emulsions, and the observations are analyzed in a similar manner. In comparison, the cloud chamber offers a less dense medium in which to observe the proton tracks, yielding greater track lengths for the same proton energy. These tracks may be measured without the use of a high-power microscope by projecting enlarged images of the cloud chamber photographs on a screen. The nature of the gas as well as the pressure of the gas in the chamber can be selected to fit the experiment. Perhaps one of the principal advantages of the cloud chamber over the emulsion is the immediate visibility of the tracks, permitting the adjustment of experimental conditions to obtain most favorable data from the experiment in progress. On the other hand, the cloud chamber, in its cycle of operation, is sensitive for only a fraction of the cycle. Furthermore the operational cycles are repeated at intervals separated by times of the order of a minute. Thus it is far from continuously sensitive throughout the experiment, as is the case of the emulsion. When a cloud chamber is designed for automatically making a large number of photographs of proton tracks, it is an elaborate piece of equipment. Once the photographs have been taken, the measurement of the tracks is only slightly less time-consuming than the similar operation for nuclear emulsions. For observations of recoiling protons, methane is commonly used as the filling gas for the cloud chamber. The pressure in the chamber may be as low as one-half atmosphere if neutrons of relatively low energy are to be detected. Bonner and co-workers (30) have used a cloud chamber to observe recoil protons from the delayed neutrons in the fission of U^{235}. Here the use of a cloud chamber was advantageous because it permitted definitely timed observations at selected intervals after the irradiation of the sample of uranium. By an appropriate selection for the timing, the effects from the emitter of delayed neutrons with a half-life of 2.1 seconds could be emphasized, this being the activity which yields the more numerous and energetic neutrons. Neutrons of energies from 0.4 to 2.4 Mev were observed in this experiment.

The adaptability of the cloud chamber to special investigations is illustrated in the study by Swartz (31) of the collisions of high-energy neutrons with helium. A cyclotron was used to accelerate protons to an energy of 235 Mev and the neutrons studied were produced when the protons struck a beryllium target. The shields and collimators around the cloud chamber were arranged according to the diagram of Fig. 10.36. The neutron beam was interrupted within the cyclotron so that neutrons reached the cloud chamber only during the sensitive part of its cycle. From the analysis of the recoil nuclei in the helium-filled cloud chamber, two major groups of tracks could be distinguished. One group of elastic helium recoils contained

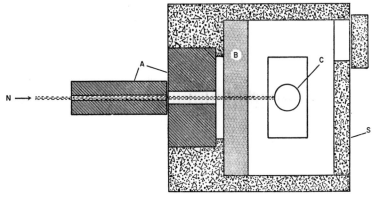

FIG. 10.36. *Cloud chamber filled with helium in a beam of neutrons for observing elastic recoil of helium nuclei. A—copper collimator and shield. B—borated water shield. C—cloud chamber. N—neutrons. S—concrete shield.*

the tracks originating from neutrons with energies in the following categories, (1) definitely less than 30 Mev, (2) probably less than 30 Mev, and (3) possibly less than 30 Mev. The histogram obtained from measuring the lengths of the recoil tracks is plotted in Fig. 10.37. The other major group was characterized by neutrons in categories of energy, (1) definitely greater than 50 Mev, (2) probably greater than 50 Mev, and (3) possibly greater than 50 Mev. The histogram for this higher energy group is shown in Fig. 10.38. In each of the above figures θ represents the angle in the lab-

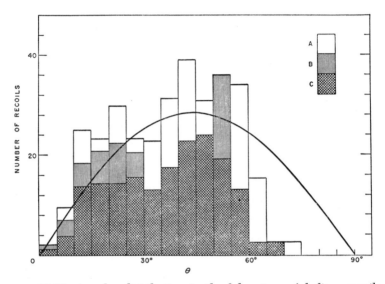

FIG. 10.37. *Angular distribution in the laboratory of helium recoils from neutrons with less than 30-Mev energy. A—neutrons with energy possibly less than 30 Mev. B—neutrons with energy probably less than 30 Mev. C—neutrons with energy definitely less than 30 Mev. The smooth curve represents the angular distribution if the scattering is isotropic in the center-of-mass system.*

oratory system between the direction of the recoiling helium nucleus and the direction of the incident neutron. The smooth curve in each figure is the calculated angular distribution if the elastic scattering were isotropic in the center-of-mass system of coordinates. The experimental distribution in Fig. 10.37 is strongly indicative that the scattering is isotropic in the center-of-mass system for neutrons with energies below 30 Mev. The data in Fig. 10.38, on the other hand, support the view that the scattering of neutrons from helium is not isotropic in the center-of-mass system for neutron energies greater than 50 Mev.

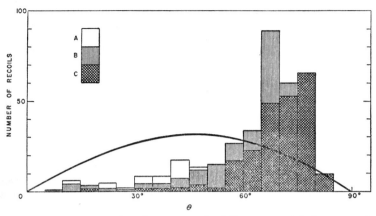

FIG. 10.38. *Angular distribution in the laboratory of helium recoils from neutrons having greater than 50-Mev energy. A—neutrons having energy possibly greater than 50 Mev. B—neutrons having energy probably greater than 50 Mev. C—neutrons having energy definitely greater than 50 Mev. The smooth curve represents what the angular distribution would be if the scattering were isotropic in the center-of-mass system.*

SYMBOLS FOR CHAPTER IV

E	kinetic energy
E_n	kinetic energy of a neutron
E_p	kinetic energy of a proton
E_γ	energy of a gamma ray
N	number of atoms per cm³ in a target
n	a neutron
n	number of neutrons
n_0	number of hydrogen atoms in a radiator
L	diffusion length for neutrons
p	proton
Q	number of hydrogen atoms per unit mass in a radiator
v	the velocity of a neutron
α	alpha particle; a neutron absorption parameter
γ	gamma ray
ϵ	an efficiency factor
θ	a recoil angle in the laboratory system
λ	disintegration constant for a radionuclide
λ_s	scattering mean free path of a neutron
λ_{tr}	transport mean free path of a neutron
μ	neutron absorption coefficient

ρ	neutron density
σ	neutron cross section
σ_{act}	neutron activation cross section
τ	mean life of a radionuclide
ϕ	recoil angle in the center-of-mass system
$\bar{\psi}$	average angle between an incident neutron and a recoil proton
Ω	a solid angle

PROBLEMS FOR CHAPTER IV

1. A manganese foil 0.1 mm thick and 2 cm on an edge was exposed to thermal neutrons for 6 hours. Twenty minutes after removal from the source of neutrons the beta particles were counted over a period of 10 min in a counter with an over-all efficiency of 0.38. The number of counts observed was 66000. Compute the neutron flux to which the neutron was exposed.

2. Compute the drain-correction factor in graphite for a detector of 1 cm radius and 1 mm thickness which has a neutron absorption coefficient of 0.6 per cm.

3. A sample of amorphous B^{10} having a thickness of 2 cm and a density of 1.8 g/cm^3 is placed in a neutron beam. Assume that the disintegration rate of the B^{10} can be measured while in the neutron beam and was found to be 4000 disintegrations per cm^2 per sec. Compute the value of the thermal flux.

4. A gold foil is irradiated in a thermal neutron flux for 2 hours. The counting rate at the moment of removal was determined as 2500 counts per min. Compute the counting rate which would have been observed if the irradiation had proceeded to saturation.

5. A proton recoil track in an emulsion is found to have a length of 50 microns. The track is inclined at an angle of 15° to the direction of the incident neutron. Compute the kinetic energy in Mev of the neutron from which the proton recoiled.

REFERENCES FOR CHAPTER IV

1. C. W. Tittle. *Nucleonics* **8**, 5 June (1951).
2. C. W. Tittle. *Nucleonics* **9**, 60 July (1951).
3. W. Bothe. *Z. Phys.* **120**, 437 (1943).
4. E. Jahnke and F. Emde. *Tables of Functions,* Dover Press, N.Y. (1943).
5. J. A. De Juren and H. Rosenwasser. *Phys. Rev.* **93**, 831 (1954).
6. A. L. Cockroft and S. C. Curran. *Rev. Sci. Inst.* **22**, 37 (1951).
7. B. Rossi and H. H. Staub. *Ionization Chambers and Counters,* McGraw-Hill (1949), p. 83.
8. D. B. James, W. Kubelka, S. A. Heiberg, and J. B. Warren. *Can. J. Phys.* **33**, 219 (1955).
9. A. O. Hanson and J. L. McKibben. *Phys. Rev.* **72**, 673 (1947).
10. R. A. Nobles, R. B. Day, R. L. Henkel, G. A. Jarvis, R. P. Kutarnia, J. L. McKibben, J. E. Perry, Jr., and R. K. Smith. *Rev. Sci. Inst.* **25**, 334 (1954).
11. S. B. Gunst, J. C. Connor, and R. T. Bayard. *Rev. Sci. Inst.* **26**, 894 (1955).
12. K. P. Nicholson and G. F. Snelling. *Brit. J. Appl. Phys.* **6**, 104 (1955).
13. R. A. Nobles and A. B. Smith. *Nucleonics* **14**, 60 Jan. (1956).
14. E. R. Rae and E. M. Bowey. *Proc. Phys. Soc.* **66A,** 1073 (1953).
15. S. G. Forbes. *Phys. Rev.* **88**, 1309 (1952).

16. R. B. Rhody and J. I. Hopkins. *Rad. Res.* **2,** 523 (1955).
17. J. Hirschfelder and J. L. Magee. *Phys. Rev.* **73,** 207 (1948).
18. H. Bethe. *Handbuch der Physik*, Vol. 24, Part I, p. 521. M. Livingston and H. Bethe. *Rev. Mod. Phys.* **9,** 263 (1937).
19. C. R. Sun and J. R. Richardson. *Rev. Sci. Inst.* **25,** 691 (1954).
20. W. F. Hornyak. *Rev. Sci. Inst.* **23,** 264 (1952).
21. J. N. McCrary, H. L. Taylor, and T. W. Bonner. *Phys. Rev.* **94,** 808A (1954).
22. J. Hadley, E. Kelly, C. Leith, E. Segrè, C. Wiegand, and H. York. *Phys. Rev.* **75,** 351 (1949).
23. C. Wiegand. *Rev. Sci. Inst.* **19,** 790 (1948).
24. E. R. Christie, B. T. Feld, A. C. Odian, P. C. Stein, and A. Wattenberg. *Rev. Sci. Inst.* **27,** 127 (1956).
25. J. B. Marion, R. M. Brugger, and R. A. Chapman. *Phys. Rev.* **101,** 247 (1956).
26. B. L. Cohen. *Nucleonics* **8,** 29 Feb. (1951).
27. H. Bradner, F. M. Smith, W. H. Barkas, and A. S. Bishop. *Phys. Rev.* **77,** 462 (1950).
28. L. Rosen. *Nucleonics* **11,** 32 July, 38 Aug. (1953).
29. J. C. Allred, A. N. Phillips, L. Rosen, and F. K. Talmadge. *Rev. Sci. Inst.* **21,** 225 (1950).
30. T. W. Bonner, S. J. Bame, Jr., and J. E. Evans. *Phys. Rev.* **101,** 1514 (1956).
31. C. Swartz. *Phys. Rev.* **85,** 73 (1952).

Chapter V

SPECTROMETERS AND MONOCHROMATORS

11.1. Early Methods for Determining Energies of Neutrons

The interactions of neutrons with nuclei frequently show rapid variations with the neutron energy. A number of examples of sharp changes in the cross section as the energy of the neutron changes have been mentioned in preceding pages. It was realized shortly after the discovery of the neutron that some method for determining energies of neutrons was essential to the investigations of neutron interactions and the interpretation of the observations. One of the first steps in the direction of estimating the neutron energy involved attempts to secure beams consisting only of slow neutrons. One method was to introduce absorbers into the beam of neutrons to remove the fast neutrons. This effort proved mainly unsuccessful because slow neutrons have attenuation coefficients in most substances as large or larger than those for fast neutrons. In limited regions, at high energies, threshold detectors proved useful in establishing reference points in neutron spectra. Threshold detectors were usually calibrated in monochromatic neutron beams of accelerators in which the energy of the accelerated beam of particles was carefully measured. Once the threshold energy for a particular detector element had been established, this element could be used anywhere. When used with accelerators, they eliminated the necessity for the accurate measurement of the energy of the beam in the accelerator. Another quite successful approach was the use of neutron absorbers which obey the $1/v$ law to estimate the energy.

11.2. Boron Absorbers for Determining Neutron Energy

It was recognized quite early in the investigations with neutrons that light elements, such as boron and lithium, which emit heavy particles on

194

capturing a neutron, should show no sharp resonance effects with slow neutrons. Consequently it was suggested that the slow neutron absorption cross section would be inversely proportional to the velocity of the neutrons. Frisch and Placzek (1) also noted that an absorber of this type could be used to identify the neutron energy, say of a monochromatic beam of slow neutrons, if the cross section for some particular energy in the $1/v$ region were known. It is now well-established that the total cross section for boron follows the $1/v$ law from the lowest neutron energies up to about 100 ev. Hence boron provides a suitable filter for measuring neutron energies in this region.

There is a variety of ways in which a boron filter may be used to determine neutron energies. A most important application has been the identification of the energies of slow neutrons captured at resonance which result in the activation of the capturing nuclei. Where resonances exist,

FIG. 11.1. *Diagram illustrating the use of boron filters to determine resonance activation energies in the slow neutron region. N—neutron beam. B—boron filter. F—activated foil.*

the activity produced in a target exposed to a beam of neutrons of heterogeneous energies may arise almost entirely from the capture of neutrons of the characteristic resonance energy. The procedure for the boron filter in this situation can be illustrated by the following hypothetical case. The example is based on the assumed existence of two activation resonances in the capturing element. The problem is even simpler when there is only one resonance. A foil of the element to be studied is exposed in a collimated beam of neutrons as indicated at F in Fig. 11.1. This beam is assumed to contain neutrons with a wide range of energies, such as a beam of moderated high-energy neutrons. It is convenient to place a cadmium filter permanently in the beam if neutrons with energy only above about 0.4 ev are desired. The activation of the foil is then measured without a boron filter in the beam and the measurement is repeated with boron filters of different thicknesses. The counting rate obtained for each step is then plotted on semilog paper versus the thickness of the boron filter, as shown by the solid curve in Fig. 11.2. The straight right-hand portion of this

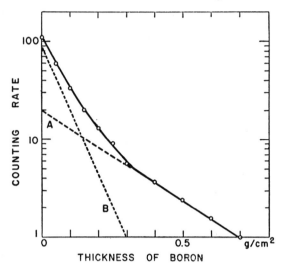

FIG. 11.2. *Graph of the counting rate from an activated foil versus the thickness of the boron filter for a hypothetical example of a foil having two resonance activations.*

curve suggests that it can be resolved into more than one logarithmic component. On extrapolating the straight section to zero boron thickness, the straight line A is obtained. Subtracting A from the solid curve gives a second straight line B with no remainder. The two straight lines, corresponding to the resonances thus revealed, can be represented by equations of the type of Eq. 4.5. Therefore the slope of each line is $-\sigma$, where σ is the total cross section in boron for the corresponding neutron energy.

We can make the following calculations to obtain the two neutron energies from the curves of Fig. 11.2. To compute σ we have

$$\frac{n}{n_0} = e^{-Nx\sigma}$$

from which

$$\ln n - \ln n_0 = -Nx\sigma \quad \text{or} \quad \sigma = \frac{\ln n_0 - \ln n}{Nx}$$

For curve A

$$\sigma = \frac{\ln 20 - \ln 1}{0.7 \, N}$$

where N is the number of boron atoms in 1 cm³ $= 6.02 \times 10^{22}$. Hence

$$\sigma = \frac{3}{0.7(6.02 \times 10^{22})} = 71.3 \text{ barns}$$

From the cross section curve for boron we find that σ has the value of 71.3 barns at $E_n = 2.9$ ev. For curve B

$$\sigma = \frac{\ln 90 - \ln 1}{0.3(6.02 \times 10^{-22})} = 377 \text{ barns}$$

For $\sigma = 377$ barns we find from the cross section curve for boron that $E_n = 0.1$ ev.

The boron filter method is less accurate than the more refined methods of measuring neutron energies, to be described below. However, it has often been used in exploratory experiments because of its simplicity. A convenient form of boron filter for some purposes is a sheet of plane-parallel borosilicate glass of known chemical composition.

11.3. Mechanical Monochromators

The velocities of slow neutrons are in a range where a mechanical device to permit the transmission of neutrons in a narrow group of velocities is readily feasible. Dunning and his co-workers (2) were the first to develop a mechanical monochromator. Their design is illustrated by Fig. 11.3. The neutrons came from a Rn-Be source mounted in a block of paraffin. The sectored disks AA, separated by a distance of 54 cm, were mounted on a rotating shaft. A similar pair of disks BB, fixed in position, served as entrance and exit slits for the neutrons. The disks BB were mounted near each disk A, as indicated in Fig. 11.3. This assembly was placed between the source of neutrons and the detector. The sectors of

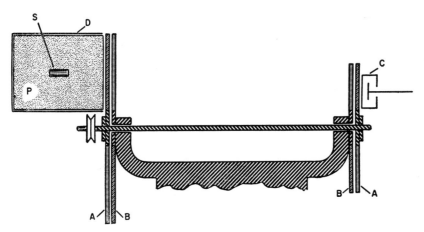

FIG. 11.3. *Diagram of the first velocity selector for measuring neutron energies. A, A—rotating sectored disks. B, B—stationary sectored disks. C—ionization chamber. D—cadmium shield. P—paraffin moderator. S—Rn-Be neutron source.*

the disks consisted of alternate cadmium and aluminum segments, each having an angular width of about 3.6°. This geometry was intended to permit the release of slow neutrons through the entrance slit as each aluminum segment came into position and to transmit through the exit slit only the neutrons with velocities which caused them to arrive at the exit slit at its next opening. Hence approximately monochromatic neutrons should emerge from the exit slit for a constant speed of rotation of the shaft carrying the disks AA. The problems of mechanical velocity selection for neutrons are not as simple as envisaged in this design. Actually this selector caused a decrease in the number of neutrons reaching the detector at certain velocities of rotation. Fig. 11.4 is a plot of the data obtained, showing the decrease as a positive ΔN. The curve is a rough

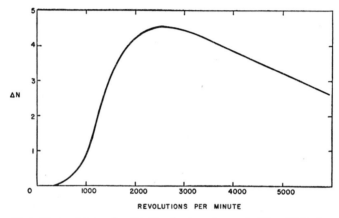

FIG. 11.4. *Data obtained with the device shown in Fig. 11.3 showing a decrease in detector response as a function of the velocity of rotation of the sectored disks.*

approximation to a Maxwellian distribution and is one of the earliest experimental demonstrations of the existence of such a distribution of velocities for neutrons of approximately thermal energies. The fact that the high-velocity end of this curve falls too slowly can be attributed to the failure of the paraffin moderator to thermalize completely the neutron beam. One of the most serious disadvantages of this early monochromator was the high background count which made accurate measurements difficult. The background resulted in part from the comparative transparency of cadmium to epithermal neutrons. It must be admitted, however, that the construction of mechanical monochromators has encountered numerous obstacles to satisfactory performance. The most accurate and detailed investigations of neutron spectra have so far been accomplished by other methods.

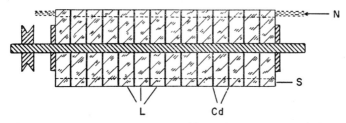

FIG. 11.5. *Cross section of rotor for neutron velocity selector designed to be opaque to epithermal neutrons. L—Lucite disks. Cd—cadmium disks. S—position of slits. N—neutron beam.*

The mechanical monochromator, or velocity selector as it is often called, has found most effective use for cold neutrons. One design, described by Dash and Sommers (3), has achieved very high opacity to epithermal neutrons. The opacity is achieved by making the rotor in the form of a cylinder, about 15 inches long and 5 inches in diameter, composed of segments of Lucite separated by disks of cadmium. The Lucite moderates the fastest neutrons so the cadmium can absorb them. Fig. 11.5 is a diagrammatic cross section of the rotor. The longitudinal slots, forming channels for the neutrons, are normally helical, and the axis of the rotor is mounted parallel to the direction of the collimated beam of neutrons. The slots may also be straight and the effect of helical slots can then be approximated by mounting the axis of the rotor at a small angle to the neutron beam. The principle by which a nominally monochromatic beam is passed through the rotor can be explained with reference to Fig. 11.6 which is a diagram of a rotor with a single helical slot to simplify the diagram. If the pitch of the helix is $dl/d\phi$ and the rotor turns at an angular

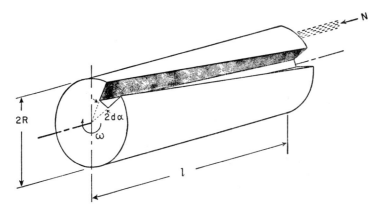

FIG. 11.6. *Diagram of a rotor of a velocity selector with a helical slot.*

velocity $\omega = d\phi/dt$, the velocity and wavelength of the selected neutrons are given by

$$v = dl/dt = (dl/d\phi)(d\phi/dt) = \omega/l\phi_0 \qquad (11.1)$$

$$\lambda = (h/m\omega)(\phi_0/l) \qquad (11.2)$$

where l is the length of the rotor and ϕ_0 is the angle of advance of the helix in this distance. The selector was calibrated with a boron absorption filter. The straight-line plot of Fig. 11.7, showing the neutron wavelength versus the reading of the tachometer used to determine the rotational velocity, was obtained by measuring the cross section of boron at two rotor speeds.

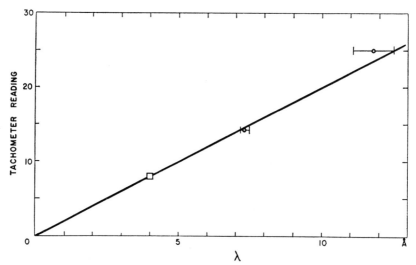

FIG. 11.7. *Calibration of a slow-neutron velocity selector showing neutron wavelength as a function of speed of rotation. 0—boron absorption measurements. □—beryllium filter measurement.*

A third point, represented by a small square on the calibration line, was obtained with a beryllium filter 4 inches thick. From the equation of the Bragg law of reflection, $n\lambda = 2d \sin \theta$, it is clear that the longest wavelength which can be reflected from a crystal, with a grating space d, is for $\sin \theta = 1$. If the maximum lattice spacing in a polycrystalline material is d_m, the longest wavelength which is reflected is

$$\lambda_m = 2d_m \qquad (11.3)$$

The crystalline filter will be transparent to all wavelengths greater than λ_m. For beryllium $2d_m = 3.95\,\text{Å}$. This point on the calibration was located by placing the beryllium filter in the neutron beam and measuring the transmitted neutron intensity at selected speeds of rotation of the rotor.

These data are plotted in Fig. 11.8. The curve indicates that the value of λ = 3.95 Å is to be assigned to a tachometer reading of approximately 8. The dependability of the calibration is considerably enhanced by this confirmation of the boron absorption measurements.

A special case of the velocity selector technique is described by Holt (4). A fundamental difficulty with crystal monochromators for neutrons is that at wavelengths greater than 1 Å, higher-order reflections may be included in the reflected beam and destroy its purity. An early method for dealing with this problem was to introduce a crystalline filter into the reflected beam. Crystals were selected which would be opaque to the shorter wavelengths of higher

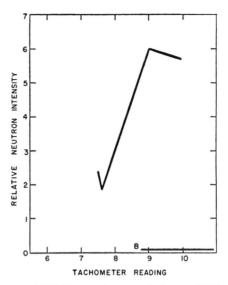

FIG. 11.8. *Determination of the* λ = 3.95 Å *point on the velocity selector calibration by means of a polycrystalline beryllium filter. The line* B *represents the background for the observations.*

orders but transparent to the long wavelengths of the principal reflection. The use of a crystalline filter for this purpose is not entirely satisfactory. To be effective, these filters must be at least several centimeters thick. Hence they also reduce

FIG. 11.9. *End view of a velocity selector rotor.*

significantly the intensity of the first-order reflection. The method developed by Holt was to replace the filter with a special velocity selector having a high transparency for neutrons of lower energy but almost opaque for higher energies. The energy of optimum transmission is varied by changing the speed of rotation. Because the neutron beam has been reflected from a crystal, epithermal neutrons are mainly absent. Referring again to Fig. 11.6, for a neutron velocity v traveling parallel to the axis of rotation, the condition that it pass through the slot in the rotor is

$$v = \frac{\omega l}{\alpha} \tag{11.4}$$

where l is the length of the rotor, ω its angular velocity, and α is the angle through which the rotor has turned as the neutron passes through. When used as a filter with a radial slit at the exit end of the rotor, the condition for blocking the second-order reflection is fulfilled if

$$v_{\max} < 2v \tag{11.5}$$

where $v_{\max}$ is the maximum velocity at which a neutron can pass through the rotor. The condition of Eq. 11.5 is given by

$$v_{\max} = \frac{\omega l}{\alpha - (2d\alpha + \beta)} = \frac{v}{1 - \dfrac{2d\alpha + \beta}{\alpha}} \cdot v \tag{11.6}$$

where $\beta = \theta l/R$ and θ is the divergence of the collimated beam of neutrons. $2d\alpha$ is the angular width of the slot.

A rotor was constructed on the basis of the preceding calculation. The rotor contained 80 helical slots, defined by cadmium-plated stainless steel vanes. Fig. 11.9 represents an end view. The pitch of the helix was 315.98 inches and the length of the rotor was 40 cm. From Eq. 11.6 for $\theta = 0.00573$ radian, the value of $v_{\max}$ is $1.57v$. The angle α was 0.313 radian and $2d\alpha = 0.0685$ radian. This rotor was tested experimentally by setting the spectrometer crystal for a wavelength of 10 Å and increasing the speed of the rotor stepwise from 2000 to 4000 revolutions per min. The maximum angular velocity at which no neutrons pass through the rotor $\omega_{\max}$ is given by

$$\omega_{\max} = \omega\left(1 + \frac{2d\alpha + \beta}{\alpha}\right) \tag{11.7}$$

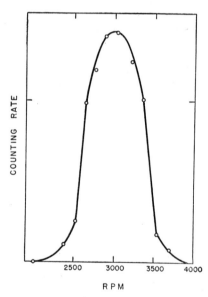

FIG. 11.10. *The counting rate as a function of angular speed of the rotor for a wavelength of 10 Å.*

In the experiment θ was equal to 0.00344 radian, giving $\omega_{\max} = 3950$ revolutions per min. The data plotted in Fig. 11.10 shows very good agreement. In this case v_{max} is $1.44v$, safely below the critical value $2v$, a requirement for excluding the second-order reflection.

11.4. Slow-Neutron Beam Choppers

Choppers use a rotating shutter which opens and closes a predetermined number of times per revolution. When closed, they effectively shut off the beam and on opening they allow a short burst of neutrons to travel to the detector over a measured path. Auxiliary devices, usually electronic circuits, measure the interval between the opening of the shutter and the response of the detector. Frequently the time for the neutron to reach the detector is obtained with a multichannel analyzer in which each channel corresponds to a narrow range of flight times. The analyzer records the number of neutrons in each of these channels (there may be several hundred) to record the distribution of velocities in the beam. Choppers have been used with neutrons having energies from 0.001 up to 10,000 ev.

An example of a chopper for slow neutrons, covering the range from 0.001 to 0.1 ev, has been described by Egelstaff (5) and is represented by the diagram of Fig. 11.11. The collimated beam from a thermal column is incident on a rotary shutter. This shutter consists of a series of alternate laminations of cadmium and aluminum. The details of this structure are shown in the cross section of Fig. 11.12 for one quadrant of the rotor. Two bursts of neutrons are released for each revolution of the shutter. The neutrons travel over a measured path to a BF_3 proportional counter tube, serving as a detector. The neutrons are recorded according to their time of arrival at the detector with reference to a flash of light on the photocell P. The light is reflected from the two-sided mirror M mounted on the shaft of the rotor. The instant, with respect to the angular position of the rotor, at which the flash of light reaches the photocell is controlled by adjusting the position of the photocell in an arc about the axis of the rotor, as indicated by the dotted lines. The response of the photocell is fed into an electronic gating unit G_1, which passes those pulses from the detector which arrive during a short, predetermined interval immediately following the pulse from the photocell. As G_1 closes, it opens G_2, permitting neutrons arriving in a subsequent interval to be recorded on the separate scaler connected to G_2. This gating process is repeated through the six gating units. In this way the scalers record six groups of neutrons which have different adjacent velocities. The circuit therefore constitutes a six-channel analyzer which can be moved over a greater range of velocities by adjusting the position of the photocell.

The graph in Fig. 11.13 shows typical measurements made with this slow neutron chopper. In the figure, the total absorption cross section of gold is plotted for flight times representing neutron energies from 0.001

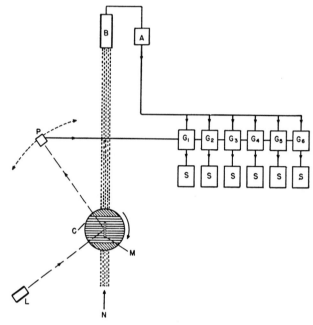

FIG. 11.11. *Diagram of a beam chopper for slow neutrons, with associated electronic circuits to determine neutron energies by measuring the time of flight from the chopper to the detector. L—light source. M—mirror. C—rotor. P—photocell. B—detector. A—amplifier. G—gating circuits. S—scalers.*

to 0.1 ev. Data for this graph were taken by introducing gold absorbers in the collimated beam of neutrons and observing the decrease in the number of neutrons in each flight channel. The curve represents the data within the limits of experimental error. The jog near the center results from a correction for the coherent scattering cross section of about 0.4 barn. A value for the absorption cross section of gold, at a neutron velocity of 2200 meters per sec, of 98.4 ± 0.9 barns was deduced from the graph of Fig. 11.13. This cross section was found to be in excellent agreement with current values reported by other investigators.

11.5. Fast-Neutron Chopper

The application of the beam chopper to slow neutrons is simplified by the large absorption cross section of cadmium for neutrons with energies less than about 0.4 ev. Thus shutters made with cadmium are quite opaque in the closed position for neutrons of lower energies. It is equally obvious that cadmium cannot be used effectively as a shutter for fast neutrons. In the search for other materials to stop fast neutrons, it became clear that

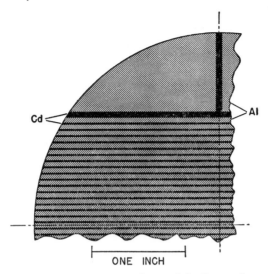

FIG. 11.12. *Detail, showing one quadrant of the beam chopper rotor in cross section.*

the size of the rotor must be greatly increased. The need for greater dimensions is a consequence of the low attenuation coefficients for fast neutrons in all substances. Fig. 11.14 is a diagram of a fast neutron chopper constructed at the Brookhaven National Laboratory (6). This design has proved efficient to a degree that it has been copied at other laboratories. The rotor is 30 inches in diameter. The shaded portions are made of phenolic laminate. The high hydrogen content of this material gives it a high stopping power for fast neutrons. The low density of the phenolic laminate is also important to the mechanical operation of the rotor, intended to be driven at speeds of 6000 to 12,000 revolutions per min. Channels through the rotor permit eight bursts of neutrons to pass for each revolution. The time resolution at 12,000 revolutions per min has roughly the form of an isosceles triangle with a full width of 0.7 microsecond at half maximum.

The essential features of an installation for the use of the fast chopper are sketched in Fig. 11.15, taken from an article by Fluharty and his co-workers (7). The shielded chopper is mounted in the collimated beam of a reactor. Usually this beam is filtered through a bismuth plug before emerging from the core of the reactor to reduce the intensity of the gamma radiation. Flight paths with lengths from 15 to 60 meters may be used. The drift tube, down which the neutrons move to the detector, is filled with helium at atmospheric pressure. Helium causes appreciably less scattering of the neutrons than air. The detector normally consists of a

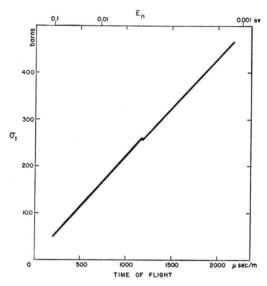

FIG. 11.13. *Typical measurements made with the apparatus of Fig. 11.11.*

bank of BF_3 proportional counter tubes to cover the area of the beam at the remote end of the drift tube. Timing for the determination of the neutron velocities is done electronically in conjunction with the passage of a beam of light through a rotor channel, coincident with the release of

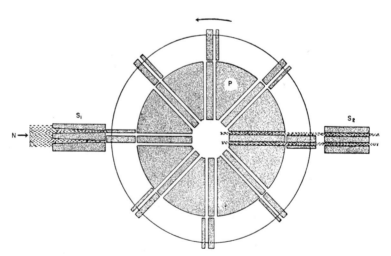

FIG. 11.14. *A beam chopper for fast neutrons. N—neutron beam. S_1—entrance slit. S_2—exit slit. P—phenolic laminate.*

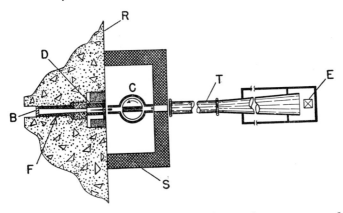

FIG. 11.15. *A diagram of a fast-neutron beam chopper mounted in front of a reactor to admit a burst of neutrons into a drift tube. B—bismuth filter, F—collimator. D—radiation door for closing the collimating system. C—beam chopper. T—drift tube. E—neutron detector.*

a burst of neutrons. This flash of light falls on a photocell to convert it into an electrical pulse. In one method of timing, the photopulse starts an electronic oscillator with a known, stabilized frequency. A scaler counts and records the number of oscillations until the oscillator is stopped by

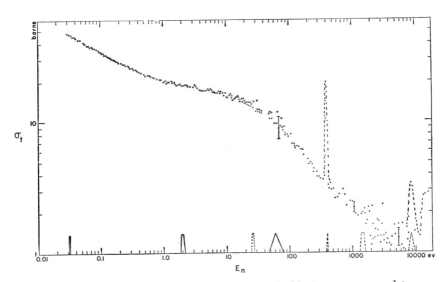

FIG. 11.16. *The total neutron cross section of chlorine as measured in part by a crystal spectrometer (open circles), and in part by a beam chopper (closed triangles).*

the arrival of the neutrons. This circuit can be made more completely automatic by having a scanning pulse transmit the reading of each scaler to one of a bank of registers, at the same time resetting the scaler to zero. This operation is completed after the arrival of the neutrons at the detector but before the next photopulse restarts the oscillator. With a sufficient number of channels in the analyzer, observations for a complete curve may be made simultaneously. Fig. 5.1 is an example of data obtained with the fast chopper. In Fig. 11.16, showing measurements by Brugger and his co-workers (8) of the neutron cross section of chlorine as a function of neutron energy, part of the measurements were made with a crystal spectrometer. The remainder, at higher energies, were obtained with a fast chopper. The two sets of data overlap in the region extending from 20 to 50 ev. The curve of Fig. 11.16 gives an approximate idea of the ranges in which these two devices for determining neutron energy conveniently operate. The resolutions at selected energies are also indicated by triangles along the x-axis. The solid triangles refer to the crystal spectrometer, and the dotted triangles to the beam chopper. The trapezoids result from averaging the resolution over a narrow range of energy.

11.6. The Pulsed Accelerators in Time-of-Flight Neutron Spectroscopy

The time-of-flight method for determining the energy of neutrons can be applied wherever bursts of neutrons of appropriate duration can be released in a drift tube for timing. The beam of a cyclotron can be interrupted internally with an abruptness and frequency suitable for this purpose. The neutrons for time-of-flight measurements with a pulsed cyclotron have usually been produced by deuterons striking a beryllium target within the cyclotron chamber. By modulating the beam of deuterons, periodic bursts of neutrons are produced. A paraffin moderator, to bring the velocities of the neutrons into the desired range, is sometimes placed in the neutron beam close to the cyclotron chamber, as indicated in Fig. 11.17. The principles by which the velocities of the neutrons are measured are basically similar to those for the neutron beam chopper. Because the chopper can be used in the intense beams from reactors and refinements in the mechanical operation can be introduced to improve the resolution, the cyclotron is now less frequently used in time-of-flight measurements of neutron spectra. However, in the period just prior to the development of the nuclear reactor, the most informative observations on neutron energies came from time-of-flight measurements with pulsed cyclotrons. An example is the study of the cross section of indium as a function of neutron energy by McDaniel (9), the results of which are shown in Fig. 11.18.

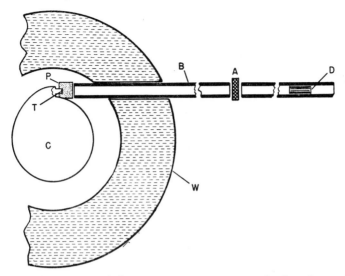

FIG. 11.17. *Diagram of the arrangement to use a pulsed cyclotron for the time-of-flight measurement of neutron energies. A—sample or absorber. B—boron-shielded tube. C—cyclotron chamber. D—neutron detector. P—paraffin moderator. T—cyclotron target. W—water tank serving as a neutron shield.*

A betatron has also been used by Yeater and his associates (10) as a pulsed neutron source in time-of-flight measurements of neutron energies. The betatron accelerates electrons by magnetic induction in a circular orbit, then rapidly contracts the electron orbit, causing the electrons to enter a thick target of uranium. Thus the bursts of neutrons from this target occur at the 60-cycle repetition rate of the betatron. Because of the very low cross sections for electron-induced nuclear reactions, the neutrons are actually released from the uranium target by the bremsstrahlung generated in the target as the electrons decelerate. By placing the uranium target within the betatron chamber, the bremsstrahlung is used with much higher efficiency than could be obtained with bremsstrahlung emerging from the betatron chamber to impinge on an external uranium target.

11.7. The Crystal Monochromator

Reference has already been made several times to neutron wavelength and Bragg reflection. In the earlier study of neutrons, sources were not strong enough to hope to be able to detect neutrons reflected from a single crystal. Very soon after nuclear reactors were put into operation, however, neutron spectrometers were constructed which were entirely analogous to the crystal spectrometers long used with x-rays. The basic principles and

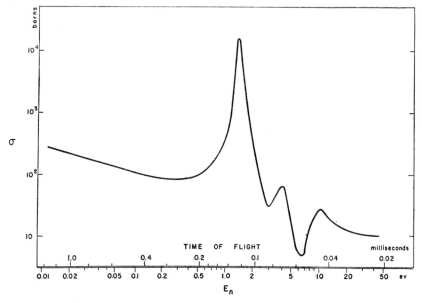

FIG. 11.18. *Cross section of indium as a function of neutron energy as determined by time-of-flight measurements with a modulated cyclotron.*

relations of reflected intensities as correlated with crystal structure are much the same in the two cases. Fig. 11.19 is a diagram of a typical installation for a neutron spectrometer at the face of a reactor. Although the gamma-ray and neutron intensity in the neighborhood of the crystal some-

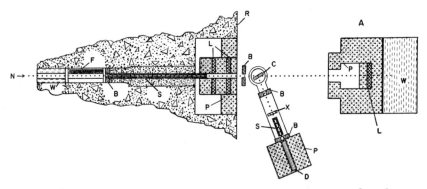

FIG. 11.19. *Diagram of a crystal neutron spectrometer mounted at the face of a reactor. A—beam catcher to absorb transmitted beam of neutrons. B—boron slits. C—crystal. D—neutron detector. F—radiation shutter. L—lead absorbers. N—neutron beam. P—borated paraffin. R—reactor shield. S—collimating slits. W—water tank.*

times is within tolerance limits for human exposure, it may be necessary in other situations to inclose the whole spectrometer within a radiation shield and operate the adjustments by remote control.

There is a variety of uses to which a neutron spectrometer may be put. Measurements of neutron cross sections, for example, have been made with crystal spectrometers up to energies that are greater than 50 ev. However, these instruments are most useful below 20 ev. In the region below 20 ev, crystal spectrometers have some advantages over the time-of-flight method, particularly with respect to resolution. The resolution in both methods is commonly expressed in terms of $\Delta E/E$, with ΔE the width at half maximum of the resolution function. The value of ΔE can be expressed approximately by the relation $\Delta E = kE^{3/2}$ with k an instrumental constant. In the comparison of the two methods, the tendency has been to express the resolution width in terms of a figure of merit K with $K = \Delta t/L$, where Δt is the uncertainty in the time to traverse the flight path of total length L. The relation between k and K becomes clearer by noting that if k is in units of $(ev)^{-1/2}$ and K in microseconds per meter, then K equals $36.15k$. Sailor and his co-workers (11) have plotted curves showing the relation between the resolution width and the neutron energy for a number of values of K. These curves are reproduced in Fig. 11.20.

The resolution function of a spectrometer is useful in ascertaining how far apart resonances must be to appear resolved in the experimental observations. This function also establishes the precision of the determination of resonance parameters and indicates the limit of sensitivity of the spectrometer. In the region of heavy nuclei, resonances are usually resolved if ΔE is not more than 3 ev. This limit is indicated by the horizontal dotted line A in Fig. 11.20. The existence of the limit can be interpreted to mean that most resonances will be observable up to 22 ev if $K = 1$ μsec/m, or up to 110 ev if $K = 0.1$ μsec/m as examples. Thus the importance of a high resolving power to the useful range of the spectrometer becomes evident. If the Breit-Wigner parameters of a resonance are of interest, the resolution width should be less than the natural width, or the doppler broadened width, of the resonance. Hence if the level width is about 1 ev, it is required that ΔE be less than 1 ev. This argument establishes another approximate limit which is indicated by the dotted horizontal line B in Fig. 11.20. Hence if $K = 1$ μsec/m, it would appear that accurate detailed analyses of resonances only up to 2.3 ev could be made. But if $K = 0.1$ μsec/m, this range is extended to 11 ev.

There are two important basic reasons for the lack of perfect resolution in the crystal spectrometer. They are the limited degree to which a neutron beam can be collimated and the departure of all crystals from the ideal crystal structure. These two effects combine to yield a reflected beam

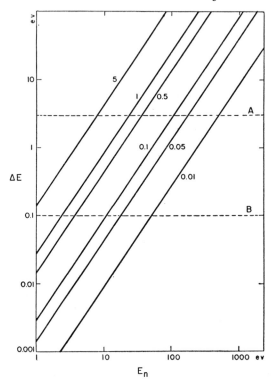

FIG. 11.20. *Resolution width* ΔE *as a function of neutron energy for several values of* K *in units of* μsec/m *in the range from 5 to 0.1. The significance of the dotted lines* A *and* B *is explained in the text.*

which has a full width at half maximum of $\Delta\theta$. Hence the resulting instrumental width $\Delta E/E$ is approximately equal to $2\Delta\theta/\theta$, where θ is the angle of reflection. The resolution can be improved by decreasing $\Delta\theta$ or by increasing θ. Better collimation will decrease $\Delta\theta$ and improvements are steadily progressing in this direction. The use of crystals with smaller lattice spacings increases θ. Progress in this direction is limited by the unfortunate fact that the intensity of the reflected beam decreases as the crystal spacing becomes smaller. By taking into account crystal defects and the divergence of the beam from a limited degree of collimation, Sailor and his colleagues (11) derive an expression for the distribution function of the reflected intensity at various values of θ. In final form this function is

$$J(\delta) = J(O)e^{-\frac{2\delta^2}{\alpha'^2}} \qquad (11.8)$$

where $J(O)$ is the intensity at the central reflection angle θ and $J(\delta)$ is the intensity at any angle θ' such that $\theta - \theta' = \delta$ and $\alpha' = \alpha/2 \, (\ln 2)^{1/2}$, with α the angle of divergence of the collimated beam.

These authors (11) give a similar expression for the rocking curve of the crystal. The rocking curve results from measurements of the intensity of the reflected beam at various angular settings of the crystal with the detector arm in a fixed position. When the widths are expressed in terms of the full width at half maximum, their equation reads

$$J(\gamma) = J(O)e^{-\frac{8(\ln 2)\,\gamma^2}{\alpha^2+\beta^2}} \tag{11.9}$$

The derivation assumes the detector arm to be set at the angle 2θ with respect to the centerline of the neutron beam. Then γ is the displacement of the crystal planes from the angle θ, the sign being positive when the Bragg angle of the individual ray is increased. $J(O)$ is the intensity of reflection at the center of the rocking curve. As before, α is the angular divergence of the collimated beam and β is the full width of the distribution caused by crystal imperfection at half maximum. Eq. 11.9 was tested experimentally for a beryllium single crystal (Be $12\bar{3}1$) using 1.26-ev neutrons. The rocking curve obtained is plotted in Fig. 11.21, the circles representing the observed intensities. The curve is drawn according to Eq. 11.9 by the method of least squares to obtain the best fit. The observations follow the theoretical equation quite closely.

It is instructive to examine the effect of an improved resolution of a spectrometer on the measurements of cross sections. Fig. 11.22 shows two experimental curves for the cross sections of the 4.28-ev resonance in tantalum, as measured by Sailor (11). The sharper curve was taken with a crystal spectrometer having $K = 0.171$ μsec/m. For the flatter curve, K had a value of 0.86 μsec/m. Obviously the data taken with the better resolution is much more suitable for the analysis of resonances.

11.8. Proton-Recoil Neutron Spectrometers

We have already mentioned the use of recoiling protons in the detection of fast neutrons. The relation, Eq. 10.17, between the energy of the incident neutron and that of the proton recoiling at an angle θ with the direction of the incident neutron has also been discussed. A considerable variety of neutron spectrometers of differing construction have been built in which the energy of the neutrons is determined from measurements of the energy of the recoiling protons. In some of these spectrometers the proton recoils are collimated as well as the incident neutrons, so that $\cos \theta = 1$. In others, the angle θ is not zero and may be changed to suit experimental conditions. A few examples will be described to illustrate some of the techniques in different regions of neutron energies.

We have already observed that proton recoil methods are mainly useful

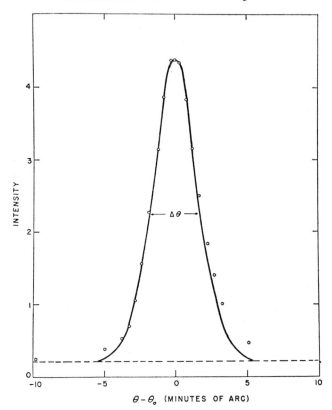

FIG. 11.21. *The rocking curve for a beryllium single crystal. The horizontal dotted line represents the background intensity.*

in the detection of neutrons when their energy exceeds 0.5 Mev. One reason for this restriction to higher energies is that solid hydrogenous radiators can be used and still the ratio t/R be kept small, where t is the thickness of the radiator and R the range of protons in the radiator. It is clear that the resolution is improved by keeping this ratio small. This dependence of the resolution on t/R results simply from the fact that as t/R approaches zero, the loss of energy in the radiator by recoil protons also approaches zero. For a well-collimated beam of neutrons, if for simplicity we neglect proportionality constants, we may write for the resolution $\Re$

$$\Re = t/R \tag{11.10}$$

Also for the efficiency ϵ we have

$$\epsilon = \sigma t \tag{11.11}$$

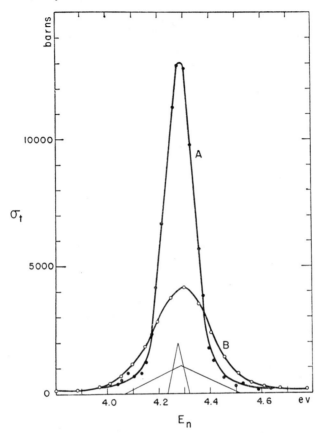

FIG. 11.22. *Observed neutron cross section for the 4.28-ev tantalum resonance. Curve B was taken by a spectrometer for which* K = 0.86 *μsec/m and curve* A *by a spectrometer having the improved resolution corresponding to* K = 0.171 *μsec/m. The triangles on the x-axis represent the resolutions in the two cases.*

where σ is the n-p scattering cross section. Introducing the value of t from Eq. 11.10 into Eq. 11.11 we obtain

$$\epsilon = \sigma \Re R \tag{11.12}$$

Hence for a constant resolution and cross section, the efficiency is proportional to the range of the protons in the radiator. Actually, of course, the cross section is not constant with energy; but its variation is smaller than the variation in the range of the protons with energy. This argument accounts qualitatively for the practical lower limit of 0.5 Mev for the energy of the neutrons incident on a solid radiator in a proton recoil spectrometer.

Perlow (12) has developed a form of proton recoil spectrometer in which

$t = R$, but which avoids the loss of resolution which would result in a solid radiator. As a result the efficiency is an order of magnitude greater than is obtained from a solid radiator of the same resolution at the same energy. In addition, this spectrometer can be used with neutrons in the range of 0.05 to 1 Mev, a considerable downward extension of the region for which the recoil method is useful. The improvement is achieved by using a gaseous radiator and by collimating the protons so that only those with a small divergence with respect to the neutron beam enter into the measurement. The spectrometer is actually a triple counter telescope with the three counter tubes interconnected so that the filling gas, CH_4, is at the same pressure in each. The gas in the first counter tube also serves as the radi-

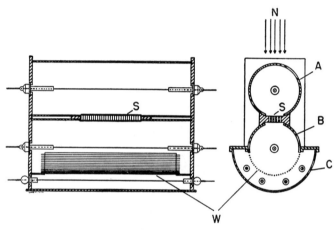

FIG. 11.23. *Proton-recoil neutron spectrometer in which methane gas used in the counter telescope also serves as a radiator. N—neutron beam. A, B, C—counter telescope. S—collimator for protons. W— wire grid forming lower half of the cathode of tube B.*

ator. The arrangement is shown in the diagram of Fig. 11.23. The two proportional counter tubes, A and B, are of the same construction, except that the lower half of B is closed electrically by a grid of fine wires. The counting chamber C has four anode wires and consists of an annular chamber attached to the lower half of B. Counter tubes A and B are joined by a collimating system S, made up of many fine holes drilled through a brass plate. The pressure of the CH_4 gas is adjusted in the range of 8 to 140 mm of mercury, depending on the energy of the neutrons under investigation. Neutrons are incident on tube A in a collimated beam from above. A recoil proton in the forward cone, formed in A, may enter B. It will also enter C only if its range is adequate for the pressure of the filling gas in use at the moment. Failure to enter C results in an anticoincidence and the energy of the proton is then given by the sum of the heights of the pulses in A and B. The collimator is sufficiently thin in comparison with the ranges of the protons to make this procedure allowable. No measurement is possible for a triple coincidence in A, B, and C or for a response in either A or B alone. Hence the operation of the spectrometer depends upon a suitable adjustment of the pressure of the filling gas. There is an upper limit to the pressure which can be used, set by double scattering of the same neutron. This also places an upper limit on

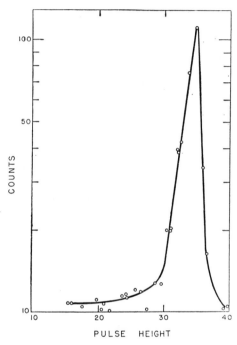

FIG. 11.24. *The pulse-height spectrum of 496-kev neutrons with a counter-gas pressure of 13.65 cm of mercury.*

the neutron energies which can be investigated. If a neutron scatters once in counter A and again in counter B, the result cannot be distinguished from a true coincidence caused by a single recoil proton. In studying neutron spectra, the coincidence output of counters A and B is recorded on a multichannel pulse analyzer. Fig. 11.24 shows the degree of resolution obtained for 496-kev neutrons at a counter gas pressure of 13.65 cm of mercury. The experimental points are uncorrected for background and efficiency. At higher neutron energies the resolution is progressively less sharp.

Johnson and Trail (13) have surveyed the deficiencies of proton recoil methods for measuring neutron energies in the region from 0.1 to 20 Mev. Calling attention to the tedious measurements required in the use of photographic emulsions and cloud chambers, they point out that the excellent characteristics of these methods of good resolution, high efficiency and ease of discriminating against background are largely nullified by the time required to measure track lengths. On the other hand, most proton-recoil counter-tube telescopes have low efficiencies, particularly with solid radiators and at low energies.

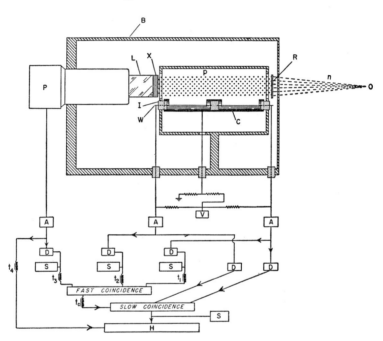

FIG. 11.25. *Proton-recoil spectrometer using a NaI (Tl) crystal to measure proton energies. O—neutron source. R—radiator. X—NaI (Tl) crystal. L—light guide. P—photomultiplier. I—insulators. C—proportional counter tube telescope. W—counter wire. B—gas-tight metal chamber.*

In attempting an improved design, Johnson and Trail concentrated on a good resolution with low background. The resulting efficiency in their design of spectrometer is low, but it is easily calculated to the accuracy with which n-p differential cross sections are known. Hence their instrument may be used to measure absolute cross sections directly. A scintillating crystal is used to measure the energy of the proton recoils. An unusual counter-tube telescope selects for recording only the protons in a narrow forward cone. Fig. 11.25 shows the relative positions of the radiator R and the counter telescope C with respect to the NaI(Tl) crystal. The telescope is composed of two counter tubes end to end, with the upper semicylinder of the cathode of each removed. The removal of the upper section of the cathode permits the counters to respond to protons which do not actually pass through the enclosed volume of the counters.

To trip both sections of the telescope, a proton must pass beyond the division between the counter tubes. To produce a triple coincidence, the same proton must also arrive at the crystal. Thus all protons which are recorded as triple coincidences have traveled from the radiator to the crystal. The residual energy of these protons is measured in terms of the height of the pulse in the photomultiplier which responds to the scintillations produced in the crystal. The neutron beam does not require strict collimation. To maintain the optimum resolution, independent of the energy, several thicknesses of radiator are required. The block diagram of Fig. 11.25 indicates the circuits by which the appropriate pulses from the photomultiplier are selected and recorded in a multichannel analyzer. The efficiency at a resolution with full width at half maximum of 5.3 percent and a background of 6 percent is 3.6×10^{-6}. The spectrum of the recoils from 13.7-Mev neutrons from the $H^3(d,n)He^3$ reaction at 117° to the deuteron beam is shown in Fig. 11.26. This curve has been corrected for the background count. The polyethylene radiator had a thickness of 15 mg/cm^2 and was 4 inches from the source.

Beghian and his associates (14) have described a fast neutron spectrometer applicable to neutrons with energies greater than about 0.5 Mev. The aim in this design was to improve the resolution compared with that usually obtained by proton recoil methods using electronic equipment. In their instrument only protons which result from a nearly head-on collision with a neutron are selected for recording and measurement. In these collisions, the scattered neutron will move in a direction, with a very low energy, at an angle of almost 90° to its original direction. It is possible to use pulses for these neutrons in a coincidence circuit, either by passing them through a system of slits at 90° to the main neutron beam or picking out only neutrons moving in this general direction with a low kinetic energy. The system of slits would reduce the intensity of the scattered beam below the limit for satisfactory operation. The problem of selecting the protons in coincidence with these slow-moving neutrons was solved by using two scintillation detectors, one for the recoiling proton and a second, in the approximately 90° position, to detect scattered neutrons with energies less than 30 kev. For neutrons having initially energies of several Mev, the protons from the collision will have more than 99 percent of the neutron energy. The pulses from the 30-kev neutrons were identified by introducing a length of path between the proton and the neutron detector so that, by delayed coincidences, the pulses of those neutrons arriving at

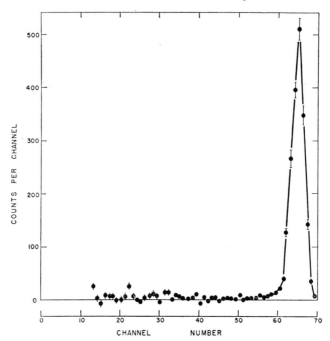

FIG. 11.26. *Proton-recoil spectrum taken with the spectrometer of Fig. 11.25. The peak contains 13.7-Mev neutrons from the* $T(d,n)He^3$ *reaction. The full width at half-maximum is 5.3 percent, attributable mainly to imperfect resolution of the scintillating crystal and to thickness of the radiator.*

the correct time, for an energy of 30 kev, entered into the coincidence. The arrangement for this special time-of-flight method of discrimination is illustrated in Fig. 11.27. Neutrons proceeding from the accelerator target T are incident on the stilbene crystal S. This crystal detects proton recoils produced in the crystal, in association with the photomultiplier P_1. Those neutrons scattered at 90° strike the silver shield E inclosing a NaI(Tl) crystal M. The crystal M responds to gamma rays excited by neutron capture in the silver. The scintillations produce pulses in the photomultiplier P_2 which can be fed into the coincidence circuit. A delay line is introduced into the coincidence circuit so that only the neutrons which have arrived at an appropriate interval after the n-p scattering in the stilbene crystal will be in coincidence with the associated proton pulse from P_1 and permit the proton pulse to be recorded in a pulse-height analyzer. A typical peak obtained with this spectrometer, in Fig. 11.28, represents observations on monochromatic neutrons of 2.8 Mev from deuterons on deuterons in an accelerator.

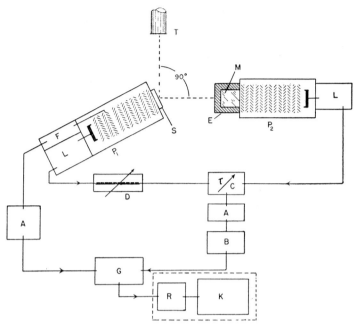

FIG. 11.27. *A scintillation-type neutron spectrometer which selects the proton recoils for recording by reference to the time of flight of the scattered neutron. T—accelerator target. S—stilbene crystal. P₁, P₂— photomultipliers. M—NaI (Tl) crystal. E—silver covering in which neutrons excite gamma rays. L—limiter circuits. F—cathode follower. A—amplifiers. D—delay line. B—discriminator. G—gate. R—am- plifier and discriminator. K—pulse-height analyzer.*

Another example of proton recoil spectrometers is the instrument de- scribed by Holt and Litherland (15). It is chosen for description because it not only illustrates the diversity of designs in this field but also applies well-established principles in an unusual way to measure the proton energy. In addition, it can be used with a minimum of auxiliary equipment to obtain useful observations quite rapidly. The diagram of Fig. 11.29 shows a cross section of the spectrometer chamber. The scattering radiator is at R. Protons released from it pass through four successive circular open- ings, closed by thin aluminum windows, which also serve as electrodes for two pulse ionization chambers A and B. A third ionization chamber, making up the remainder of the volume of the gas-tight chamber, has H for the high-voltage electrode and a shallow collection volume between the grid G and the collecting electrode C. The windows collimate the protons within an angle of 13° of the forward direction. When the chamber is filled with argon at a measured pressure, the range of the protons which just

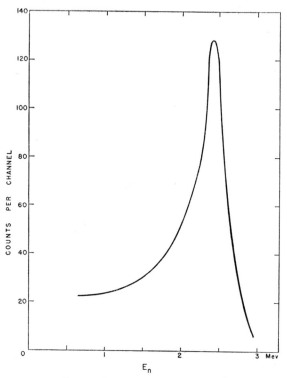

FIG. 11.28. *The peak of 2.8-Mev neutrons from the* D-D *reaction as observed with the spectrometer of Fig. 11.27.*

emerge through the fourth aluminum window H can be computed by adding the thicknesses of the windows to the thickness of the argon in this path. In actual measurements, the pressure of the argon is adjusted so that protons, for which the range is to be determined, pass through H but fail to reach G. Thus the protons stop at some distance x, as indicated in Fig. 11.29, from G. The measurement of this distance permits a computation of the total range. The distance x is measured by the time required by electrons released in the argon to move from the point where the proton stops to the grid G. This measurement is accomplished by connecting chambers A and B in coincidence. The coincidence pulse generated by a proton passing through both A and B triggers the sweep of an oscilloscope which also receives the pulse from C on its deflection plate. This pulse, produced by the arrival of electrons at G, has a sharp leading edge which marks the instant of arrival of the electrons from the nearest point on the proton path. Hence the distance on the oscilloscope trace from the start of the trace to the point of deflection is directly proportional to x. The

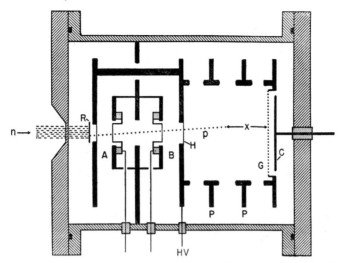

FIG. 11.29. *A fast-neutron spectrometer for the region between 5 and 25 Mev. n—neutron beam. R—radiator. A and B—pulse ionization chambers. H—entrance, covered by thin aluminum foil, to the main chamber. G—grid. C—collecting electrode. PP—field-shaping rings. HV—high-voltage electrode. p—path of a proton from the radiator.*

calibration for this measurement consists simply in adjusting conditions so that protons just emerge through the window H. This gives a length of oscilloscope trace which corresponds to the total depth of the main chamber, from H to G. This chamber has field-shaping rings PP to insure a uniform electric field between H and G. Spurious pulses on the oscilloscope screen may be eliminated from measurement by visual discrimination. This is possible because of the marked difference in the shape of most spurious pulses from the pulses produced by protons. The observations may be recorded very simply by applying cross section paper to the oscilloscope screen and filling in the appropriate square for each trace. This procedure permits a histogram to be constructed rapidly to reveal the more important features of a neutron spectrum very clearly. An example of a histogram is shown in Fig. 11.30 representing the results obtained for a part of the $Al^{27}(d,n)Si^{28}$ spectrum generated by 8.5-Mev deuterons. Although it seems likely that pulse-height analyzers could be used with this instrument, part of its appeal is the simplicity and rapidity of recording while the whole procedure is under direct visual observation. This spectrometer has found considerable application in studying the angular distributions of neutrons from deuteron stripping reactions (16). It is reported to be relatively trouble-free and to have adequate sensitivity and resolution for this work.

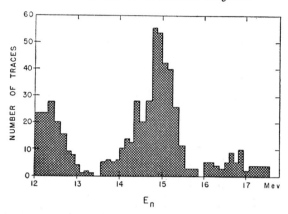

FIG. 11.30. *Histogram made visually by applying cross-section paper to the screen of an oscilloscope and filling in the appropriate squares for each trace produced by the spectrometer of Fig. 11.29. The histogram represents part of the spectrum from the* $Al^{27}(d,n)Si^{28}$ *reaction with 8.5-Mev deuterons.*

11.9. Proton-Recoil Spectrometers at Higher Energies

As neutrons of higher energies are generated by synchrocyclotrons and other types of ultra-high-energy accelerators, a need has developed for neutron spectrometers in the corresponding region of energies. The proton recoil method is still useful here, particularly when the proton energy is measured by a crystal phosphor. This form of detector lends itself naturally to measurements at the high energies here under consideration because a significant fraction of the energy of the protons can be absorbed in crystals of moderate thickness, say 1 or 2 cm. Some of the commonly used crystal phosphors also offer moderately good resolution for proton energies up to 200 Mev.

Guernsey and his co-workers (17) have constructed a high-energy neutron scintillation spectrometer for the range from 50 to 230 Mev in neutron energies. The protons were generated in the usual radiator placed in the neutron beam. The proton telescope, consisting of four scintillating crystals, was set at an angle θ with respect to the neutron beam. The fourth crystal of the telescope also served to measure the energy of the protons. Two different crystals were used for the measurement of the proton energy at various stages of the investigation. One was an anthracene crystal 1.09 cm thick, and the other was stilbene 2.2 cm thick. Fig. 11.31 indicates the relative positions of the crystals in the spectrometer. The pulse heights from the photomultiplier connected with the fourth crystal were recorded in the usual multichannel pulse-height analyzer, in conjunction with a coincidence analyzer, gating circuits, and delay lines. A block diagram of these connections is shown in Fig. 11.32.

The resolving power, defined in the customary way as the pulse height divided by the full width at half maximum, and therefore equal to $1/\mathfrak{R}$, if $\mathfrak{R}$ is the resolution, is ordinarily proportional to the square root of the pulse height in scintillation spectrometers for measuring the energies of gamma rays. This relation exists because the full energy of the secondary electrons is absorbed in the crystal.

In the case of fast protons, here considered, which are not stopped in the crystal, there are marked fluctuations in the energy absorbed from the protons by the crystal. These fluctuations can be attributed mainly to variations in the small number of collisions in the crystal in which the proton loses a large fraction of its energy in a single encounter. The theoretical derivation of equations describing this effect by Landau (18) reveals that, as an example, a 6-Mev proton stopped in an anthracene crystal 1 cm thick might give a resolution of 4 percent. However, a 240-Mev proton giving up 6 Mev of its energy in passing through the same crystal would have a resolution of about 15 percent. Guernsey measured the resolutions of the two crystals which he used at several proton energies in the range under discussion. Monoenergetic protons selected magnetically from the beam of a synchrocyclotron were used in

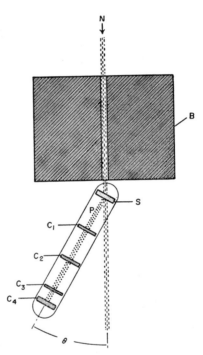

FIG. 11.31. *A fast neutron scintillation spectrometer.* N—*neutron beam.* S—*radiator.* C_1, C_2, C_3, C_4—*scintillation crystal telescope.*

the measurement of resolution. The observed points are plotted in Fig. 11.33. Although the observations for the stilbene crystal, corresponding to curve S, show somewhat better resolutions than predicted by theory, shown by the solid curve, the reverse is true of curve A for the anthracene crystal. In neither case is the agreement with theory very good.

It is evident that this scintillation spectrometer requires a calibration in terms of the pulse heights of the photomultiplier and the energies of the protons entering the crystal telescope. This calibration was made by measuring pulse heights for protons of a single energy at a number of

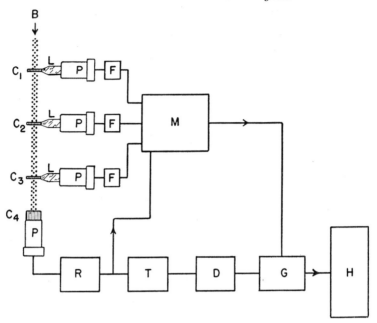

FIG. 11.32. *Block circuit diagram for the scintillation spectrometer of Fig. 11.31. B—proton beam from radiator. L—light guides. P—photo-multipliers. F—cathode followers. M—coincidence analyzer. R—amplifier. T—attenuator. D—delay line. G—gated amplifier. H—pulse-height analyzer.*

different proton energies, again using a proton beam from the synchro-cyclotron. The results for the stilbene crystal in this calibration were indistinguishable from those for the anthracene crystal. The calibration curve, which represents the data for both crystals within limits of experimental error, is shown in Fig. 11.34. As a further indication of the performance of the instrument, a spectrum obtained with 131-Mev protons incident on the fourth crystal, the solid curve in Fig. 11.35, may be compared with the dotted curve. The dotted curve is a plot of the pulse heights after an absorber was introduced into the proton beam to reduce the proton energy to 121 Mev. Both the dispersion and the resolution become worse as the energy of the protons increases. This deterioration is in part the result of the approach to the energies for minimum ionization by protons, as can be seen from the calibration curve of Fig. 11.34. At 240 Mev the specific ionization of the protons is only twice the minimum, which sets a practical limit to the usefulness of this spectrometer. The improvement in resolution obtainable with crystals of greater thickness is unavailable here because of the increased nuclear absorption of the protons in the

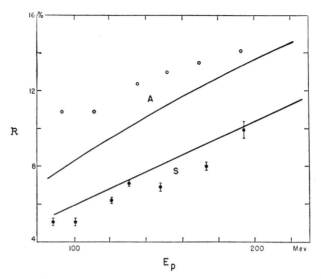

FIG. 11.33. *Resolution of* (A) *a 1.09-cm anthracene crystal and* (S) *of a 2.2-cm stilbene crystal as a function of proton energy. The solid lines indicate the prediction of the theory.*

crystals. This absorption introduces spurious pulse heights which may constitute 5 percent or more of the response for crystals thicker than 1 inch.

11.10 The Nuclear Track Emulsion as a Neutron Spectrometer

The use of photographic emulsions in the detection of neutrons has been described in 10.16. At the same time the principles were outlined by which the energy of the neutron can be computed from the measurement of the length of track of the recoiling proton in the emulsion. Thus the emulsion method constitutes a type of neutron spectrometer which still finds occasional use in spite of the time-consuming operations connected with the measurements.

SYMBOLS FOR CHAPTER V

Å	Ångstrom unit
d	lattice spacing in a crystal
E	kinetic energy of a neutron
J	intensity of a beam of neutrons after reflection from a crystal
K	figure-of-merit for a neutron spectrometer
m	mass of a neutron

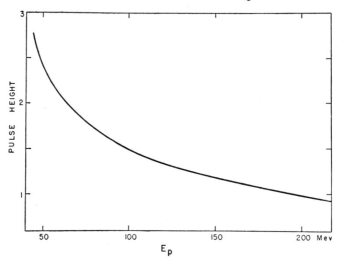

FIG. 11.34. *Calibration curve for the crystal scintillation telescope spectrometer.*

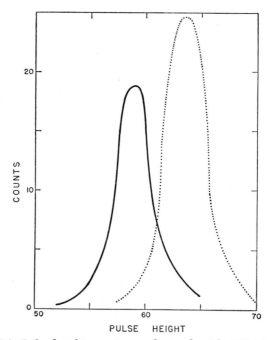

FIG. 11.35. *Pulse-height spectrum obtained with 131-Mev protons incident on the fourth crystal of the spectrometer of Fig. 11.31. The dotted curve was obtained when an absorber was introduced into the proton beam to reduce its energy to 121 Mev.*

R	range of protons on a proton-recoil radiator
$\mathfrak{R}$	resolution of a neutron spectrometer
v	velocity of a neutron
α	angle of advance of the rotor of a neutron velocity selector
α	angular divergence of a collimated beam of neutrons
β	full width at half maximum of the rocking curve of a crystal
γ	angular displacement of a crystal in a crystal spectrometer
ϵ	efficiency factor
θ	angle of recoil of a proton in n-p scattering
θ	Bragg angle of reflection from a crystal
θ	angular divergence of a collimated beam of neutrons
λ	neutron wavelength
ϕ	angle of rotation of a rotor in a neutron velocity selector
ω	angular velocity of a rotor

PROBLEMS FOR CHAPTER V

1. Boron filters of the thicknesses indicated in the table below were introduced into a beam of neutrons incident on a foil detector which gave a saturated counting rate in each instance as indicated.

Thickness of boron filter	Counting rate per sec
0.2 g/cm^2	102
0.4	53
0.6	27

Determine the energy in electron volts of the neutrons responsible for the induced activity.

2. The first-order neutron reflection from a crystal with a grating space equal to 1.8 Å is at $\theta = 15°$. Calculate the energy in electron volts of the neutrons in the reflected beam.

3. The time required for neutrons to traverse a distance of 35 meters was found to be 0.00145 sec. Compute the kinetic energy of the neutrons in electron volts.

4. Compute the maximum number of ion pairs that can be produced by the complete absorption of a proton which has recoiled from a neutron with $E_n = 3$ Mev, in a gas for which the energy per ion pair is 28 ev. Compute the number of ion pairs which can be produced by a proton which recoils at an angle of 30° to the direction of the incident neutron.

5. The rotor of a neutron beam chopper rotates at a speed of 9000 revolutions per min. Compute the width of a neutron channel at the circumference of a rotor 30 cm in diameter if the rotor is to open for a maximum of 0.5×10^{-6} sec.

6. The crystal planes in a crystal spectrometer are set at an angle of 12° to the incident beam of neutrons. The lattice spacing in the crystal is 3.84 Å. Compute the wavelength of the first-order reflection from the crystal. A sheet of boron is placed in the reflected beam with its plane perpendicular to the beam. If the boron

is 0.1 mm thick, compute the fraction of the reflected beam transmitted through the boron.

7. The transmission of a sheet of material containing $.139 \times 10^{19}$ atoms per cm² was measured in a time-of-flight neutron spectrometer to obtain the following data.

Time of flight (μsec/meter)	Transmission
29.0	1.00
29.5	0.99
30.0	0.98
30.5	0.95
31.0	0.90
31.5	0.75
32.0	0.92
32.5	0.97
33.0	0.99
33.5	1.00

From the data plot the curve of cross section versus neutron energy and, assuming the natural width is much less than the instrumental resolution width, compute the resolution of the spectrometer in percent.

REFERENCES FOR CHAPTER V

1. O. R. Frisch and G. Placzek. *Nature* **137,** 357 (1936).
2. J. R. Dunning, G. B. Pegram, G. A. Fink, D. P. Mitchell, and E. Segrè. *Phys. Rev.* **48,** 704 (1935).
3. J. G. Dash and H. S. Sommers, Jr. *Rev. Sci. Inst.* **24,** 91 (1953).
4. N. Holt. *Rev. Sci. Inst.* **28,** 1 (1957).
5. P. A. Egelstaff. *J. Nuc. Energy* **1,** 57 (1954).
6. F. G. P. Seidl, D. J. Hughes, H. Palevsky, J. S. Levin, W. Y. Kato, and N. G. Sjöstrand. *Phys. Rev.* **95,** 476 (1954).
7. R. G. Fluharty, F. B. Simpson, and O. D. Simpson. *Phys. Rev.* **103,** 1778 (1956).
8. R. M. Brugger, J. E. Evans, E. G. Joki, and R. S. Shankland. *Phys. Rev.* **104,** 1054 (1956).
9. Boyce D. McDaniel. *Phys. Rev.* **70,** 832 (1946).
10. M. L. Yeater, E. R. Gaerttner, and G. C. Baldwin. *Rev. Sci. Inst.* **28,** 514 (1957).
11. V. L. Sailor, H. L. Foote, Jr., H. H. Landon, and R. E. Wood. *Rev. Sci. Inst.* **27,** 26 (1956).
12. G. J. Perlow. *Rev. Sci. Inst.* **27,** 460 (1956).
13. C. H. Johnson and C. C. Trail. *Rev. Sci. Inst.* **27,** 468 (1956).
14. L. E. Beghian, R. A. Allen, J. M. Calvert, and H. Halban. *Phys. Rev.* **86,** 1044 (1952).
15. J. R. Holt and E. Litherland. *Rev. Sci. Inst.* **25,** 298 (1954).
16. J. M. Calvert, A. A. Jaffe, A. E. Litherland, and E. E. Maslin. *Proc. Phys. Soc.* **68A,** 1008 (1955).
17. G. L. Guernsey, G. R. Mott, B. K. Nelson, and A. Roberts. *Rev. Sci. Inst.* **23,** 476 (1952).
18. L. Landau. *J. Phys. U.S.S.R.* **8,** 201 (1944).

Chapter VI

INTERACTIONS OF NEUTRONS
WITH MATTER

Our main concern up to the present stage of the discussion of neutrons has been with the results of interactions of neutrons with individual particles and nuclei. In describing some of the methods by which these interactions are studied, frequent allusions have been made to processes involving the interaction of neutrons with masses of material in which encounters with many nuclei by many neutrons contribute to the final effects. Such processes as moderation and crystalline diffraction are examples of two general types of interactions of neutrons with matter, using the term in the ordinary sense of bulk material. Moderation, or the slowing down of neutrons, is brought about by repeated collisions of neutrons with nuclei in large masses of matter. In these collisions the neutrons act independently of each other and of the presence of other nuclei at each encounter. The main effect is the scattering of the neutrons, and the process is called incoherent or diffuse scattering. The results can be computed in many cases in terms of nuclear cross sections and densities of the material through which the neutrons pass. Diffraction, on the other hand, is a coherent process in which the structure of the matter has a controlling influence on the results. The wave nature of the neutron then becomes important and we enter the field often called neutron optics. Actually the basic elastic scattering interaction is much the same in both coherent and incoherent scattering. If the medium consists of randomly distributed and oriented nuclei, the interference effects, characteristic of coherent interactions, cancel out in the summation of the individual processes. When the atoms of the scattering medium are in a spatially periodic arrangement, analogous to an optical diffraction grating, coherent scattering becomes possible. Some aspects of both types of interactions constitute the topics of this chapter.

12.1. Moderation of Neutrons: The Elastic Collision

When neutrons with high velocities are released in a medium with a low neutron capture cross section, the neutrons begin to lose energy by collisions with nuclei in the medium. Under suitable conditions the slowing down process continues until the neutrons have velocities in equilibrium with the velocities, arising from thermal agitation, of the nuclei. Under practical conditions, some neutrons will be lost by capture and some may escape through the boundaries of the finite medium.

These and similar effects are important in the design of nuclear reactors, as an example. In general, such details of reactor theory are beyond the scope of this book. Such information is available in numerous volumes about reactors listed in a special bibliography at the end of the Appendix. The discussion here will be restricted to the simplest elementary considerations to serve as an introduction to the field.

The collisions of neutrons with nuclei can be represented by a simple

LABORATORY   CENTER OF MASS

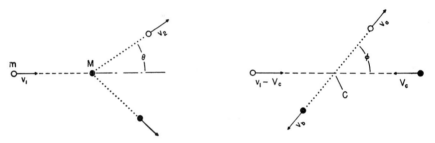

FIG. 12.1. *Representation of the collision of a neutron with a nucleus in the laboratory and in the center-of-mass system of coordinates. m— mass of neutron. M—mass of nucleus. V$_c$—velocity of the center of mass in the laboratory system. C—center of mass. Dashed lines represent paths of motion of the collision. The nucleus is initially at rest in the laboratory system.*

mechanical picture. In the description it will be helpful to review the use of the center-of-mass system of coordinates in the analysis. In the usual diagrams to show the differences between the center-of-mass system of Fig. 12.1, a neutron of mass m and velocity v_1 collides with a nucleus of mass M at rest in the laboratory system. In the illustration, dashed lines refer to events prior to the collision and the dotted lines to events occurring afterwards. After the collision, the neutron moves with a velocity v_2 at an angle θ with respect to its original direction, in the laboratory system. In the center-of-mass system, however, the center of mass is assumed to be at rest and the nucleus moves toward it with a velocity V_c, which is the velocity of the center of mass in the laboratory system. The neutron moves toward the center of mass with a velocity $v_1 - V_c$. After the collision, still in the center-of-mass system, the neutron moves with a velocity v_a away from the center of mass at an angle ϕ with respect to its original direction. The nucleus recoils with a velocity v_b in a directly opposite direction. One of the simplifications introduced by the use of the center-of-mass system is to make the total momentum zero before the collision. This means, of course, that the momentum is also zero after the collisions. This fact can be deduced from Fig. 12.1. We obtain

$$V_c = \frac{mv_1}{M + m} \tag{12.1}$$

$$v_1 - V_c = \frac{Mv_1}{M + m} \tag{12.2}$$

The total momentum is then

$$m\frac{Mv_1}{M + m} - M\frac{mv_1}{M + m} = 0 \tag{12.3}$$

Another simplification is that the speeds of the neutron and of the nucleus after the collision are the same as before it. The conservation of momentum requires

$$mv_a = Mv_b \tag{12.4}$$

The conservation of energy requires

$$\tfrac{1}{2}m\left(\frac{Mv_1}{M + m}\right)^2 + \tfrac{1}{2}M\left(\frac{mv_1}{M + m}\right)^2 = \tfrac{1}{2}(mv_a{}^2) + \tfrac{1}{2}(Mv_b{}^2) \tag{12.5}$$

From Eq. 12.4 and Eq. 12.5 we obtain

$$v_a = \frac{Mv_1}{M + m} = v_1 - V_c \tag{12.6}$$

and

$$v_b = \frac{mv_1}{M + m} = V_c \tag{12.7}$$

Hence in the center-of-mass system the velocities before and after the collision differ only in direction. The value of v_2 in the laboratory system may now be computed from the center-of-mass analysis as the vector sum of the velocity of the neutron in the center-of-mass system and the velocity of the center of mass in the laboratory system, as illustrated in Fig. 12.2(a).

In the moderation process we are mainly interested in the loss of energy by the neutron. There are two limiting cases for the value of ϕ which help to reveal the relation between ϕ and the loss of energy. In the diagram of Fig. 12.2(a) when $\phi = 0$ we find $v_2 = v_1$. If the initial energy of the neutron is E_1, then the energy after the collision, E_2, is also equal to E_1. Consequently the interaction is a glancing impact in which the neutron loses no energy. When $\phi = 180°$ we find

$$v_2 = \frac{M - m}{M + m}v_1 \quad \text{and} \quad E_2 = \left(\frac{M - m}{M + m}\right)^2 E_1 \tag{12.8}$$

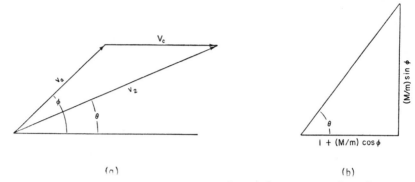

FIG. 12.2. *Vector diagram showing relations between* V_c *the velocity of the center of mass in the laboratory system,* v_2 *the velocity of the neutron after collision in the laboratory system,* v_a *the velocity of the neutron after collision in the center-of-mass system, and the angles* θ *and* ϕ *of Fig. 12.1.*

In this case we have a head-on collision in which the neutron loses the maximum energy. For a hydrogen nucleus, $M = m$, the value of E_2 becomes zero. The neutron loses all of its energy in a single impact. For carbon, frequently used as a moderator in reactors,

$$E_2 = \left(\frac{12 - 1}{12 + 1}\right)^2 E_1 = 0.72 \, E_1 \tag{12.9}$$

The maximum loss of energy is thus proportional to the initial energy with the proportionality constant for a given medium.

12.2. Average Logarithmic Energy Decrement

The constant maximum fractional loss of energy by a neutron in a series of collisions suggests the use of a logarithmic scale of energy. The convenience in calculations of the use of the logarithm of the energy can be seen by assuming that a neutron has an energy E_n before the first collision. In each collision the neutron loses a constant fraction, which we will represent by $1/\alpha$, of the energy which it had prior to the collision. The successive energies may be represented by $E_1 = E_n$, $E_2 = (1/\alpha)E_n$, $E_3 = (1/\alpha^2)E_n$, $E_4 = (1/\alpha^3)E_n$, ... If we write $\ln E_1 = a$, $\ln E_2 = b$, $\ln E_3 = c$, $\ln E_4 = d$, . . . we note that $a - b = b - c = c - d = \ln \alpha = a$ constant. Hence the scale of the decrease of the logarithm of the energy is linear. From the triangle of Fig. 12.2(a), using the law of cosines, we obtain

$$v_2^2 = v_1^2\left(\frac{M}{M + m}\right)^2 + v_1^2\left(\frac{m}{M + m}\right)^2 + 2v_1^2\left(\frac{M}{M + m}\right)\left(\frac{m}{M + m}\right)\cos\phi \tag{12.10}$$

Hence the ratio of E_2 to E_1 is

$$\frac{E_2}{E_1} = \frac{v_2^2}{v_1^2} = \frac{M^2 + m^2 + 2Mm \cos \phi}{(M + m)^2} \tag{12.11}$$

For simplification we introduce the ratio $r = \left(\dfrac{M - m}{M + m}\right)^2$ so that Eq. 12.11 becomes

$$\frac{E_2}{E_1} = \frac{1 + r}{2} + \frac{1 - r}{2} \cos \phi \tag{12.12}$$

This leaves undisturbed the relation between ϕ and the loss of energy in a collision. When $\phi = 180°$ and $\cos \phi = -1$, we find $E_2 = rE_1$, representing the largest loss of energy. When $\phi = 0$ and $\cos \phi = 1$, we have $E_2 = E_1$, therefore no loss of energy. The relation between the angle ϕ and θ in the two coordinate systems is indicated in Fig. 12.2(b) from which

$$\cot \theta = \frac{\cos \phi + (m/M)}{\sin \phi} \tag{12.13}$$

$$\cos \theta = \frac{1 + (M/m) \cos \phi}{1 + (M/m)^2 + 2(M/m) \cos \phi} \tag{12.14}$$

When the ratio M/m is very large, the angle ϕ becomes nearly equal to the angle θ and the laboratory and center-of-mass systems are almost identical.

Because the average loss of energy by neutrons is the quantity of practical interest, we must investigate how the probability of the scattering in the center-of-mass system depends on the angle ϕ. We have seen that, both experimentally and theoretically, the scattering is isotropic in the center-of-mass system, at least for neutrons with energies below about 10 Mev. Therefore the differential cross section for neutrons scattered into a solid angle $d\Omega$ is $\sigma_s/4\pi d\Omega$, with σ_s the scattering cross section defined in earlier chapters. The element of solid angle between ϕ and $\phi + d\phi$ is $2\pi \sin \phi \, d\phi = -2\pi d (\cos \phi)$ and isotropic scattering requires all values of $\cos \phi$ to be equally probable. Furthermore E_2/E_1 is a simple linear function of $\cos \phi$. Consequently all values of E_2/E_1 from 1 to r are also equally probable. The probability PdE that a neutron will lose energy in one collision from an initial energy E_1 to a final energy in the range from E_2 to $E_2 + dE$ is then given by

$$PdE = \frac{dE}{E_1 - rE_1} \tag{12.15}$$

where $E_1 - rE_1$ is the whole energy interval into which the neutron may be scattered. It is now a simple step to calculate the average logarithmic energy decrement, represented by ξ. This decrement is defined as the average loss in the logarithm of the energy in a single collision. From the definition we have

$$\xi = \overline{\ln E_1 - \ln E_2} = \overline{\ln (E_1/E_2)} \tag{12.16}$$

To determine the average we write

$$\xi = \int_{rE_1}^{E_1} \ln \frac{E_1}{E_2} \, PdE = \int_{rE_1}^{E_1} \ln \frac{E_1}{E_2} \frac{dE}{E_1 - rE_1}$$

To solve the integral, let $E_2/E_1 = x$ which gives

$$\xi = \frac{1}{1 - r} \int_1^r \ln x \, dx \quad \text{from which}$$

$$\xi = 1 + \frac{r}{1 - r} \ln r \tag{12.17}$$

where, as before, $r = \left(\dfrac{M - m}{M + m}\right)^2$. When M/m is larger than 10, Eq. 12.17 is approximated to within about 1 percent by

$$\xi = \frac{2}{M/m + 2/3} \tag{12.18}$$

When $M/m = 1$, with $r = 0$, Eq. 12.17 becomes indeterminate. To determine ξ in this case we must evaluate the indeterminate form

$$\lim_{r \to 0} \frac{r}{1 - r} \ln r$$

We need only consider the problem of finding $\lim\limits_{r \to 0} r \ln r$ because $1 - r$ becomes negligibly different from unity. Now making the substitution $\ln r = -y$ with $r = e^{-y}$ we obtain $\lim\limits_{y \to \infty} \dfrac{-y}{e^y}$. By l'Hospital's rule we may replace the numerator and denominator respectively by their derivatives and then have

$$\lim_{y \to \infty} \frac{-1}{e^y} = \frac{1}{\infty} = 0$$

Therefore for $M/m = 1$ we find that Eq. 12.17 gives the value $\xi = 1$, representing collisions in hydrogen. Hence on the average after a collision a neutron has $1/e$ times its energy prior to the collision. For the case where M/m is very large, ξ approaches zero and the neutron loses practically no energy. Hence nuclei at the heavy end of the periodic table are poor moderators. A knowledge of ξ for a moderator permits the immediate calculation of the average number of collisions which a neutron must undergo in slowing down from one energy to another. This number is simply the total loss in the logarithm of the energy divided by ξ. For example, to find the average number of collisions required for a neutron to slow down from 2 Mev to 1/40 ev, that is down to thermal energy, the computation is approximately

$$\frac{\ln (2 \times 10^6) - \ln (1/40)}{\xi} = \frac{\ln (8 \times 10^7)}{\xi} = \frac{18.2}{\xi}.$$

In Table 12.1 the values of the mass numbers, of ξ, and of $18.2/\xi$, are given for a few substances.

Table 12.1

AVERAGE LOGARITHMIC ENERGY DECREMENTS
FOR A FEW SUBSTANCES

Substance	Mass Number	ξ	$18.2/\xi$
Hydrogen	1	1	18.2
Deuterium	2	0.725	25.1
Helium	4	0.425	43
Lithium	7	0.268	68
Beryllium	9	0.209	87
Carbon	12	0.158	115
Oxygen	16	0.120	152
Uranium	238	0.00838	2172

We have based our computations on the isotropic scattering of neutrons in the center-of-mass system. The scattering in the laboratory system will not be isotropic, except for large values of M where the two systems are almost identical. The departure in the laboratory system from spherical symmetry is proportional to the average value of $\cos \theta$, that is, to $\overline{\cos \theta} = (1/4\pi) \int \cos \theta \, d\Omega$. Using the value of $\cos \theta$ from Eq. 12.14, we obtain

$$\overline{\cos \theta} = \tfrac{1}{2} \int_0^\pi \frac{1 + (M/m) \cos \phi}{\sqrt{1 + (M/m)^2 + 2(M/m) \cos \phi}} \sin \phi \, d\phi$$

which on integration gives

$$\overline{\cos \theta} = \frac{2}{3(M/m)} \tag{12.19}$$

For heavy nuclei $\overline{\cos \theta}$ is very small and the angles of deflection are practically isotropic in the laboratory system. For hydrogen, $\overline{\cos \theta} = 2/3$, and the neutrons are scattered mainly in the forward direction in the laboratory system. However, in the center-of-mass system the scattering is still spherically symmetrical.

12.3. Slowing-Down Density

We will conclude this elementary account of moderation with a description of what is commonly called the slowing-down density. Again we will neglect absorption of neutrons in the medium and neutron leakage from it. The concept of a slowing-down density can be explained by assuming that the neutrons are being produced, with an initial energy E_1, in the moderating medium. We let q equal the number produced per cubic centimeter per second. Therefore q also represents the number which slow down past some other energy E per cubic centimeter per second. The neutrons leaving an interval of energy dE will be those scattered out of it, expressed by $n(E) \, dE \, v\Sigma_s$, where $n(E) \, dE$ is the number of neutrons per cm³ in the interval of energy from E to $E + dE$, Σ_s is the macroscopic scattering cross section, and v the velocity of the neutron. $\Sigma_s v$ then is the probability per second that a neutron will undergo scattering. At equilibrium as many neutrons enter dE as leave it. Therefore $n(E) \, dE \, v\Sigma_s$ is also the number of neutrons scattered into the energy range dE from higher energies. If we fix our attention on the range of energies between

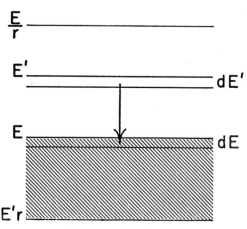

FIG. 12.3. *Energy diagram for computing the slowing-down density* $q(E)$.

E and $E + dE$ and recall that the energy of a neutron can at most go from E_1 to rE_1 in a collision, we see that the maximum energy from neutrons can be scattered into dE is given by E/r. We now consider neutrons scattered into dE from a region dE' at an energy E' between E and E/r, as indicated in the diagram of Fig. 12.3. The number of neutrons scattered into dE from higher energies is equal to the integral over the energy range of the number of scattering collisions in dE', that is, $n(E') \, v'\Sigma'_s \, dE'$, multiplied by the probability that an energy loss will occur which brings the energy from dE' to dE, given by $\dfrac{dE}{E' - E'r}$. In other words,

$$n(E)v\Sigma_s \, dE = \int_E^{E/r} n(E') \, dE' \, v'\Sigma'_s \frac{dE}{E' - E'r} \qquad (12.20)$$

A solution is $n(E)v\Sigma_s = c/E$ with c a constant.

To evaluate c, we can develop an expression for $q(E)$. The number of neutrons per cubic centimeter per second slowing down past E and coming from dE' is given by the number of scattering collisions in dE' multiplied by the fraction of the neutrons from dE' that lose more energy than $E' - E$ and thus enter the shaded region of Fig. 12.3, between E and $E'r$. This multiplication may be written

$$n(E')v'\Sigma'_s \, dE' \frac{E - E'r}{E' - E'r}$$

To obtain $q(E)$ we integrate over the whole energy region and write

$$q(E) = \int_E^{E/r} n(E')v'\Sigma'_s \, dE' \frac{E - E'r}{E' - E'r} \tag{12.21}$$

which by substitution of $n(E')v'\Sigma'_s = c/E'$, following Eq. 12.20 reduces to

$$q = c\left[1 + \frac{r}{1 - r}\ln r\right] \tag{12.22}$$

which is independent of the energy. We recognize the quantity in the brackets of Eq. 12.22 as ξ. Hence $c = q/\xi$ and we have

$$\Sigma_s n(E)v = \frac{q}{\xi E} \tag{12.23}$$

and the slowing-down flux is

$$n(E)v = \frac{q}{\xi\Sigma_s}\frac{1}{E} \tag{12.24}$$

Therefore the flux in the energy range dE is inversely proportional to the energy E past which the neutrons slow down.

12.4. Space Distribution of the Slowing-Down Density

In discussing cross sections we found that the neutron has a mean free path which is the reciprocal of the macroscopic cross section. Thus for absorption the mean free path λ_a is $1/\Sigma_a$. Similarly, for scattering the mean free path λ_s is $1/\Sigma_s$. Because the scattering in the laboratory system is not spherically symmetrical for nuclei which make good moderators, there is a preferential scattering in the forward direction. From the preceding section $\overline{\cos\theta} = \dfrac{2}{3A}$, where θ is the angle of deflection in the laboratory system and $A = M/m$ so that, for neutrons, A is the mass number of the scattering nucleus. Therefore, in addition to the mean free path for scattering, λ_s, we need a corresponding quantity which will take into account the excess forward scattering. This quantity is called the transport mean free path, represented by λ_{tr}. It is defined in terms of $\overline{\cos\theta}$ as

$$\lambda_{tr} = \frac{\lambda_s}{1 - \overline{\cos \theta}} = \frac{1}{\Sigma_s(1 - \overline{\cos \theta})} \tag{12.25}$$

The spatial distribution of the slowing-down density of neutrons is mainly of interest in reactor theory. However, a preliminary account of it will be given here because in this way the meaning of neutron "age" can be illustrated. Although the age, usually represented by τ, also occurs in reactor theory, it does have other uses. The slowing-down density is naturally, in any physical medium, a function of the x, y, z coordinates as well as of E.

Qualitatively, the conditions in a reactor can be described by letting $Q(E_1)$ represent the initial production of fast neutrons of energy E_1 by fission, per cubic centimeter per second. The resulting neutron flux nv at thermal energies will be proportional to $Q(E_1)$. Because of nonproductive absorption and neutron leakage by scattering, there will be a loss of neutrons. We will here concentrate on the loss by scattering. The thermal flux in a reactor is at a maximum at the center of the reactor. There is a continuous current of neutrons toward the boundaries of the moderator. In the process of diffusion the neutrons lose energy and the general nature of the spatial distribution of neutrons is that the lower the energies of the neutrons the more space they occupy. In a steady state the number of neutrons which escape from a cubic centimeter per second in the energy range E to $E + dE$ is $-(\lambda_{tr}/3)\nabla^2 n(E)v\,dE$. This loss must be balanced by $Q(E)dE$ which we may write

$$Q(E)dE = q(E + dE) - q(E) = \frac{\partial q}{\partial E}\,dE \tag{12.26}$$

where $q(E)$ is the slowing-down density already described. Equally we have

$$-\frac{\lambda_{tr}}{3}\nabla^2 n(E)v\,dE = \frac{\partial q}{\partial E}\,dE \tag{12.27}$$

where ∇^2 is the Laplacian operator explained in the next section on diffusion of neutrons. By introducing the slowing-down flux, $n(E)v = \dfrac{q}{\xi\Sigma_s E}$, Eq. 12.27 becomes

$$\frac{\lambda_{tr}}{3}\frac{1}{\xi\Sigma_s E}\nabla^2 q + \frac{\partial q}{\partial E} = 0 \tag{12.28}$$

which may be simplified by introducing the quantity τ defined by the equation

$$d\tau = \frac{\lambda_{tr}}{3\xi\Sigma_s}\,dE \tag{12.29}$$

so that Eq. 12.28 becomes

$$\nabla^2 q + \frac{\partial q}{\partial \tau} = 0 \tag{12.30}$$

Here q is a function of the coordinates and of the energy associated with τ. The integration of Eq. 12.29, defining τ, is carried out in a way to make $\tau = 0$ for thermal energies. Hence

$$\tau(E) = \int_{E_{th}}^{E} \frac{\lambda_{tr}}{3\xi\Sigma_s} \frac{dE}{E} = \int_{E_{th}}^{E} \frac{1}{3\Sigma_s\xi\Sigma_{tr}} \frac{dE}{E} \tag{12.31}$$

The integration defines $\tau(E)$, which has the dimensions of a length squared and is not concerned with time. However, an element of time can be associated with the definition of τ if we write

$$\tau(E) = \int_{E_{th}}^{E} \frac{\lambda_{tr}\lambda_s}{3\xi} \frac{dE}{E} = \int_{E_{th}}^{E} \frac{\lambda_{tr}v}{3\xi} \frac{\lambda_s}{v} \frac{dE}{E}$$

$$= \int_{t_1}^{t_2} \frac{\lambda_{tr}v}{3} dt \tag{12.32}$$

The time $t_2 - t_1$ is now the slowing-down time because λ_s/v is the average time between collisions and ξ is the loss in $\ln E$ in a collision.

By defining appropriate average values of λ_{tr} and Σ_s we find by integrating Eq. 12.31 that

$$\tau(E) = \frac{\bar{\lambda}_{tr}}{3} \left[\frac{\ln (E/E_{th})}{\xi\bar{\Sigma}_s} \right] \tag{12.33}$$

Because the quantity within the brackets of Eq. 12.33 is the average total zigzag distance x covered by neutrons in the slowing down from E to E_{th} we may write

$$\tau(E) = \frac{\bar{\lambda}_{tr}}{3} x \tag{12.34}$$

We will now consider the application of Eq. 12.30 to the simple example of a point source, at $x = y = z = 0$, which emits Q_0 neutrons per sec, all with the same energy E_0 with $\tau = \tau_0$. The boundary conditions that the total neutron current through a sphere of radius r must approach Q_0 as r approaches zero and that the neutron flux is finite and constant at all points may then be expressed as

$$q(x,y,z,\tau_0) = Q_0\delta(x,y,z)$$

where $\delta(x,y,z)$ is the delta function which is zero at all points except at the origin and $\int \delta(x,y,z)dV = 1$ if the volume of integration includes the origin. Eq. 12.30 then has a solution

$$q(x,y,z,\tau) = \frac{Q_0}{[4\pi(\tau_0 - \tau)]^{3/2}} e^{-\frac{r^2}{4(\tau_0 - \tau)}} \tag{12.35}$$

where $r^2 = x^2 + y^2 + z^2$. This solution reveals that $q(r)$ has a separate Gaussian distribution for each particular value of τ. The Gaussian curves have a height and a width dependent on τ, with a width of $2\sqrt{\tau_0 - \tau}$ at $1/e$ of their full height. Examples of curves of q versus r are given in Fig. 12.4. The solid curve corresponds to a high energy and the dotted curve to a low energy.

In making measurements of τ it is usual to determine the quantity $\bar{r}^2$. The relation between τ and $\bar{r}^2$ can be obtained by taking $\bar{r}^2$ to represent the mean square distance from a point source, say of fission neutrons, at which the neutrons just become thermal, where $\tau = 0$. Then

$$\bar{r}^2 = \frac{\int r^2 q_{\text{th}}(r)dV}{\int q_{\text{th}}(r)dV} = \frac{\int_0^\infty r^2 e^{-(r^2/4\tau_0)}4\pi r^2 dr}{\int_0^\infty e^{-(r^2/4\tau_0)}4\pi r^2 dr} = 6\tau_0 \qquad (12.36)$$

When a sufficiently large volume of moderator around a source is used to reduce neutron leakage to negligible proportions, the distribution of neutrons is spherically symmetrical about the source. Foil detectors will then acquire an activity A which will be a function of their distance r from the source. Under these conditions

$$\bar{r}^2 = \frac{\int A(r)r^4 dr}{\int A(r)r^2 dr} \qquad (12.37)$$

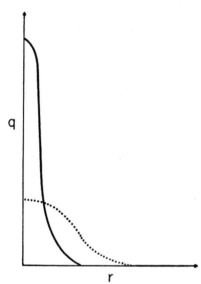

q

r

FIG. 12.4. *The slowing-down density* q *as a function of* r, *the distance from a point source of neutrons. The solid curve shows this curve for neutrons of high initial energy* $\tau \cong \tau_0$, *and the dotted curve for low initial energy,* $\tau \cong 0$.

As a rough numerical example to illustrate the method for determining τ from an evaluation of $\bar{r}^2$, we may consider the data of Table 12.2. The first column contains observed values of A for corresponding values of r in the second column. By numerical integration a more precise value of $\bar{r}^2$ could be obtained, but for this illustration we may use approximate values of the integrals of Eq. 12.37 simply from the addition of the last two columns of Table 12.2. Thus we have $\bar{r}^2 = 8,757,500/16,400 = 534$ cm² from which $\tau_0 = 534/6 = 89$ cm². If the foil detector is mainly activated at a resonance energy, as in the case of an indium foil covered with cadmium, which captures neutrons of 1.44 ev, then the activation method for determining $\bar{r}^2$ gives the age

Table 12.2

DATA FOR DETERMINING $\bar{r}^2$

A	r (cm)	Ar^2	$A\bar{r}^4$
44	5	1100	27,500
35	10	3500	350,000
14	20	5600	2,240,000
6	30	5400	4,860,000
0.5	40	800	1,280,000
		16,400	8,757,500

from the initial energy down to the energy of resonance capture. In experiments of this kind it is then necessary to compute a correction to bring the age down to 0.025 ev, if the thermal age is required. Similarly, corrections are required for neutrons outside the range of r where the induced activity can be measured experimentally. In this region the induced activity will decrease exponentially and no longer follow a Gaussian curve. Because neutrons at considerable distance from the source have not been in many collisions, the neutron intensity I is given by

$$I = \frac{C}{r^2} e^{-(r/\lambda_s)}$$

where C is a constant and not by the Gaussian distribution

$$I = Ce^{-(r^2/4\tau)}$$

This discussion has been based on the assumption that neutrons slow down in a continuous process. From the very nature of the collision mechanism this assumption does not correspond to the facts. Nevertheless the results of the computations are adequate for moderators such as graphite, where ξ is small. The equations do not apply very well to water, where in a single collision with a hydrogen nucleus a neutron may lose nearly all of its energy.

13.1. Diffusion of Neutrons

The development of the diffusion theory as applied to neutrons came about mainly because of its usefulness in the design of nuclear reactors. The diffusion of neutrons is an important process in reactors. There are, of course, other uses for the concepts of the diffusion theory in the measurement of neutrons. Enough of an introduction to the diffusion theory of neutrons will be presented here to aid in making these concepts intelligible. For applications in reactor theory, the reader is referred to books, listed in the bibliography, which go into many of the details with examples of practical uses in the study of reactors.

As electrically neutral particles, neutrons can be expected to have many of the properties of ordinary atoms and molecules. In particular, the Boltzmann equation for diffusion in gases can be applied directly to the diffusion of neutrons. This makes it possible, as an example, to refer to the temperature of neutrons. At an absolute temperature T, neutrons have an average kinetic energy of $kT/2$ ergs per degree of freedom and an average translatory kinetic energy of $3kT/2$ ergs, entirely analogous to gaseous diffusion. Kinetic theory is more readily applied to movements of neutrons when they exhibit the least of their special properties associated with their absorption in nuclei. In media where the capture cross section is small in comparison with the scattering cross section, neutrons have a chance to diffuse among the nuclei much as atoms and molecules in a gas. Therefore diffusion of neutrons is an important process in materials which are good moderators. To be a good moderator, a substance must be composed of atoms of low mass and low neutron capture cross section.

The expression usually called the diffusion equation defines the condition of continuity after equilibrium has been established and the neutron density n is constant with time at any particular point in the medium. The diffusion equation may be written, for ease of explanation, as

$$\frac{\lambda_{tr} v}{3} \nabla^2 n(x,y,z) - \frac{v}{\lambda_a} n(x,y,z) + q(x,y,z) = \frac{dn}{dt} = 0 \qquad (13.1)$$

Here, as previously, q is the rate of production of neutrons per cubic centimeter. ∇^2 is a shorthand notation for the Laplacian operator representing the divergence of the gradient of the neutron density. Applied to the neutron density n in rectangular coordinates, it may be written out as

$$\nabla^2 n = \frac{\partial^2 n}{\partial x^2} + \frac{\partial^2 n}{\partial y^2} + \frac{\partial^2 n}{\partial z^2}$$

The significance of each term in Eq. 13.1 is readily recognized. The first term represents the diffusion of neutrons in and out of the element of volume. The second is the loss of neutrons in this volume by absorption. The third term represents any production of neutrons within the volume. We have not mentioned any specific velocity for the neutrons but it is obvious that the diffusion equation is most useful in the thermal region. Therefore the production of thermal neutrons in the element of volume will usually come about by the slowing down of fast neutrons which become thermal in it. We also neglect, for the present discussion, the fact that thermal neutrons have a Maxwellian distribution of velocities and assume v to be the same for all neutrons. To bring Eq. 13.1 into the more familiar form of the diffusion equation, we divided by $\lambda_{tr} v/3$ and obtain

$$\nabla^2 n - \frac{3}{\lambda_{tr}\lambda_a} n + \frac{3q}{\lambda_{tr} v} = 0 \qquad (13.2)$$

13.2. Diffusion of Thermal Neutrons from a Plane Source

This example of the diffusion of neutrons is selected because of its simplicity. In the diagram of Fig. 13.1 the y,z plane, shown shaded, is a portion of an infinite plane which emits Q neutrons per cm² per second. We will consider only those neutrons which diffuse into a medium extending in the direction of positive values of x. Hence the source strength to be considered is $Q/2$. The medium into which the neutrons diffuse is also assumed to have infinite dimensions, which further simplifies the compu-

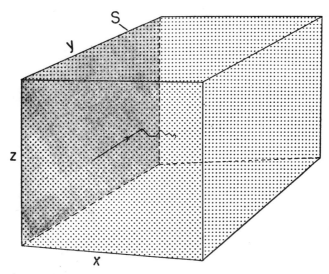

FIG. 13.1. *Diffusion of neutrons from an infinite plane source into a nonabsorbing medium.*

tation. The neutron density n is constant in the y and z directions for any value of x. The Laplacian is $\nabla^2 n = d^2n/dx^2$ and the diffusion equation is simply

$$\frac{d^2n}{dx^2} = \frac{3}{\lambda_{tr}\lambda_a} n \tag{13.3}$$

As we shall see presently, the factor $\dfrac{3}{\lambda_{tr}\lambda_a}$ may be replaced by $1/L^2$ where L is called the diffusion length. Eq. 13.3 has a solution

$$n(x) = Ce^{-x/L} \tag{13.4}$$

with L the distance over which the neutron density drops by a factor of *e.* To evaluate C, we use the fact that the net neutron current across a unit area is

$$j_x = - \frac{\lambda_{tr} v}{3} \frac{dn}{dx}$$

and from Eq. 13.4 $dn/dx = -(C/L)e^{-x/L}$. Hence

$$j_x = \frac{\lambda_{tr} v}{3} \frac{C}{L} e^{-x/L}$$

Then at $x = 0$,

$$j_{x_0} = \frac{\lambda_{tr} v}{3} \frac{C}{L} = \frac{Q}{2}$$

from which

$$C = \frac{3LQ}{2\lambda_{tr} v} = n_0$$

Thus Eq. 13.4 becomes

$$n(x) = n_0 e^{-x/L} \tag{13.5}$$

which is plotted in Fig. 13.2.

The diffusion length L may be expressed as $L = \sqrt{\frac{\lambda_{tr}\lambda_a}{3}}$ and is the geometric mean of λ_{tr} and λ_a divided by $\sqrt{3}$. L is also the average shortest point-to-point distance from the plane $x = 0$ which neutrons reach before absorption. This can be seen by computing the average statistical values of x from Eq. 13.5. The total average path of the neutrons, over their zigzag route between collisions, is λ_a. However, the average point-to-point

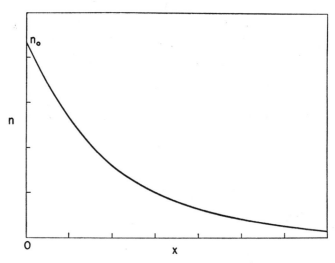

FIG. 13.2. *Neutron density as a function of* x, *the distance from an infinite plane source.*

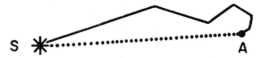

S ✳ A

FIG. 13.3. *The zigzag path of the neutron between the source* (S) *and the point of absorption* A *represents* λ_a. *The straight dotted line between the two points is* L.

distance is shorter by the factor $\sqrt{\lambda_{tr}/3\lambda_a}$. The diagram of Fig. 13.3 illustrates the relation between λ_a and L. The simple form of the diffusion equation used here is only valid if the capture cross section of the medium is small, in other words when $\lambda_a \gg \lambda_{tr}$. The diffusion length is a useful parameter of the diffusing medium. Its value has been measured, or computed from other measured constants, for a number of substances suitable as moderators. Some typical values are given in Table 13.1.

Table 13.1

TYPICAL DIFFUSION CONSTANTS OF SOME SUBSTANCES
USED AS MODERATORS

Substance	L (cm)	λ_{tr} (cm)	λ_a (cm)
Water	2.73	0.45	49
Deuterium oxide	171	2.40	36700
Beryllium	20.8	1.43	906
Carbon	50.8	2.75	2820

13.3. Diffusion of Thermal Neutrons from a Point Source

Another simple example is diffusion of neutrons from a point source. Here the value of n depends only on r, the radial distance from the source. The Laplacian for this case is

$$\nabla^2 n(r) = \frac{d^2 n}{dr^2} + \frac{2}{r}\frac{dn}{dr}$$

By introducing a new variable F where

$$F = nr \text{ with } \frac{d^2 F}{dr^2} = \frac{d^2 n}{dr^2} r + 2\frac{dn}{dr}$$

and substituting in Eq. 13.2 we obtain

$$\frac{1}{r}\frac{d^2 F}{dr^2} = \frac{F}{r}\frac{1}{L^2} \tag{13.6}$$

which has a solution

$$F = \frac{C}{r} e^{-r/L}$$

On substitution of nr for F we have

$$n = \frac{C}{r} e^{-r/L} \tag{13.7}$$

To evaluate C we put the total neutron absorption rate equal to the strength of the source and write

$$\int_0^\infty \frac{nv}{\lambda_a} 4\pi r^2 dr = Q$$

Introducing the value of n from Eq. 13.7, we have

$$\frac{4\pi vC}{\lambda_a} \int_0^\infty e^{-r/L} r\, dr = Q = \frac{4\pi CvL^2}{\lambda_a}$$

from which

$$C = \frac{3Q}{4\pi\lambda_{tr}v}$$

so that Eq. 13.7 becomes

$$n = \frac{1}{r} \frac{3Q}{4\pi\lambda_{tr}v} e^{-r/L} \tag{13.8}$$

From Eq. 13.8 we note that the scattering and absorption processes in diffusion cause the neutron density to decrease inversely as the distance from the source. This relation replaces the inverse square law which is characteristic of, for example, electromagnetic radiation. If there were no scattering of the neutrons they would also decrease in intensity in accordance with the inverse square law. We can compute the mean square distance which neutrons traverse before absorption from Eq. 13.8 as

$$\bar{r}^2 = \frac{\int_0^\infty r^2 n(r) r^2 dr}{\int_0^\infty n(r) r^2 dr} = 6L^2 \tag{13.9}$$

14.1. Neutron Diffraction

The wave properties of neutrons have been investigated almost from the time of the discovery of the neutron. Because these properties become more readily observable at low energies, the earliest studies were hampered by the low intensities of slow neutrons then available. Nevertheless, as early as 1936, Mitchell and Powers (1) succeeded in demonstrating conclusively the existence of Bragg reflection of neutrons by single crystals. The diagram of their experiment is shown in Fig. 14.1. A Ra-Be neutron source

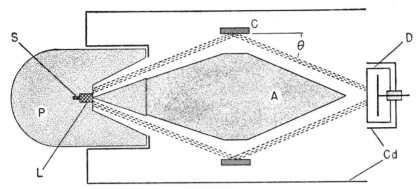

FIG. 14.1. *The method used by Mitchell and Powers (1) to demonstrate Bragg reflection of neutrons by single crystals. A—absorber. C—ring of magnesium oxide single crystals. S—neutron source. L— lead screen. P—paraffin. D—detector. Cd—cadmium shielding. θ— Bragg angle.*

mounted in a paraffin moderator was used as a source of slow neutrons. One of the difficulties of the experiment was that many fast neutrons escaped from the moderator and contributed to a high background at the detector. To provide a detectable intensity in the reflected beam, the crystal assembly consisted of a complete ring of magnesium oxide single crystals. The ring of crystals was mounted so that the average angle of incidence θ for the neutrons was 22°. The reflected wavelengths should then be around 1.5 Å, corresponding to the lattice spacing in the magnesium oxide crystals, $2d = 4.0$ Å. To test the presence of Bragg reflection, the crystals were tilted about 25° from the normal position and the counting rate of the neutron detector compared with that for the normal position. An increase of six to eight times the background was observed when the crystals were brought into the normal angle for a Bragg reflection. The large angular divergence in the neutron beam permitted a considerable range of wavelengths to be reflected into the detector and thus contributed to the success of the experiment in spite of the low intensity of the neutrons.

When much more intense beams of slow neutrons became available, the reflection of monochromatic beams of neutrons from one single-crystal became observable. In using the term monochromatic with reference to neutrons, a distinction must be noted from the analogous case of x-rays. From the nature of the characteristic line spectra of x-rays, it is possible by crystal reflection to isolate a single x-ray line with a definite wavelength. The beam of neutrons incident on a crystal has no characteristic lines in its spectrum and the crystal can only select a narrow band of wavelengths. The width of this band, as we saw in the discussion of neutron crystal spectrometers in Chapter V, depends mainly on the angle of divergence of the collimated beam. Another difference is that a very small fraction of the incident beam of neutrons is reflected. Consequently single crystals may be used to produce monochromatic beams of neutrons by what is called transmission. Here the reflected beam passes through the main body of the crystal. Basically there is no difference in the diffraction process for the two ways of using a crystal.

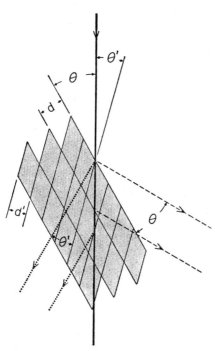

The relation between the reflection method and the transmission method is illustrated in the diagram of Fig. 14.2, showing a portion of a crystal assumed to have two sets of planes at 45° to each other. A beam of neutrons is incident in a vertical direction from above, as indicated by the heavy lines. This beam makes an angle θ with the direction of the longitudinal planes of the crystal. The beam reflected from these planes in the direction of the broken lines represent the case of reflection. The incident beam also makes an angle θ' with the direction of the transverse planes and neutrons reflected in the direction of the dotted lines represent the case of transmission. Obviously any set of planes can be selected, according to the orientation of the crystal, for the transmission process. By the transmission method a crystal of much smaller width is adequate to intercept the full width of the collimated beam at the small values of θ ordinarily used.

FIG. 14.2. *Diagram of neutron diffraction by transmission (dotted lines), and by reflection (dashed lines), with the relation of the corresponding Bragg angles. In this hypothetical case θ and θ' are different. This is also true of* d *and* d' *and of the diffracted wavelengths.*

The strong beams from nuclear reactors have also been used to demonstrate the existence of diffraction patterns produced by neutrons, analogous to the Laue patterns produced by x-rays. Fig. 14.3 is a diagram of the experimental assembly used by Wollan, Shull, and Marney (2) to obtain from a single crystal of sodium chloride the neutron Laue pattern represented by Fig. 14.4. A collimated beam of neutrons from a reactor traversed the crystal of NaCl and the diffracted neutrons impinged on the sheet of indium foil which covered an x-ray photographic film. The main beam passed through a central hole in the indium foil. The indium foil was needed because neutrons do not produce photographic effects directly. The beta-activity induced in the indium exposed the photographic film over areas activated by the diffracted neutrons. A boron carbide plastic shield, also with a central hole, screened the film from the back. The incident beam of neutrons had a continuous spectral distribution from 0.5 Å to 3.0 Å. The central white disk in Fig. 14.4 represents exposure of the film by neutrons and gamma rays scattered back from the film cassette through the central hole in the boron shield.

In spite of considerable differences in detail, to be discussed later, between the interference phenomena of x-rays and of neutrons, practically every kind of diffraction experiment possible with x-rays has its counterpart in neutron diffraction. Thus the rotating-crystal method of studying crystal structure, illustrated by the diagram of Fig. 14.5, was used in early experiments with beams of thermal neutrons from a reactor by Fermi and Marshall (3). In this work the experimenters were mainly interested in determining the phase of the scattered neutron wave in comparison with that of the incident wave. Using the apparatus shown

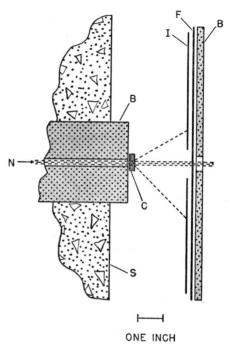

ONE INCH

FIG. 14.3. *Photographic film in position at the opening of a reactor for recording the diffraction pattern of neutrons by the Laue method. N—beam of neutrons. C—single crystal of NaCl. B—borated plastic neutron shield. S—reactor shield. I—indium foil to be activated by the diffracted neutrons. F—photographic film.*

diagrammatically in Fig. 14.6, they were able to show, mainly from measurements of the intensities at various Bragg orders of reflection, that the phase difference between the incident and the scattered wave is usually 180°. In the few cases, such as hydrogen, titanium, and manganese, where the phase difference is zero, this fact is explained by the existence of resonances at energies much greater than the energy of thermal neutrons. For manganese, as an example, there are resonances at

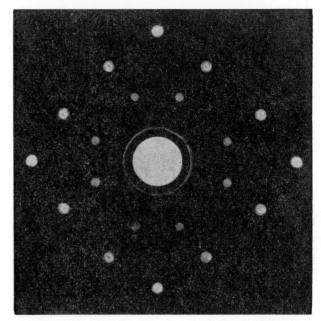

FIG. 14.4. *Diagram of the Laue photograph obtained by the arrange-ment in Fig. 14.3.*

300 ev and at 2400 ev, both of which contribute to the zero difference in phase between the incident and the scattered waves.

The Debye-Scherrer method of studying crystal structure, using x-rays, has found frequent use in experiments in which monochromatic neutrons replaced the x-radiation. The crystalline material is in the form of a powder or other polycrystalline preparation. Here the scattered neutrons appear in a conical distribution about the incident beam, as indicated in Fig. 14.7.

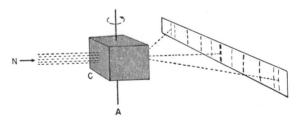

FIG. 14.5. *The rotating-crystal method of observing neutron diffraction. N—monochromatic beam of neutrons. A—axis of rotation. C—single crystal. The lines in the photograph correspond to the various planes of the crystal as they are brought into the Bragg position by rotation. In the case of neutrons, BF₃ proportional counters are used for detec-tion in place of photographic film.*

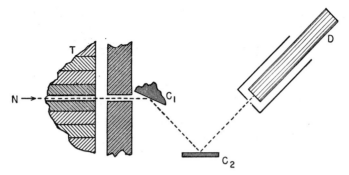

FIG. 14.6. *Monochromator in position to observe the intensities of the various Bragg orders of reflection of neutrons. N—neutron beam from thermal column T of the reactor. C_1—monochromator crystal. C_2— crystal under investigation. D—BF_3 neutron detector.*

The angular divergence of each cone is 2θ, with θ the Bragg angle for the particular set of crystal planes involved. In this powder diffraction method, the neutron intensity at any small region on a ring is relatively low because the scattered neutrons for a given θ are distributed over the entire ring. This is a handicap where neutron counters must be used to detect the scattered neutrons. This disadvantage can be overcome only by the use of much stronger incident beams than would otherwise be needed. Fermi, Sturm, and Sachs (4) were the first to study the transmission of slow neutrons through microcrystalline substances. Using crystals of less than

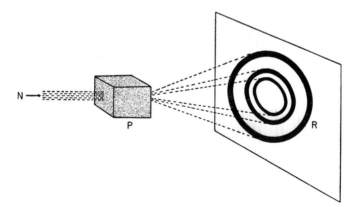

FIG. 14.7. *Diagram of the Debye-Sherrer method for observing neutron diffraction by a sample of powdered crystals or other polycrystalline material. N—monochromatic beam of neutrons. P—powder sample. R—Debye-Sherrer rings. For a particular Bragg angle the reflected intensity is distributed over the entire ring.*

a micron in linear dimensions, they measured the scattering cross section of beryllium as a function of neutron energy. The cross sections were determined from measurements of the transmission T defined as

$$T = \frac{R_a}{R_o} \qquad (14.1)$$

where R_a is the net counting rate with the crystalline preparation in the monochromatic beam and R_o is the counting rate for the open beam. The scattering cross section σ_s is given by

$$\sigma_s = -\frac{\ln T}{N} \qquad (14.2)$$

where N is the number of beryllium atoms per cm³. A typical curve for σ_s as a function of neutron energy is shown in Fig. 14.8.

14.2. Coherent Neutron Scattering

The optical type of interference of neutron waves depends upon the existence of coherent scattering. Associated with coherent scattering is a corresponding cross section σ_{coh}. The values of this cross section for individual types of nuclei, together with structural parameters of the scattering medium, will control the nature of the interference between the scattered wave and the wave of the incoming neutrons. In discussing coherent scattering, we concentrate our attention on the so-called potential scattering, idealized as scattering from a nucleus regarded as an impene-

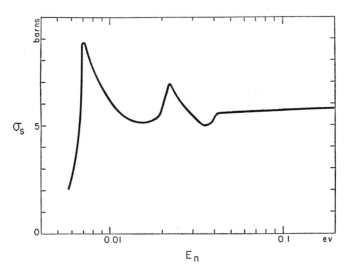

FIG. 14.8. *The scattering cross section σ_s of beryllium oxide as a function of neutron energy E_n.*

trable sphere. This concept distinguishes potential scattering from resonance scattering in which the incident neutron is not merely reflected from the surface of the nucleus but actually interacts with the components of the nucleus. Not all potential scattering will be of the coherent type. Diffuse scattering will occur in the absence of some uniform array of scattering nuclei or whenever the pattern of this array and its components are defective from the standpoint of interference phenomena. Consequently it is often convenient to consider the total scattering cross section σ_s as the sum of the coherent and the diffuse cross sections and write

$$\sigma_s = \sigma_{\mathrm{coh}} + \sigma_{\mathrm{dif}} \tag{14.3}$$

We have analogies to these two scattering processes in the scattering of light. If there is a random distribution of the separation distances between scattering centers, we have diffuse scattering of light with no interference effects. This is also true of neutrons. However, there are other causes for the incoherent scattering of neutrons. One is the presence of isotopes of differing masses and different scattering cross sections in an otherwise uniform array of scattering centers. Also there is incoherence arising from difference in the orientation of the spin of the nucleus with respect to that of the scattering nucleus.

14.3. The Wave Equation for Neutron Scattering

We consider a plane wave of neutrons represented by the wave function

$$\Psi = e^{ikz} \tag{14.4}$$

where $k = 2\pi/\lambda$ is the wave number. When this wave strikes a nucleus, a spherically symmetrical scattered wave will be generated having the form

$$\Psi = -\frac{a}{r} e^{ikr} \tag{14.5}$$

with r the distance from the scattering center at which the nucleus is rigidly fixed. The quantity a is the scattering amplitude. The neutron wave after scattering accordingly will be represented by

$$\Psi = e^{ikz} - \frac{a}{r} e^{ikr} \tag{14.6}$$

Ordinarily the scattering amplitude is a complex quantity represented by

$$a = \alpha + i\beta \tag{14.7}$$

but in the absence of absorption, a is entirely real. The scattering cross section may then be defined as

$$\sigma_s = 4\pi a^2 \tag{14.8}$$

which is the familiar formula for the potential scattering cross section with the nuclear radius replaced by the scattering amplitude.

14.4. Coherent and Diffuse Scattering Cross Sections

The effect of the spin of the scattering nucleus can be illustrated by selecting a scattering substance containing only one isotope with a spin "i" not equal to zero. The resultant spin of the compound nucleus may then be either $(i + \frac{1}{2})$ or $(i - \frac{1}{2})$. There will be a separate scattering amplitude for each of these cases which can be represented by a_+ and a_-, respectively. Blatt and Weisskopf (5) show that, for unpolarized neutrons, the relative probability $g(S)$ that an incident particle will be found to have the same channel spin S is

$$g(S) = \frac{2S + 1}{(2s + 1)(2i + 1)}$$

where s is the spin of the particle, and S, the vector sum of i and s, is called the *channel spin* of the compound nucleus. When, as for the neutron, $s = \frac{1}{2}$ and $S = i \pm \frac{1}{2}$, we have

$$g(S) = \frac{1}{2}\left(1 \pm \frac{1}{2i + 1}\right) \quad \text{for } l = 0$$

where l is the quantum number of the orbital angular momentum in a channel. When $S = i + \frac{1}{2}$ we have

$$g(S)_+ = \frac{i + 1}{2i + 1}$$

and for $S = i - i/2$

$$g(S)_- = \frac{i}{2i + 1}$$

Hence

$$\frac{g(S)_+}{g(S)_-} = \frac{i + 1}{i} \tag{14.9}$$

Using the statistical weighting factor of Eq. 14.9, the average coherent scattering amplitude is

$$a_{\text{coh}} = 4\pi\left(\frac{i + 1}{2i + 1}a_+ + \frac{i}{2i + 1}a_-\right)^2 \tag{14.10}$$

The quantity a_{coh} is the scattering amplitude involved in the optical properties of neutrons, such as interference and refraction. From a_{coh} we obtain directly a cross section

$$\sigma_{\text{coh}} = 4\pi a^2_{\text{coh}} \tag{14.11}$$

The total scattering cross section can be computed from the sum of the scattering amplitudes for the individual spins, again weighted according to statistical probability of occurrence. Hence

$$\sigma_s = 4\pi\frac{i + 1}{2i + 1}a_+{}^2 + 4\pi\frac{i}{2i + 1}a_-{}^2 \tag{14.12}$$

The diffuse scattering cross section then is

$$\sigma_{\text{dif}} = \sigma_s - \sigma_{\text{coh}}$$

$$= 4\pi \left[\frac{i+1}{2i+1} a_+{}^2 + \frac{i}{2i+1} a_-{}^2 - \left(\frac{i+1}{2i+1} a_+ + \frac{i}{2i+1} a_- \right)^2 \right]$$

$$= 4\pi \frac{i(i+1)}{(2i+1)^2} (a_+ - a_-)^2 \tag{14.13}$$

From the diffuse scattering cross section, the diffuse scattering amplitude is obtained as

$$a_{\text{dif}} = \sqrt{\frac{\sigma_{\text{dif}}}{4\pi}} = \frac{\sqrt{i(i+1)}}{2i+1} (a_+ - a_-) \tag{14.14}$$

This analysis of the relations between coherent and diffuse scattering gives a certain practical insight into the behavior of the corresponding cross sections. For example, we see that the diffuse scattering will be zero if $a_+ = a_-$, since then σ_s will be equal to σ_{coh}. If the two terms on the right hand of Eq. 14.10 happen to be equal and the individual scattering amplitudes of opposite sign, then a_{coh} becomes zero as also does σ_{coh}. There is abundant experimental evidence to confirm the reliability of these relations between the various cross sections for scattering.

It is possible to trace both spin-diffuse and isotopic-diffuse scattering effects in the measured values of scattering amplitudes and of cross sections. For example, hydrogen has a total scattering cross section of 81.4 barns with a coherent cross section of only 1.79 barns. This difference must be a spin-diffuse cross section. This large diffuse cross section arises from an a_+ coupled with an a_- which is large enough to overcome slightly the adverse statistical weighting of 3 to 1 and yield a small negative coherent scattering amplitude. On the other hand, the principal isotopes of nickel are all of even mass and hence have zero spin. Any diffuse scattering must arise from an isotopic incoherence because of mass differences. The measured value for the element of σ_s is 18 barns, and of σ_{coh}, 13.4 barns. The coherent scattering amplitudes of the isotopes have been measured by Koehler, Wollan, and Shull (6) and the results of their measurements are given in Table 14.1. From the measured value of $\sigma_{\text{coh}} = 13.4$ barns we

Table 14.1

SCATTERING AMPLITUDES FOR ISOTOPES OF NICKEL

Abundance (percent)	Isotope	a (10^{-12} cm)	a corrected for abundance
67.8	Ni^{58}	1.47	1.00
26	Ni^{60}	0.28	0.073
3.7	Ni^{62}	−0.85	−0.034
	Total		1.04

would expect

$$a_{\mathrm{coh}} = \sqrt{\frac{13.4 \times 10^{-24}}{4\pi}} = 1.03 \times 10^{-12} \text{ cm}$$

which gives adequate confirmation of the correctness of the preceding analysis. In the case of isotopic incoherence, the relative abundances of the isotopes replace the statistical weighting factor used in computing spin-diffuse cross sections for scattering.

In this discussion, the isotopic and spin-dependent scattering have been treated as involving similar random variations in scattering amplitudes from the various different nuclei in the scattering medium. This treatment leads to correct estimates of cross sections, but it obscures differences in the detailed physical processes in the two types of scattering. Isotopic incoherent scattering produces no changes in the scattering nuclei and leaves the spin of the emergent neutrons unchanged. However, there is a possibility that the spin of the neutron may be reversed in the spin-dependent scattering process. Thus the spin of the scattering nucleus will also be changed by $\hbar$, that is one unit. Halpern and Johnson (7) have computed the probability of this spin-flip as

$$P = \frac{2i(i + 1)(a_+ - a_-)}{3(2i + 1)[(i + 1)a_+{}^2 + ia_-{}^2]} \tag{14.15}$$

In terms of the cross sections we can write

$$P = \frac{2}{3} \frac{\sigma_{\mathrm{dif}}}{\sigma_s} \tag{14.16}$$

Thus we see at once that the maximum value of P is $\frac{2}{3}$, independent of i. The importance of this probability can be illustrated by considering a beam of polarized neutrons, with all spins aligned in the same direction. One totally incoherent spin-dependent scattering will leave only one-third of the spins in their original direction. The remaining two-thirds of the neutrons will have their spins reversed. Examples of completely spin-dependent incoherent scattering are rare. However, at least two elements show this property to a considerable degree. Hydrogen has a value of 1.8 barns for σ_{coh} and a value of 38 barns for σ_s. Similarly for vanadium σ_{coh} is 0.032 barn and σ_s is 5 barns. Hydrogen of course can be considered mono-isotopic and V^{51} makes up 99.8 percent of that element. Isotopic incoherence is therefore negligible for both elements. Also the coherent scattering amplitude a is negative in both cases. Meyerhof and Nicodemus (8) used the apparatus sketched in Fig. 14.9 to measure the spin-flip probability in carbon, hydrogen, and phosphorus. Measurements on carbon and hydrogen were used chiefly to test the reliability of the method. Six measurements of the intensity of the transmitted beam of neutrons were required for a determination. Four of these measurements were made with

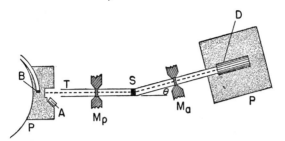

FIG. 14.9. *Arrangement to study depolarization, or spin-flip, on scattering. B—beryllium target of cyclotron. P—paraffin moderator. A—neutron monitor. T—cadmium drift tube. Mp—polarizing magnet. S—scattering sample. M_a—analyzing magnet. D—BF_3 proportional counter. The angle θ was fixed at 14°.*

a straight cadmium tube, not shown in the figure, and with no scattering material in the beam. These intensities were

I_D intensity with both polarizer and analyzer magnetized
I_P intensity with polarizer only magnetized
I_A intensity with analyzer only magnetized
I_0 intensity with both polarizer and analyzer unmagnetized

From these measurements the double transmission effect η_D was computed as

$$\eta_D = \frac{I_D - I_0}{I_0}$$

the single transmission effect with polarizer on η_P as

$$\eta_P = \frac{I_P - I_0}{I_0}$$

and the single transmission effect with analyzer on η_A as

$$\eta_A = \frac{I_A - I_0}{I_0}$$

For the measurements on the scattering material with the bent cadmium tube, as shown in Fig. 14.9, the intensities measured were I^*_D = intensity with both polarizer and analyzer magnetized and the scatterer in place and I^*_0 = intensity with both polarizer and analyzer unmagnetized and the scatterer in place. From these two intensities the double transmission effect on scattering η^*_D was computed as

$$\eta^*_D = \frac{I^*_D - I^*_0}{I^*_0}$$

The authors were able to show that the spin-flip probability P is then given by the formula

$$P = \frac{\eta_D - H\eta^*_D}{2[\eta_D - (\eta_P + \eta_A)]} \tag{14.17}$$

in which H is a correction factor, close to unity, which is calculated from the theory of neutron polarization in magnetized iron, which we will discuss a little later. The experimental results for carbon yielded a value of $P = -0.09 \pm 0.21$, consistent with the theoretical prediction of $P = 0$ and in agreement with the absence of a measurable spin-dependent incoherent scattering for carbon. For hydrogen, the experiments gave $P = 0.56 \pm 0.10$ consistent with the value $P = 0.650$ obtained in substituting the theoretical diffuse scattering cross section of 19.9 barns and the total scattering cross section of 20.4 barns in Eq. 14.16. For phosphorus, a value of $P = 0.73 \pm 0.15$ was obtained, leading to a spin-dependent incoherent cross section of $\sigma_{dif} = 3.7 \pm 0.8$ barns and a value for σ_{coh} of less than 0.5 barn. It should be noted that incoherent scattering is isotropic, as far as spin-dependent and isotopic effects are concerned. The scattering intensities rather than the amplitudes are added to obtain the total effect from a large number of atoms. On the other hand, the total coherent scattering is obtained by adding coherent amplitudes for all atoms and squaring the sum, as suggested by Eq. 14.8.

In comparing x-ray and neutron diffraction, differences as well as similarities are encountered. One of the more notable differences is the behavior of the scattering amplitude for different angles between the incident and scattered directions. For x-rays, the scattering amplitudes decrease sharply with increase in the Bragg angle θ. However, neutron scattering amplitudes show no variation with θ. The difference in behavior is illustrated in the graph of Fig. 14.10, taken from Bacon (9), in which the dotted curve gives the scattering amplitudes of the potassium atom as a function of $\sin \theta/\lambda$ for x-rays and the solid horizontal line gives the corresponding information for neutrons. The explanation offered for this difference is that the electronic shells of the atom are comparable in dimensions with x-ray wavelengths. In the case of neutrons, the nucleus is quite small in comparison with the neutron wavelengths.

A similarity between x-ray and neutron diffraction is the effect of temperature on the scattering. Because the atoms of a crystal vibrate with temperature about an average lattice position, coherent scattering of both x-rays and neutrons will be decreased from that of fixed atoms by an amount depending on the temperature, the wavelength, and the angle of scattering. This correction to the fixed-atom coherent cross section can be obtained by using the well-known Debye-Waller (10) factor which leads to the formula

$$\sigma_{coh}(\text{eff}) = \sigma_{coh}e^{-K(\sin \theta/\lambda)^2} \tag{14.18}$$

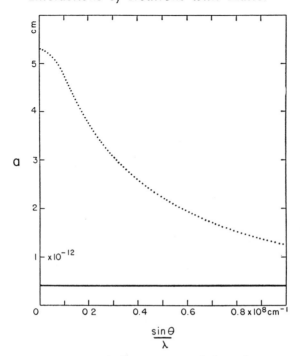

FIG. 14.10. *Comparison of the variation of the coherent scattering amplitude with* sin θ/λ *for x-rays (the dotted curve), and for neutrons (the horizontal line). These curves are for the potassium atom.*

in which $\sigma_{\text{coh}}(\text{eff})$ is the cross section which is observed as a result of temperature vibrations and K is defined as

$$K = \frac{3h^2}{Mk\Theta}\,(\phi(x)/x)$$

where M is the mass of the atoms, h is Planck's constant, k is Boltzmann's constant, Θ is a characteristic temperature of the crystal and $x = \Theta/T$, with T the absolute temperature of the crystal at the time of observation. The quantity $\phi(x)$ is defined by

$$\phi(x) = \frac{1}{x}\int_{0}^{x}\frac{\zeta d\zeta}{e^{\zeta}-1}$$

As has been indicated previously, the expressions for σ_{coh} have all assumed the nucleus to be in a fixed location. Eq. 14.18 gives the decrease in the coherent scattering with temperature but does not permit the computation of the thermal diffuse scattering resulting from the temperature vibrations of atoms in the crystal lattice. The thermal diffuse scattering can be studied beyond the Bragg cutoff at $\lambda > 2d$, where there is no coherent scattering. In this region of long wavelengths, the total cross section can be represented by

$$\sigma_t = \sigma_a + \sigma_{\text{dis}} + \sigma_{\text{inel}} \tag{14.19}$$

where σ_a is the $1/v$ absorption cross section, σ_{dis}, independent of λ, is the "disorder" cross section, resulting from imperfections in the crystal, and σ_{inel} represents inelastic scattering arising from exchange of energy between the neutrons and the vibrating atoms. In this exchange, the neutron may either lose or gain energy. The inelastic cross section shows variations both with λ and with temperature. In fact the rapid increase of the inelastic cross section with increasing temperature of the crystal is one means by which it may be identified.

14.5. Powder Diffraction

We cannot include within the limits of this book much of the detailed information which has been acquired by the study of neutron diffraction. Consequently we will devote most of the discussion of this topic to an introduction to the methods of obtaining neutron powder diffraction patterns with only brief reference to the data obtained. The powder diffraction technique has been widely used and offers at least two advantages over methods requiring single crystals. An obvious advantage is that powdered crystalline material is much easier to obtain than single crystals. In addition, the powder technique provides the most convenient procedure for determining absolute values of scattered intensities. Also, when compared with x-ray diffraction, the study of powder diffraction patterns permits the determination of the position of hydrogen atoms in crystal lattices. It is practically impossible to locate hydrogen atoms with x-rays because of the very low reflecting power of the hydrogen atom for x-rays. The low reflecting power of hydrogen is illustrated by the curves of Shull and Wollan (11), reproduced in Fig. 14.11. The powder diffraction patterns from NaH obtained by x-rays and by neutrons show pronounced differences in this graph. These differences result from the differing degree of reflection of the two types of waves from sodium and from hydrogen atoms. In the x-ray curve, reflections are recorded only from those planes defined by sodium atoms. Conversely, the neutron curve contains reflections only from planes defined by hydrogen atoms. From these patterns, it was possible to ascertain that NaH has a face-centered cubic structure. This ability of neutron diffraction to locate light atoms in crystals is one of its most valuable properties.

The crystalline preparations used in neutron diffraction may contain the powder in a thin rectangular parallelepiped as an envelope, or the container may be a vertical circular cylinder. In either case, the transmission

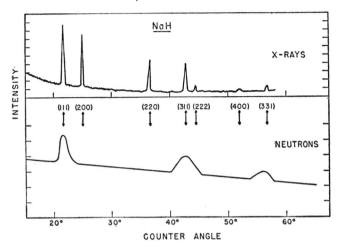

FIG. 14.11. *Comparison of x-ray and neutron powder diffraction patterns from NaH. The pattern for x-rays is determined solely by sodium atoms and the differences between the patterns reveal the effect of neutron scattering by hydrogen.*

method is commonly used, as indicated in Fig. 14.12. The rectangular preparation intercepts the whole monochromatic beam of neutrons, whereas the cylindrical specimen has cross-sectional dimensions smaller than the cross-sectional area of the beam. Consequently it is convenient to use a cylindrical sample when small amounts of crystalline material are available. The rate of deflection I of neutrons into the neutron counter from the rectangular sample is given by

$$I = I_0 \frac{\lambda^3 h e^{-\mu t \sec \theta}}{4\pi r \sin^2 \theta} \frac{t \rho'}{\rho} j N_c^2 F^2 e^{-K(\sin \theta/\lambda)^2} \qquad (14.20)$$

where I_0 is the rate at which monochromatic neutrons are incident on the sample, h is the height of the counter slit, r is the distance from the sample to the counter, t is the thickness of the sample, μ is the linear coefficient of absorption for neutrons in the sample, j is the number of cooperating planes in the reflection under measurement, ρ' is the apparent density of the powder, ρ the density of the solid crystal, N_c is the number of unit cells per cm³, and F the structure factor. In a set of crystal planes (h,k,l) the structure factor, familiar to x-ray crystallographers, is defined as

$$F_{h,k,l} = \sum_j a_j e^{2\pi i(hx_j + ky_j + lz_j)} \qquad (14.21)$$

where the summation is taken over the atoms of a unit cell, using the coordinates x_j, y_j, z_j and the coherent amplitudes a_j. The term $e^{-\mu t \sec \theta}$ of Eq. 14.20 is the effect of absorption in the sample and μt can be evaluated by transmission measurements at $\theta = 0$.

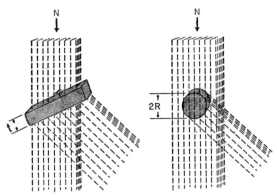

FIG. 14.12. *With rectangular powder diffraction samples, the specimen is larger than the cross-sectional area of the beam, and the diffracted beam has a larger area than the incident beam, as shown at the left. Cylindrical specimens are completely immersed in the incident beam, and the diffracted beam has a smaller cross-sectional area than the incident beam, as shown at the right.*

For the cylindrical sample the formula becomes

$$I = I_0 \frac{\lambda^3 h}{4\pi r} \frac{V\rho'}{\rho \sin\theta \sin 2\theta} jN_c^2 F^2 A_{hkl} e^{-K(\sin\theta/\lambda)^2} \qquad (14.22)$$

where now I_0 is the rate of incidence per unit area of monochromatic neutrons, V is the volume of the sample, and A_{hkl} is an absorption factor. The absorption here cannot be determined directly as in the rectangular sample. Bacon (9) has prepared a table giving values of a_{hkl} for various values of μR and θ, where R is the radius of the sample. These data are given in Table 14.2.

As a convenient example of the application of the powder diffraction method, we select the monochromator and spectrometer described by

Table 14.2

VALUES OF THE ABSORPTION FACTOR A_{hkl}
FOR CYLINDRICAL SAMPLES

θ / μR	0°	22.5°	45°	67.5°	90°
0.1	0.845	0.845	0.847	0.852	0.857
0.2	0.718	0.718	0.719	0.724	0.729
0.3	0.610	0.611	0.612	0.621	0.628
0.4	0.518	0.519	0.528	0.545	0.554
0.5	0.440	0.442	0.458	0.478	0.491
0.6	0.374	0.377	0.397	0.420	0.437
0.7	0.318	0.323	0.345	0.372	0.390
0.8	0.272	0.278	0.304	0.332	0.352

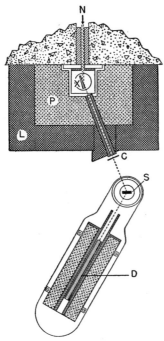

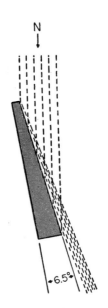

FIG. 14.13. *Plan of a mono-chromator for observing neutron diffraction patterns from a powder specimen. N—neutron beam. X—crystal of mono-chromator. P—borated paraffin. L—lead. C—neutron shutter. S—powder sample. D—BF₃ proportional counter.*

FIG. 14.14. *Diagram of a crystal cut according to the suggestion of Fankuchen.*

Wollan and Shull (12). The general plan of the apparatus is shown in Fig. 14.13. Particular care was taken in the design of this equipment to obtain a concentrated monochromatic beam. The crystal of the monochromator, operated in a fixed position, was mounted as close as possible to the opening in the shield of the reactor. In addition, this sodium chloride crystal was cut, as suggested by Fankuchen (13), at an angle of 6.5° to the (200) plane. Then neutrons from a primary beam 1 inch in width were diffracted into a beam only $\frac{3}{8}$ inch wide, as shown in Fig. 14.14. Much of the tedium attendant on taking spectrometer readings was eliminated by automatic rotation of the sample table and the counter arm and by using a printing recorder to take the data. Furthermore, automation permitted the apparatus to be operated at night when there was less interference from other equipment. The energy spectrum from the NaCl crystal, including also a scale of wavelengths, in Fig. 14.15, reveals the diffracted beam to have a

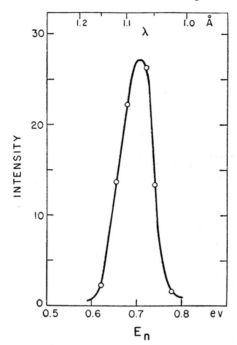

FIG. 14.15. *Energy and wavelength distribution from the crystal of the monochromator.*

spread of about 10 percent. The maximum intensity is at 1.06 Å which is in the neighborhood of the peak of the Maxwell distribution for thermal neutrons. Careful study with a second crystal on the spectrometer table detected diffusely scattered radiation of about 3 percent of the diffracted beam and a second order reflection of about 1.6 percent, corresponding to $n = 2$ in the Bragg formula.

Fig. 14.16 is an example of a neutron powder diffraction pattern observed by Hastings and Corliss (14). The observations, represented by dots, trace out well-defined reflections from the various planes of the $MnFe_2O_4$ crystal. The planes for the three most intense reflections are identified in the figure but the remaining peaks can also be associated with appropriate planes.

Although the Debye-Waller temperature factor of Eq. 14.18 can be computed, it is frequently more convenient to determine the corresponding correction experimentally. Fig. 14.17 illustrates how the correction was measured by Shull and Wollan (15) for the diffraction pattern from a sample of powdered lead. The observed data corresponding to the crystal structure scattering amplitude factor F are plotted on a log scale for the y-axis against the corresponding values of $(\sin \theta/\lambda)^2$ on the linear x-axis.

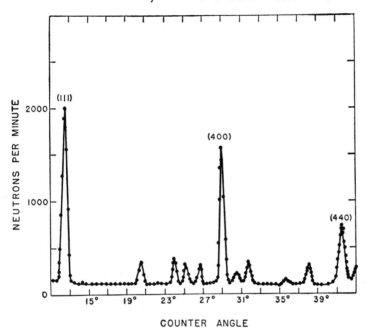

FIG. 14.16. *Neutron diffraction pattern of polycrystalline* $MnFe_2O_4$ *at room temperature.*

Extrapolating the line connecting the observed points to $x = 0$ gives the coherent scattering amplitude for lead, independent of the Debye-Waller temperature factor.

Shull and Wollan (15) have also developed a graphical method for evaluating the spin-scattering amplitudes. The method is illustrated by Fig. 14.18 for cobalt. From Eq. 14.12 for the total scattering cross section we obtain

$$\sigma_s = 4\pi(w_+a_+{}^2 + w_-a_-{}^2) \tag{14.23}$$

where w_+ and w_- represent the statistical weighting factors of Eq. 14.12. From Eq. 14.23 we have

$$\frac{a_+{}^2}{\sigma_s/4\pi w_+} + \frac{a_-{}^2}{\sigma_s/4\pi w_-} = 1 \tag{14.24}$$

which is the equation of the ellipse of Fig. 14.18. This ellipse gives all combinations of spin amplitudes represented by the measurements of the total scattering cross section. The straight line reveals the possibilities allowed by the coherent scattering amplitudes of known algebraic sign. The two points of intersection of the straight line with the ellipse represent alternative scattering amplitudes. The ambiguity arises from the random alignment of the scattering nuclei. This ambiguity can be resolved by

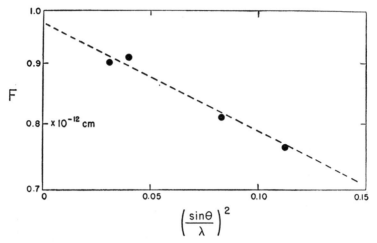

FIG. 14.17. *A plot of the observed scattering amplitude F on a log scale versus* $(\sin \theta/\lambda)^2$ *for lead. The dotted line shows the expected variation in F for a Debye temperature of 88°K. The intercept at zero scattering angle represents the coherent scattering amplitude for lead.*

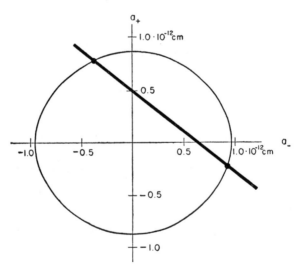

FIG. 14.18. *A graphical method for evaluating the spin-scattering amplitude applied to cobalt. Intersection of the straight line representing the coherent scattering amplitudes with the ellipse representing the total scattering gives the two alternative spin-scattering amplitudes.*

experiments on nuclei with spins uniformly oriented with respect to a beam of polarized neutrons.

14.6. Neutron Diffraction in Fluids

Neutron diffraction has also been applied to the structure of gaseous molecules in an extension of the powder technique. Alcock and Hurst (16) used the arrangement sketched in Fig. 14.19 to measure the variation of scattered intensity with Bragg angle for 0.07-ev neutrons. The curve of Fig. 14.20 represents their measurements for oxygen gas. This curve reveals evidence of a pattern produced by the structure of the molecule. In further measurements (17) in which neutron patterns for the gases nitrogen, carbon tetrafluoride, and methane were observed, the same authors were able to show that the coherent scattering cross sections of nitrogen and fluorine are nearly equal to the total cross sections. Hence σ_{dif} and σ_a are both very small. Moreover, they measured the length of the C–F bond in carbon tetrafluoride as 1.33 Å. The structure of liquefied gases have also been studied with neutrons. Henshaw, Hurst, and Pope (18) have measured

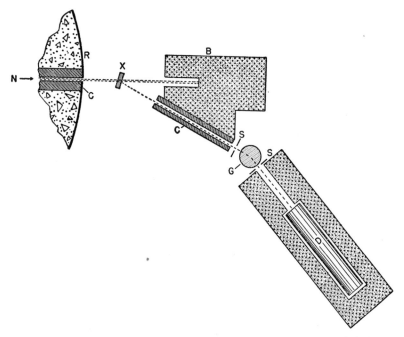

FIG. 14.19. *Diagram of a neutron crystal spectrometer modified to study the diffraction of neutrons in gases. R—shield of reactor. N— neutron beam. C—steel collimators. B—beam catcher of borated paraffin. G—gas chamber. S—slits. X—spectrometer crystal.*

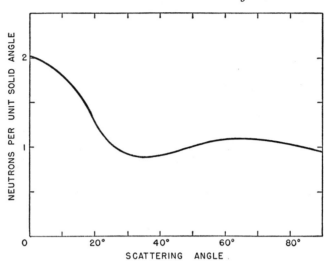

FIG. 14.20. *Angular distribution of 0.07-ev neutrons scattered from oxygen gas, giving a slight indication of the form of the molecule.*

the diffraction patterns from liquid nitrogen, oxygen, and argon. Liquids give more definite peaks than gases, as can be seen from the curve for liquid nitrogen in Fig. 14.21. This curve was interpreted to indicate a single neighbor at a spacing of 1.1 Å for each nitrogen atom, corresponding

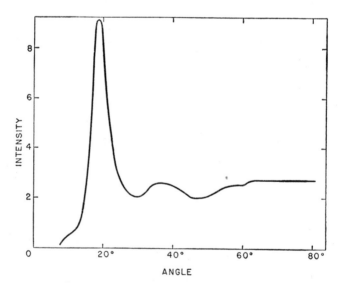

FIG. 14.21. *Diffraction pattern of neutrons scattered by liquid nitrogen at 77.4°K for a neutron wavelength of 1.08 Å.*

to a diatomic molecule in the liquid. In liquid oxygen, 1.5 neighbors at approximately 1.25 Å from each atom were found, indicating that the liquid molecule has a structure more complex than diatomic and not inconsistent with an O_4 molecule.

14.7. Neutron Diffraction in Magnetic Substances

We will conclude this outline of neutron diffraction with a brief discussion of investigations of magnetic materials. Currently the study of magnetic properties of the solid state is one of the more important developments in the general field of the coherent scattering of neutrons. The results have contributed significantly to the understanding of the fundamentals of magnetism, and it is apparent that much more is to be learned in this way.

The diffraction of neutrons in magnetic crystals has two components, one the coherent scattering from nuclei which we have been considering, the second a magnetic component which is the result of the interaction of the magnetic moment of the neutron with the magnetic lattice. This lattice is made up of a symmetrical alignment of the spins of unpaired electrons of the array of atoms in the crystal. Thus the magnetic scattering of neutrons is analogous to the scattering of x-rays, in the sense that both are produced by atomic electrons. The outstanding difference between them is that all atomic electrons contribute to x-ray scattering but only the electrons responsible for the magnetic properties of the atom are involved in the magnetic scattering of neutrons. Because the magnetic scattering of neutrons comes from a structure with dimensions comparable with the wavelengths of the neutrons, we can expect that the distribution of the magnetic scattering about the atom will not be isotropic.

This similarity to x-ray scattering has been verified experimentally in numerous cases. An example of the angular dependence of the amplitude on the magnetic scattering angle for the Mn^{++} ion is shown in Fig. 14.22. The form of this curve was deduced by Shull, Strauser, and Wollan (19) from the measurements of the antiferromagnetic reflections from MnO at low temperatures. The magnetic amplitude for factor f of Fig. 14.22 is dependent on the spatial distribution of the magnetic electrons. The form factor originates, in definition, in the theory of magnetic scattering of neutrons by Halpern and Johnson (20). They could show that, for randomly oriented paramagnetic ions, the differential paramagnetic cross section is given by

$$d\sigma_{\text{pm}} = \frac{2}{3} S(S + 1) \left(\frac{c^2\gamma}{mc^2}\right)^2 f^2 d\Omega \qquad (14.25)$$

where S is the spin quantum number, γ is the magnetic moment of the neutron in Bohr magnetons, with e and m the electronic charge and mass,

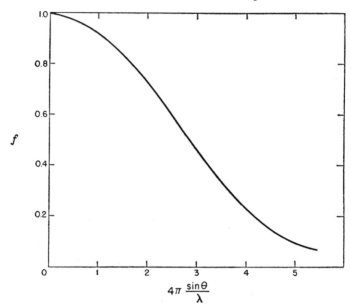

Fig. 14.22. *Magnetic form factor* f *for* Mn++ *ions.*

respectively. The corresponding value for the paramagnetic scattering cross section becomes

$$\sigma_{pm} = \frac{8\pi}{3} S(S+1) \left(\frac{e^2\gamma}{mc^2}\right)^2 \bar{f}^2 \tag{14.26}$$

with $\bar{f}^2$ the integral of the form factor representing the average value of f^2 integrated over the total solid angle. For ferromagnetic substances, where the atoms have their magnetic moments either in parallel or antiparallel positions, the differential cross section can be shown to take the form

$$d\sigma_m = q^2 S^2 \left(\frac{e^2\gamma}{mc^2}\right)^2 f^2 d\Omega \tag{14.27}$$

where **q** is a magnetic interaction vector with

$$\mathbf{q} = \epsilon(\epsilon\mathbf{K}) - \mathbf{K} \tag{14.28}$$

where **K** is a unit vector in the direction of the atomic magnetic moment and ϵ is a unit vector called the scattering vector. The relation between these vectors is shown in the diagram of Fig. 14.23. Because, in magnetic materials, coherence can occur for waves scattered from the atomic magnetic moments in a definitely oriented array, diffraction phenomena can be anticipated. Magnetic neutron diffraction was predicted by Halpern and Johnson (20) who defined the magnetic scattering amplitude D as

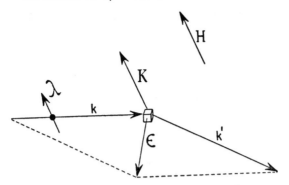

FIG. 14.23. *Diagram of unit vectors determining diffraction from a magnetized crystal.* κ—*vector of propagation for incident neutron.* κ'—*vector of propagation for reflected neutron.* K—*vector of magnetization,* ϵ—*scattering vector.* λ—*polarization vector.* H—*magnetic field.*

$$D = \frac{e^2\gamma}{mc^2} Sf \qquad (14.29)$$

The amplitude D is analogous to the nuclear scattering amplitude a. Referring back to Fig. 14.22, we now see from Eq. 14.29 that the quantity f is the scattering amplitude multiplied by the constants of Eq. 14.29. Hence the curve of Fig. 14.22 reveals the course of the magnetic scattering amplitude as a function of the scattering angle. The total differential scattering cross section per atom was found by Halpern and Johnson to be

$$F^2 = d\sigma_s = a^2 + 2aD\mathbf{q\lambda} + q^2D^2 \qquad (14.30)$$

with $\boldsymbol{\lambda}$ the unit vector in the direction of the polarization of the neutron, as shown in Fig. 14.23. In the case of an unpolarized beam of neutrons, $\mathbf{q\lambda} = 0$ and

$$d\sigma_s = a^2 + q^2D^2 \qquad (14.31)$$

showing that in this case the intensities, and not the amplitudes, of the nuclear and magnetic components are additive. Other simplifications can be represented by the following cases for the direction of magnetization

$$d\sigma_s = a^2 \qquad \epsilon \parallel \mathbf{K} \qquad (14.32)$$

$$d\sigma_s = a^2 + D^2 \qquad \epsilon \perp \mathbf{K} \qquad (14.33)$$

$$d\sigma_s = a^2 + \tfrac{2}{3} D^2 \quad \text{unmagnetized} \qquad (14.34)$$

The literature dealing with aspects and applications of the magnetic diffraction of neutrons is rapidly becoming voluminous. One or two of the simpler examples will be mentioned. The articles cited contain references to other work which will introduce the reader, wishing to pursue the subject further, to this general field. It is natural to consider first an example of observations on the coherent scattering of neutrons by iron, although this was not the first substance to be investigated for magnetic scattering of neutrons. We select the neutron powder diffraction pattern observed by Shull, Wollan, and Koehler (21), reproduced in Fig. 14.24. The values deduced for the differential coherent cross sections from this pattern are plotted in Fig. 14.25 as open circles. In this graph the origin has been suppressed. Hence the major contribution to the differential cross section is the isotropic nuclear scattering represented by the horizontal dotted line. The dashed line represents the best fit to the data of a computed curve, using the magnetic form factor derived by Steinberger and Wick

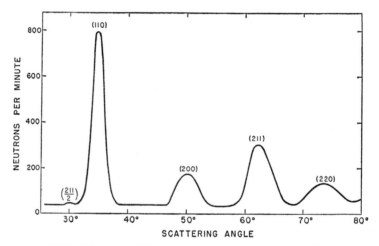

FIG. 14.24. *Neutron diffraction pattern for polycrystalline iron.*

(22). The good agreement between the data and the theoretical curve gives added confidence in the interpretation of the observations as the addition of the effects of magnetic scattering from the iron atoms to the isotropic scattering from the nuclei of these atoms.

Further confirmation of the effects of diffraction originating from the magnetic properties of the scattering material is provided by the study of McReynolds and Riste (23). They used the experimental arrangement of Fig. 14.26 to measure the intensity of neutrons diffracted from a crystal of Fe_3O_4 at a fixed angle of $\theta = 16°$ as the temperature of the crystal was raised from 0° to 700°C. Their observations are plotted in Fig. 14.27. The solid curve shows the data obtained with the crystal unmagnetized. The dotted curve represents the data with the crystal magnetized parallel to the scattering vector ϵ of Fig. 14.23. The dashed line is the background

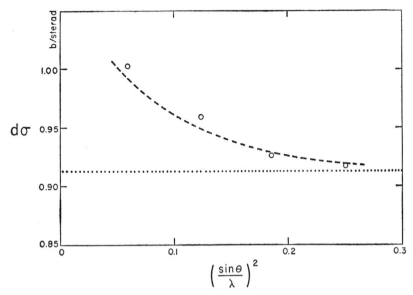

FIG. 14.25. *The observed differential coherent scattering cross section as a function of scattering angle represented by the circles, as deduced from the data of Fig. 14.24. The horizontal dotted line represents the isotropic nuclear scattering. The dashed line is the computed curve for the magnetic scattering.*

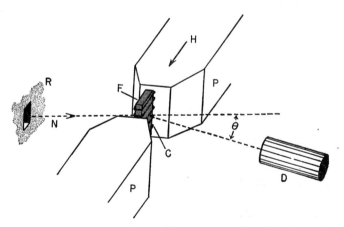

FIG. 14.26. *Apparatus for observation of magnetic diffraction of neutrons from a Fe_3O_4 single crystal as a function of the temperature of the crystal.*

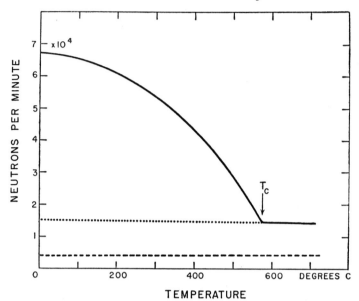

FIG. 14.27. *The solid line represents the total observed intensity of neutrons diffracted from the (111) planes of the Fe_3O_4 crystal of Fig. 14.26 when unmagnetized. The dotted line is the curve when the crystal is magnetized parallel to the scattering vector. The dashed line is the background.*

counting rate with the crystal turned out of alignment. Here we have an example of a large magnetic scattering compared with the nuclear scattering. For the solid curve, $d\sigma_s = a^2 + \frac{2}{3} D^2$ and hence is the sum of the magnetic and nuclear scattering. For the dotted curve, $d\sigma_s = a^2$ and therefore represents the isotropic nuclear scattering. The striking result from the magnetic point of view is that the solid curve merges into the dotted curve at and above the Curie temperature T_c for the crystal. In other words, the magnetic scattering goes sharply to zero at the Curie temperature where the crystal undergoes a transition from ferromagnetic to paramagnetic behavior.

15.1. Reflection of Neutrons

Fermi and Zinn (24) called attention to the fact that neutrons should have an index of refraction n with $(n - 1)$ negative or positive and of the order of 10^{-6}. When $n < 1$ there should be total reflection at angles of a few minutes. Fermi and Zinn observed this total reflection experimentally. Subsequently Fermi and Marshall (3) investigated the total reflection in more detail. The index of refraction may be computed from

$$n = 1 - \frac{\lambda^2 N a}{2\pi} \tag{15.1}$$

where N is the number of atoms per cm³ and a is the coherent scattering amplitude for the mirror. The limiting glancing angle θ_c for total reflection is approximately

$$\theta_c = \sqrt{2(1 - n)} = \lambda \sqrt{\frac{N a}{\pi}} \tag{15.2}$$

Fermi and Marshall used the monochromator sketched in Fig. 15.1 to observe total reflection from metallic mirrors which were suspected to have a positive value for a. Their data are quoted in Table 15.1.

Table 15.1

LIMITING ANGLE FOR TOTAL REFLECTION
OF NEUTRONS OF 1.873 Å

Mirror	Limiting Angle (min)	
	Observed	Calculated
Be	12.0	11.1
C	10.5	8.4
Fe	10.7	10.0
Ni	11.5	11.8
Zn	7.1	6.9
Cu	9.5	9.5

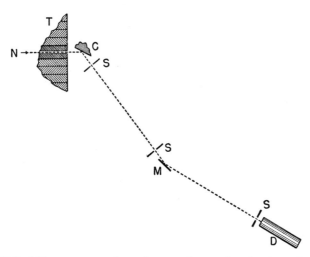

FIG. 15.1. *Mirror arranged to observe the total reflection of monochromatic neutrons. N—neutron beam. T—thermal column of a reactor. C—monochromator crystal. S—slits. M—mirror. D—BF₃ proportional counter.*

The circumstance that total reflection can occur only when the coherent scattering amplitude is positive can be used to identify the sign of a. Actually at the present time total reflection is the only direct experimental means of determining this sign. Another important aspect of total reflection is that when θ_c and λ are known, the value of a for the mirror is uniquely determined. The form factor for coherent scattering is unity in this case and does not appear in Eq. 15.2. Therefore total reflection plays an important role in the determination of coherent scattering amplitudes. The method is particularly valuable when these amplitudes are relatively inaccessible by other methods. A few examples will be described.

The uncertainties in the temperature correction factors and the measurement of the absolute intensities of the diffracted beams impair the accuracy of the determination of coherent scattering cross sections by the diffraction method. The use of total reflection to measure coherent scattering cross sections obviates these sources of error. Also in reflection experiments, small amounts of the reflecting material are required, of the order of milligrams. Thus measurements can be made on samples of separated isotopes or wherever there is a scarcity of the substance to be investigated. The low depth of penetration of a neutron beam into a mirror requires the surface material to be pure. The depth of penetration can be computed as approximately $\lambda/2\pi\theta_c$ which, for usual conditions, is a depth of about 100 atoms.

Heindl and his co-workers (25) have investigated procedures for producing mirrors specially suited for use in reflection experiments with neutrons. To make use of small amounts of the reflecting substance, the evaporation technique was chosen for depositing the sample on a rigid support. Vanadium was selected for the base material. The principal reason for this choice is the extremely low coherent cross section of vanadium, equal to 0.028 ± 0.005 barn. Consequently a deposited sample with positive scattering amplitude a will produce only one reflection, the one at the air-sample interface. No complicating reflection will occur at the sample-vanadium interface. The surface of the vanadium slab was ground flat, lapped, and electropolished to a high luster. This preparation insured the deposition of a smooth mirror which produced good reflections of neutrons.

Measurements were made on the angle of total reflection of several evaporated mirrors arranged as indicated in Fig. 15.2. The neutrons emerging through the shield of the reactor had passed through a filter F of beryllium and beryllium oxide 10 inches thick. The filter removed all neutrons with wavelengths less than 4.68 Å, with a sharp cutoff on the short-wavelength side. The filter has the advantage over a monochromator of yielding relatively high intensities. The filtered beam was collimated by slits with openings of only 0.0075 inch, at the face of the reactor and at the mirror. A similar slit in front of the detector could be moved by a microme-

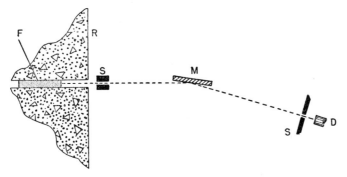

FIG. 15.2. *Measurement of critical angle of neutron reflection from specially prepared mirrors. F—beryllium filter. R—reactor shield. S, S—slits. M—mirror. D—BF$_3$ proportional counter.*

ter screw at right angles to the axis of the beam. It served as a scanning slit. The quality of the mirrors is evidenced by the curves of Fig. 15.3. They show the profiles of the direct and of the reflected beams in their normal angular relation. The curves of Fig. 15.3 are for Te^{130} deposited on vanadium. There is a considerable increase in the half-width at half-maximum on reflection. However, reflection from a copper mirror deposited on glass showed a negligible increase in the half-width. Thus the quality of the reflection is directly correlated with the smoothness of the mirror.

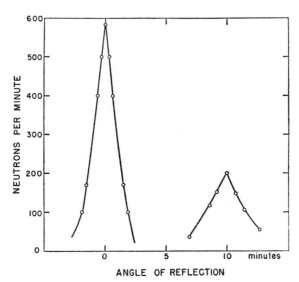

FIG. 15.3. *Profiles of direct and reflected beam for Te^{130} deposited on a polished vanadium base.*

The method by which θ_c was located is illustrated by the curve of Fig. 15.4. The circles represent the observed neutron counting rates as the angle θ was increased from zero with the scanning slits simultaneously moved so that they were always at an angle 2θ with respect to the direct beam. As can be seen, the intensity of the reflected neutrons initially increases linearly with θ. As θ_c is approached, the intensity suddenly begins to fall off and finally drops sharply toward zero. The intersection of the two extrapolated curves gives the value of θ_c for the neutron wavelength

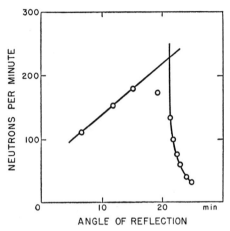

FIG. 15.4. *Observations for locating θ_c.*

of 4.4 A, the cutoff wavelength of the filter. Using the procedure described, Heindl and co-workers obtained the coherent cross sections of tellurium and copper given in Table 15.2.

Table 15.2

VALUES OF σ_{coh} OBTAINED BY TOTAL
REFLECTION FROM A MIRROR

Reflecting Material	θ_c (min)	σ_{coh} (barns)
Cu	21.2	6.8 ± 0.5
Te	11.0	4.0 ± 0.4
Te^{130}	11.1	4.1 ± 0.4
Te^{123}	11.3	4.2 ± 0.5

The values for Cu and for Te agree almost exactly with the best values obtained from diffraction measurements. The agreement has been taken as an indication that at least as good measurements can be obtained by reflection as by diffraction, with the advantage that the reflection method can be used on samples where the diffraction method cannot be used.

16.1. Polarization of Neutrons

Bloch (26) originally suggested that neutrons might be polarized by passing them through magnetized iron. He concluded that the coherent scattering cross section per nucleus for magnetically saturated iron could be expressed as

$$\sigma = \sigma_0 \pm \sigma_p \qquad (16.1)$$

where σ_0 is the cross section for completely demagnetized iron and σ_p is the polarization cross section. The polarization cross section is the result of the interference of the neutron wave scattered by the magnetic field of the iron atoms with the wave scattered by the nucleus. This polarization is not the familiar property of electromagnetic radiation. It refers rather to the spin of the neutron associated with its magnetic moment. A beam of neutrons having their spins all aligned in one direction is considered to be completely polarized. In cases of partial polarization, the degree of polarization P is

$$P = \frac{n_+ - n_-}{n_+ + n_-} \qquad (16.2)$$

where n_+ is the number of neutrons with spins in the positive direction and n_- is a lesser number with spins in the negative direction. Early attempts at polarizing neutrons were only qualitatively successful. One reason for the disappointing results is that in the absence of complete and uniform magnetization of the iron there will be depolarizing effects arising from inhomogeneities in the magnetic field.

The method of studying the polarization of neutrons suggested by Bloch involves the single-transmission effect η_1 in magnetized iron expressed by

$$\eta_1 = \frac{I}{I_0} - 1 \qquad (16.3)$$

where I is the intensity of neutrons emerging from a magnetized block of iron and I_0 is the emergent intensity when the iron is unmagnetized. Therefore the neutron intensity incident on the iron block is $I_0/e^{-N\sigma_t d}$, where N is the number of scattering centers per unit volume in the iron, σ_t is the total cross section for unmagnetized iron and d is the thickness of the block. This reveals one of the disadvantages in the use of magnetized iron for obtaining polarized neutrons—a considerable reduction of the intensity of the neutrons in the polarizing process. The polarization P can be shown to be given, for completely saturated iron, by

$$P = \sqrt{1 - (\eta_1 + 1)^2} \qquad (16.4)$$

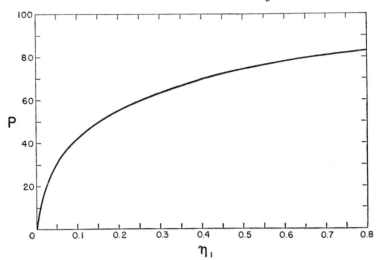

FIG. 16.1. *Polarization versus the single transmission effect η_1 for complete saturation.*

Eq. 16.4 has been plotted by Stanford and his co-workers (27) and the graph is shown in Fig. 16.1. The value of σ_p may be deduced from the relation

$$\eta_1 = \cosh (N\sigma_p d) - 1 \tag{16.5}$$

which for $N\sigma_p d \ll 1$ is given approximately by

$$\eta_1 = \tfrac{1}{2} N\sigma_p^2 d^2 \tag{16.6}$$

If the iron is not completely saturated, Eq. 16.6 becomes

$$\eta_1 = \tfrac{1}{2} N^2 \sigma_p^2 d^2 f(q/\epsilon d) \tag{16.7}$$

with $f(x) = 2x^2(e^{-1/x} + 1/x - 1)$ and $\epsilon = \dfrac{M_\infty - M}{M}$ in which M_∞ is the saturation magnetization and M the actual magnetization. The parameter q is related to the size of the microcrystals in the iron, as described by Fleeman, Nicodemus, and Staub (28), who designate this quantity by λ.

The polarization cross section σ_p for iron has been measured, using the single-transmission method, at a number of wavelengths by Stanford and co-workers (27). The neutron energies were selected, in most of the observations, by a quartz crystal monochromator. Four measurements were also obtained using a single crystal of magnetized magnetite to analyze the beam emerging from the iron polarizer. By this procedure, the magnetite crystal also acted as a monochromator. Their data, combined with observations by other investigators, are plotted in Fig. 16.2. The two discontinuous curves A and B in this graph represent the results of theoretical

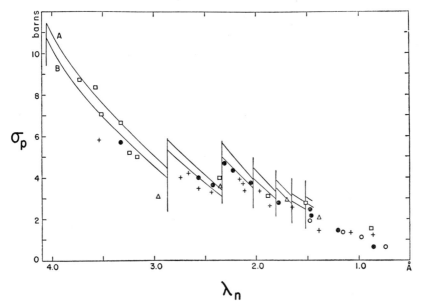

FIG. 16.2. *Polarization cross section in magnetized iron as a function of neutron wavelength. The curves are computed from theory, using the value $\sigma_{coh} = 11.4$ barns for iron. Curve A results from assuming that the wave function of the third shell is zero, and curve B from assuming that the derivative of this function is zero at the atomic radius.*

computations of σ_p. Curve A is calculated on the assumption that the wave function of the $3d$ shell, responsible for the magnetic properties of iron atoms, is zero at the atomic radius. Curve B was obtained on the assumption that the derivative of the wave function is zero at the atomic radius. The observations, shown by the plotted points, are too scattered to distinguish between these two possibilities. However, the observed points do follow the general course of the curves sufficiently well that the deviations can be assigned to imperfections in the iron polarizer. In particular, the calculations of the theoretical curves assumed a random distribution of the microcrystals in the iron. This condition was not completely met in the actual block of iron.

16.2. Polarization of Neutrons by Reflection

Hughes and Burgy (29) have investigated the suggestion by Bloch (26) that the index of refraction of magnetized iron should have two values. These two values originate from the fact that the total scattering amplitude a_t can be represented by $a_t = a \pm D$. The value of the magnetic scattering amplitude D is added or subtracted according to the orientation of the magnetic moment of the neutron with respect to the magnetization of the microscopic magnetic domains in the iron. For the case of magnetization in the direction of incidence of the neutrons, the index of refraction can be expressed as

$$n^2 - 1 = \frac{\lambda^2 Na}{\pi} \pm \frac{\mu B}{E_n} \tag{16.8}$$

for the forward direction. Here μ is the magnetic moment of the neutron and B is the magnetic induction with $B = H + 4\pi M$, where M is the intensity of magnetization. The corresponding general expression for the critical angle for total reflection would be

$$\theta_c = \sqrt{\frac{\lambda^2 Na}{\pi} \pm \frac{\mu(H + 4\pi CM)}{E_n}} f(\phi) \tag{16.9}$$

where C is a constant introduced by Bloch (26) which would be zero for the dipole-dipole neutron-electron interaction which he proposed. The function $f(\phi)$ expresses the dependence of θ_c on ϕ, the angle between the direction of propagation of the neutron and the magnetic field. For $\phi = 0$, an experimental condition which can be arranged, $f(\phi)$ has a value of zero. For the Dirac type of electron-neutron interaction, discussed by Ekstein (30), the Bloch constant C would have the value of unity. If $C = 0$ there should, from Eq. 16.9, be only one value of θ_c. The magnetic term disappears because H, the magnetic field, is small in comparison with B. An experiment to distinguish between these two possibilities was performed by Hughes and Burgy (29). The magnetized mirror was mounted in front of an opening to the thermal column of a reactor, as indicated in Fig. 16.3. The emergent neutrons passed through a filter of beryllium oxide within the thermal column to exclude from the beam all wavelengths less than 4.4 Å. The results of measurement of the intensity of the reflected beam as

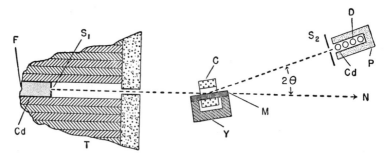

FIG. 16.3. *Apparatus for investigation of the reflection of neutrons from magnetized iron mirrors. F—beryllium filter. Cd—cadmium shield. T—thermal column of reactor. S_1—slit to define neutron beam. C—magnet coil. Y—magnet yoke. M—magnetized mirror. S_2—scanning slit. P—paraffin. D—BF_3 proportional counters.*

a function of θ are plotted in Fig. 16.4. The upper curve, labeled B, is computed with the constant $C = 0$. The curve D corresponds to $C = 1$. There is no doubt that the plotted observations favor the curve D. In fact a value of $C = 0.9$ can be computed from these measurements. The results also confirm that it is the saturated value of the magnetic induction and not the magnetic field strength which determines the index of refraction for neutrons in magnetized iron. Also the two critical angles for total reflection are independent of the direction of magnetization. The three points in Fig. 16.4 represented by crosses were taken with $\phi = 90°$, but they lie on the same curve with the other observations taken with $\phi = 0°$.

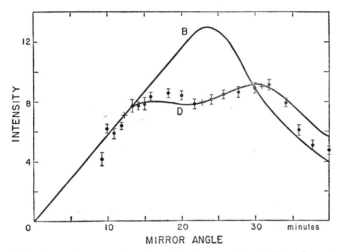

FIG. 16.4. *Intensity as a function of mirror angle of filtered neutrons reflected from a magnetized iron mirror. Curve B corresponds to C = O and curve D to C = 1. The three observations indicated by crosses were taken at $\phi = 90°$, otherwise $\phi = 0°$.*

The data plotted in Fig. 16.4 indicate that the critical angles for total reflection are different for the two spin states of the neutron. This difference immediately suggests that the neutrons in these states might be separated, hence polarized, by reflection from a magnetized mirror. Hamermesh (31) called attention to the fact that polarization by this process would be difficult to accomplish with iron. In iron the coherent scattering amplitude is greater than the magnetic amplitude and the index of refraction is less than unity for both spin states. Both spins, therefore, can be totally reflected. Because the critical angle is proportional to the wavelength, there will be an overlap for the two spin states, unless monochromatic neutrons are used. To resort to the selection of a narrow band of neutron energies would reduce intensities to such an extent as to make this process unprofitable as a source of polarized neutrons. The case of a magnetized cobalt mirror is, however, quite different. When magnetized in the direction of the propagation of the neutrons, an exact analog to a Nicol prism for light is obtained with a cobalt mirror. The coherent cross section for cobalt is 1.06 ± 0.06 barn, about a tenth of the coherent cross section for iron. On the other hand, the magnetic scattering amplitude for cobalt is around 4×10^{-13}cm, to be compared with about 6×10^{-13} cm for iron. Hence in cobalt the magnetic amplitude is greater than the nuclear amplitude. The consequence is that the indices of refraction for the two neutron spin states will be on opposite sides of unity for all wavelengths. Therefore only one spin state can be totally reflected and a

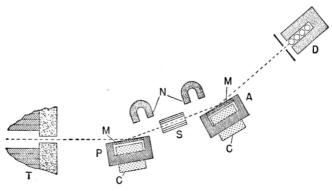

FIG. 16.5. *Apparatus for producing complete neutron polarization by reflection from a magnetized cobalt mirror. T—thermal column of reactor. P—polarizing magnet. C—magnet coils. M—cobalt mirrors. A—analyzing magnet. S—magnetic shield. N—permanent magnets. D—BF_3 proportional counters.*

completely polarized reflected beam should be produced, independent of wavelength.

Hughes and Burgy (29) investigated the polarization produced by a magnetized cobalt mirror, using a second magnetized cobalt mirror as an analyzer. The cobalt was electroplated on copper to form the mirrors. The mirrors were mounted across the yokes of electromagnets, as shown in Fig. 16.5. The use of the analyzer mirror was based on the expectation that, with the second mirror magnetized in the same direction as the first, there would be no loss of intensity on reflection of a completely polarized beam incident on the second mirror. If the magnetization of the second mirror were reversed, no reflection should occur in the second mirror. The conduct of an experiment of this type involves a number of difficulties. To obtain a magnetic scattering amplitude greater than the nuclear scattering amplitude, the magnetic induction of the mirror must be greater than 82 percent of saturation. This degree of saturation is not readily obtained in cobalt. Another problem was revealed when, in the first trials, no change of intensity was observed on reversal of the magnetic field of the analyzer. The failure was traced to a reorientation and partial depolarization of the polarized beam before reaching the analyzer. For successful results, the field reversal must be accomplished in a time short compared with the Larmor precession time of the neutron. The angular velocity of the Larmor precession is $\omega = 4\pi\mu H/h$, where h is Planck's constant. At thermal energies, neutrons travel a distance of $80/H$ cm during one Larmor precession, where H is the magnetic field in gauss. Hence the field between the magnets must be reduced to a negligible value at some point in this region and then the field must be reversed in the space of a few millimeters. To satisfy this condition required the addition of concentric iron shields S around the neutron beam and the introduction of the two small permanent magnets N, shown in Fig. 16.5. This modification permitted observations on the polarization. It was finally found desirable to detect the polarization by inserting a sheet of unmagnetized iron into the neutron beam between the mirrors, both mirrors being magnetized in the same direction. The iron sheet served as a depolarizer. This depolarization method of observing the effect demonstrated that, with high magnetization currents and long neutron wavelengths, approximately 100 percent polarization was achieved. Therefore the reflection method has two advantages over the transmission method for polarizing neutrons. First, there is no loss of intensity by absorption on reflection; and it is possible to polarize neutrons of long wavelengths by reflection. The polarization of neutrons with long wavelengths is impossible by the transmission method because iron is practically transparent to neutrons with wavelengths greater than 4.04 Å.

SYMBOLS FOR CHAPTER VI

A	activity induced in nuclei by neutron absorption
a	nuclear scattering amplitude
B	magnetic induction
D	magnetic scattering amplitude
E, E_n	neutron energy
H	magnetic field strength
i	nuclear spin
K	unit vector in direction of the atomic magnetic moment
k	neutron wave number
L	neutron diffusion length
m	mass of the neutron
M	mass of a nucleus

M	intensity of magnetization
N	number of atoms per cm^3
n	neutron density
n	index of refraction for the neutron
nv	neutron flux
P	probability of spin flip
Q	rate of emission of neutrons from a source
q	slowing-down density for neutrons
$\mathbf{q}$	magnetic interaction vector
s	spin of the neutron
S	spin quantum number
v	velocity of a neutron
V_c	velocity of the center of mass in the laboratory
w	statistical weighting factor
γ	magnetic moment of the neutron
$\boldsymbol{\epsilon}$	scattering vector
η	transmission effect—fractional change in neutron intensity on passing through a sample of matter
θ	angle in the laboratory between the direction of a neutron before and after a collision
θ_c	critical angle for total reflection of neutrons
λ_a	absorption mean free path for neutrons
λ_s	scattering mean free path
λ_{tr}	transport mean free path
λ	wavelength of a neutron
$\boldsymbol{\lambda}$	unit vector in the direction of the polarization of a neutron
μ	linear coefficient of absorption for neutrons
ξ	average loss in the logarithm of the energy of a neutron in a single collision
ρ	density of matter
Σ_a	macroscopic cross section for absorption
Σ_s	macroscopic cross section for scattering
σ_a	$1/v$ absorption cross section
σ_{coh}	coherent scattering cross section
σ_{dif}	diffuse scattering cross section
σ_p	polarization cross section
σ_s	scattering cross section
σ_t	total cross section
τ	neutron "age"
ϕ	angle in center-of-mass system between the direction of a neutron before and after a collision
Ψ	neutron wave function

PROBLEMS FOR CHAPTER VI

1. Compute the maximum amount of energy which a neutron with energy E_n can lose on collision with (1) an atom of aluminum, (2) an atom of beryllium, (3) an atom of gold, and (4) an atom of bismuth.

2. Compute the average value of the cosine of the angle through which a neutron is scattered (1) by carbon atoms, (2) by gold atoms.

3. Compute the value of λ_{tr} for thermal neutrons in gold if σ_s for gold is 9 barns.

4. In bismuth for thermal neutrons σ_a is 0.032 barn and σ_s is 9.4 barns. Compute the diffusion length.

5. The measured value of σ_{coh} for a substance is 10 barns. Compute the scattering amplitude in cm.

6. The limiting glancing angle for total reflection of neutrons from a beryllium mirror was found to be 20 min. Compute the wavelength of the neutrons.

7. Derive the formula for the limiting glancing angle for total reflection of neutrons.

8. Measurements of neutron flux at increasing distances from a constant point source of neutrons yielded the following data, where A is the value of the thermal flux and r the distance from the source.

A	r	A	r
200	10 cm	80	45 cm
160	25	40	63
120	35	20	80
		10	100

Compute the value of the neutron age τ_0.

9. A point source of thermal neutrons in the center of a large tank of water produces 4×10^8 neutrons per sec. Compute the neutron flux at a distance of 20 cm from this source. Make the same computation when the water has been replaced by heavy water.

10. If Q thermal neutrons per sec are produced in each cubic centimeter of an infinite diffusing medium, compute the thermal neutron flux at any point in the medium.

11. Thermal neutrons diffuse from an infinite plane source emitting Q neutrons per cm² per sec into a tank of heavy water. Compute the neutron density at a distance of 30 cm from the source. Make the same computation with the heavy water replaced by beryllium metal.

12. Compute the velocity of recoil of the target nucleus when a 3-Mev neutron collides with a proton which recoils at an angle of 15° to the direction of the incident neutron. Repeat the computation with an oxygen nucleus as the target for the neutron.

13. Measurements of the intensity of indium resonance neutrons at various distances from a fast neutron source yielded the following data.

Neutron intensity	Distance	Neutron intensity	Distance
454	5 cm	140	20 cm
358	10	73	25
243	15	29	30
		11	35

Compute τ to the indium resonance energy.

14. The intensity of indium resonance neutrons from a fast neutron source was measured at various distances from the source in a beryllium moderator giving the following data.

Neutron intensity	Distance from source
29000	10 cm
8250	20
1330	30
240	40
41	50
10	60

Plot the data on semilog paper, using neutron intensity multiplied by the square of the distance from the source as ordinates along the log scale and distance from the source as abscissa on the linear scale. Explain the shape of the curve between 30 cm and 60 cm in terms of an equation.

REFERENCES FOR CHAPTER VI

1. D. P. Mitchell and P. N. Powers. *Phys. Rev.* **50,** 486 (1936).
2. E. O. Wollan, C. G. Shull, and M. C. Marney. *Phys. Rev.* **73,** 527 (1948).
3. E. Fermi and L. Marshall. *Phys. Rev.* **71,** 666 (1947).
4. E. Fermi, W. J. Sturm, and R. G. Sachs. *Phys. Rev.* **71,** 589 (1947).
5. J. M. Blatt and V. F. Weisskopf. *Theoretical Nuclear Physics*, Wiley (1952), p. 423.
6. W. C. Koehler, E. O. Wollan, and C. G. Shull. *Phys. Rev.* **79,** 395 (1950).
7. O. Halpern and M. H. Johnson. *Phys. Rev.* **55,** 898 (1939).
8. W. E. Meyerhof and D. B. Nicodemus. *Phys. Rev.* **82,** 5 (1951).
9. G. E. Bacon. *Neutron Diffraction*, Oxford (1955).
10. I. Waller. *Z. Phys.* **51,** 213 (1928).
11. C. G. Shull and E. O. Wollan. *Science* **108,** 69 (1948).
12. E. O. Wollan and C. G. Shull. *Phys. Rev.* **73,** 830 (1948).
13. I. Fankuchen. *Nature* **139,** 193 (1937).
14. J. M. Hastings and L. M. Corliss. *Phys. Rev.* **104,** 328 (1956).
15. C. G. Shull and E. O. Wollan. *Phys. Rev.* **81,** 527 (1951).
16. N. Z. Alcock and D. G. Hurst. *Phys. Rev.* **75,** 1609 (1949).
17. N. Z. Alcock and D. G. Hurst. *Phys. Rev.* **83,** 1100 (1951).
18. D. G. Henshaw, D. G. Hurst, and N. K. Pope. *Phys. Rev.* **92,** 1229 (1953).
19. C. G. Shull, W. A. Strauser, and E. O. Wollan. *Phys. Rev.* **83,** 333 (1951).
20. O. Halpern and M. H. Johnson. *Phys. Rev.* **55,** 898 (1939).
21. C. G. Shull, E. O. Wollan, and W. C. Koehler. *Phys. Rev.* **84,** 912 (1951).
22. J. Steinberger and G. C. Wick. *Phys. Rev.* **76,** 994 (1949).
23. A. W. McReynolds and T. Riste. *Phys. Rev.* **95,** 1161 (1954).
24. E. Fermi and W. H. Zinn. *Phys. Rev.* **70,** 103 (1946).
25. C. J. Heindl, I. W. Ruderman, J. M. Ostrowski, J. R. Ligenza, and D. M. Gardner. *Rev. Sci. Inst.* **27,** 620 (1956).
26. F. Bloch. *Phys. Rev.* **50,** 259 (1936); **51,** 994 (1937).
27. C. P. Stanford, T. E. Stephenson, L. W. Cochran, and S. Bernstein. *Phys. Rev.* **94,** 374 (1954).
28. J. Fleeman, D. B. Nicodemus, and H. H. Staub. *Phys. Rev.* **76,** 1774 (1949).
29. D. J. Hughes and M. T. Burgy. *Phys. Rev.* **81,** 498 (1951).
30. H. Ekstein. *Phys. Rev.* **76,** 1328 (1949).
31. M. Hamermesh. *Phys. Rev.* **75,** 1766 (1949).

Chapter VII

CALIBRATIONS AND STANDARDS

Some of the measurements involving neutrons, such as determination of strengths of neutron sources, of flux, and of cross sections, are ultimately referred to absolute standard values. In consequence, most of the measurements are simply, directly or indirectly, comparisons with standards. Because relative magnitudes can be measured more readily and accurately than absolute values, considerable effort is saved by use of standards as compared with that required for absolute measurements in every case. Moreover, in the preparation of standards, specimens can be selected for absolute measurement which lend themselves conveniently to this process. Some of the methods by which absolute measurements are made will be described in this chapter. These descriptions are intended to serve as an introduction to the principles of absolute measurements. They are not to be regarded as ideal models to be followed in every detail nor as a complete survey of the field.

17.1. Boric Acid Solution Method for Absolute Measurement of the Strength of a Source

The method to be described here is applicable to small compact neutron sources, of which Ra-Be(α,n) preparations containing from 1/2 to 1 g of radium might be considered examples. Such sources emit roughly from 0.5 to 1×10^7 neutrons per sec. No longer considered strong enough for most neutron studies, these sources are useful in the calibration of equipment where measurements are to be based on absolute intensities of neutrons. Standard sources also may be used to produce standards of neutron flux. The procedure for measurement is to place the source to be calibrated at the center of a tank containing a solution of boric acid of known concentration. The volume of the solution is made sufficient to slow down and capture all but a negligible fraction of the neutrons emitted by the source. The rate of emission of neutrons from the source is equal to the rate at which they are absorbed in the solution. If, in particular, the rate of absorption as a function of the distance from the source could be determined

291

with a detector composed of boron, the measurement would become very simple and direct. It would then be unnecessary to know the energies at which the neutrons were absorbed or the cross sections involved. Such an ideal experiment cannot be performed conveniently.

Walker (1) has described, in a laboratory report, detailed procedures for the use of a boric acid solution in absolute measurements of source strengths which approximate the ideal experiment. Because this particular experiment does not seem to be described in any journal, these details will be given here. The assumption underlying the procedure is that most of the neutrons from the source mounted at the center of the boric acid solution will be slowed down and absorbed at energies below the cadmium absorption cutoff. Then only a small correction will be required for neutrons absorbed at higher energies. The number of neutrons of thermal energies captured per cm^3 per sec at a distance r from the source can be computed as

$$nv(M_B\sigma_B + M_H\sigma_H) \tag{17.1}$$

where nv is the thermal flux at the distance r from the source, M_B and M_H are the moles per cm^3 of boron and hydrogen, respectively, in the solution, and σ_B and σ_H are the thermal capture cross sections per mole for boron and hydrogen. The number of neutrons captured at energies above the cadmium cutoff is taken care of by letting k stand for the fraction of those neutrons captured at low energies which the number captured above the cadmium cutoff represents. Hence if, in a given set of conditions, the number captured at thermal energies is n, the number captured above the cadmium cutoff is kn. Then the source strength Q can be written as

$$Q = 4\pi \int_0^\infty nv(M_B\sigma_B + M_H\sigma_H)(1 + k)\, r^2 dr \tag{17.2}$$

representing an integration of the absorption rate over the volume of the sphere surrounding the source. Rearranged, Eq. 17.2 becomes

$$Q = 4\pi\left(M_B + M_H \frac{\sigma_H}{\sigma_B}\right)\int_0^\infty nv\sigma_B(1 + k)r^2 dr \tag{17.3}$$

The quantity $nv\sigma_B$ under the integral is the rate of absorption of thermal neutrons per cm^3 per mole of boron at the distance r from the source. The value of $nv\sigma_B$ is determined by use of an unknown and unmeasured flux $(nv)_B$ produced inside a BF$_3$ counter by an auxiliary neutron source mounted in a moderating medium, independent and separated from the main equipment of the experiment. The procedure is first to place the counter, containing a measured quantity of BF$_3$, in the flux $(nv)_B$ to determine, from the counting rate, the number of disintegrations per second per mole of boron I_B in this flux. Then

$$I_B = (nv)_B\sigma_B \tag{17.4}$$

The ratio between nv and $(nv)_B$ must now be determined. This can be done by some foil detector, obeying the $1/v$ law, and thin enough to produce negligible changes in the neutron densities by its presence. If A_{th} is the saturated activity produced in the foil by slow neutrons at a distance r from the source in the boric acid solution and A_B is the corresponding saturated activity produced in the foil at the position of the BF_3 counter in the flux $(nv)_B$ then

$$\frac{nv}{(nv)_B} = \frac{A_{th}}{A_B} \tag{17.5}$$

from which, in combination with Eq. 17.4

$$nv\sigma_B = A_{th}\frac{I_B}{A_B} \tag{17.6}$$

We can introduce this value of $nv\sigma_B$ into Eq. 17.3 and obtain

$$Q = \left(M_B + M_H\frac{\sigma_H}{\sigma_B}\right)\frac{I_B}{A_B}\, 4\pi \int_0^\infty A_{th}(1+k)r^2 dr \tag{17.7}$$

The calibration requires a knowledge of M_B, M_H, and of the ratio σ_H/σ_B. Also the ratio I_B/A_B must be evaluated and A_{th}, the saturated activity of the foil detector induced by thermal neutrons, must be measured as a function of r. The selection of σ_H/σ_B as one of the constants of Eq. 17.7 is based on the relative ease with which the ratios of cross sections can be measured in comparison with the determination of absolute values. Furthermore the ratios can often be computed from data on relative values of cross sections appearing in the literature. Although formerly the values of cross sections were not known very accurately, tables now exist giving cross sections which are sufficiently accurate for most calibrations (see reference 8 of Chapter II). In setting up these equations descriptive of the calibration process, it is assumed that all cross sections, including the activation cross section of the detecting foil, follow the $1/v$ law at energies below the cadmium cutoff.

The major portion of the integral of the foil activity

$$4\pi \int_0^\infty A_{th}r^2 dr$$

was obtained by use of a mechanical integrator. The integrator consisted of a mechanical arrangement to move the foil from a position $r = r_1$ to a position $r = r_2$ in such a way that the activity acquired by the foil in this interval is proportional to the integral

$$4\pi \int_{r_1}^{r_2} A_{th}r^2 dr$$

The design of the integrator is based on the requirement that the motion of the foil must allow for the decay of its activity as well as take into account the geometrical integral. The requirement can be met by use of the following computation in the design. If $A_{th}(r)$ is the saturated activity of the foil produced by slow neutrons at the distance r, and A_i is the initial counting rate of the foil, corresponding to the time t_2 when the foil has reached r_2, we require that

$$A_i = K4\pi \int_{r_1}^{r_2} A_{th}(r)r^2dr \qquad (17.8)$$

To determine the value of the constant K, we note that

$$dA_i = 4\pi K A_{th}(r)r^2dr \qquad (17.9)$$

Also this increment of activity can be expressed as

$$dA_i = A_{th}(r)\lambda e^{-\lambda(t_2-t)}dt \qquad (17.10)$$

where λ is the decay constant of the activity induced in the foil. Eq. 17.10 merely computes the increment of activity produced by irradiation for a time dt at a distance r, in accordance with the theory of radioactive transformations. Equating the left-hand member of Eq. 17.9 to that of Eq. 17.10 gives

$$4\pi K r^2 dr = \lambda e^{-\lambda(t_2-t)}dt$$

which on integration becomes

$$\tfrac{4}{3}\pi K r^3 = e^{-\lambda(t_2-t)} + C \qquad (17.11)$$

Using the boundary conditions to evaluate the constant of integration C,

when $\qquad\qquad r = r_2, t = t_2 \qquad C = \tfrac{4}{3}\pi K r_2^3 - 1$

when $\qquad\qquad r = r_1, t = t_1 \qquad C = \tfrac{4}{3}\pi K r_1^3 - e^{-\lambda T}$

with $T = t_2 - t_1$, from which we obtain

$$K = \frac{3(1 - e^{-\lambda T})}{4\pi(r_2^3 - r_1^3)} \qquad (17.12)$$

Introducing the value $C = (4/3)\pi K r_1^3 - e^{-\lambda T}$ into Eq. 17.11

$$\tfrac{4}{3}\pi K(r^3 - r_1^3) = e^{-\lambda(t_2-t_1)} - e^{-\lambda T} = e^{-\lambda t_2}(e^{\lambda t} - e^{\lambda t_1})$$

from which

$$r^3 - r_1^3 = \frac{3}{4\pi}\frac{4\pi(r_2^3 - r_1^3)}{3(1 - e^{-\lambda T})} e^{-\lambda t_2}(e^{\lambda t} - e^{\lambda t_1})$$

or

$$r^3 = r_1^3 + r_1^3\frac{(r_2^3/r_1^3) - 1}{e^{\lambda t_2} - e^{\lambda t_1}}(e^{\lambda t} - e^{\lambda t_1})$$

Finally

$$r = r_1\left[1 + \left(\frac{r_2^3}{r_1^3} - 1\right)\frac{e^{\lambda(t-t_1)} - 1}{e^{\lambda T} - 1}\right]^{1/3} \qquad (17.13)$$

Eq. 17.13 defines the value of r at any time t in terms of measurable constants r_1, r_2, t_1, t_2, and λ.

The essential element of the integrator is a cam rotated at a uniform speed having a shape which will give the relation between r and t specified by Eq. 17.13. The value of λ will control the choice of $T = t_2 - t_1$. Normally T will be approximately twice the half-life of the foil activity. The value of r_1 will be determined by the closest convenient approach to the source and r_2 will be located at the distance where the neutron density be-

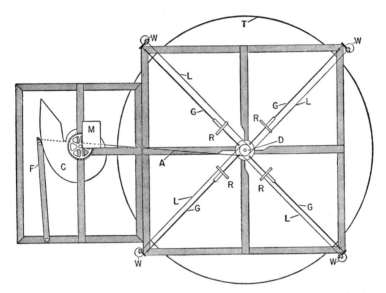

FIG. 17.1. *Diagram of top view of the mechanical integrator. A—cable for rotating the drum D. C—cam controlling movement of follower arm F. G—guide wires supporting riders R from which the activation foils are suspended. L—cables wrapped around the drum D and passing over pulleys to weights W hanging down the outside of the tank T. The cables L follow the motion of the drive cable A.*

comes a small fraction of the average neutron density in the capturing volume.

Fig. 17.1 is a diagram of the principal features of an integrator. It is a plan looking vertically down into the top of the tank T. The cam C is rotated at a uniform speed by the electric clock mechanism M to give a complete rotation in time T. The precise shape of the cam is outlined, starting with a rough blank approximately of the final form, by drawing radial lines from the center of rotation corresponding to equal intervals of time. At each radial position the follower at F is adjusted to place the riders R at the correct distance r from the center of rotation of the drum D. The best approximate point for the periphery of the finished cam is marked on the blank for this radial position. The process is repeated at other radial positions of the cam until a smooth curve can be drawn connecting the marked points. The cam is then machined to this curve. Finally the cam is tested in operation and deviations from Eq. 17.13 corrected by further machining of the periphery.

The source to be calibrated is suspended midway from the bottom of the tank, directly below the center of the drum D. Each rider slides on a guide wire G and is clamped to a cable L. Each cable is attached to the periphery of the drum and makes one or two turns around it before passing out over the pulleys at the corners of the frame. Weights attached to the free ends of the cables hang down the sides of the tank to hold the cables taut against the tension of the driving cable A, attached to the follower arm. As the follower arm moves back and forth, following the contour of the cam, the

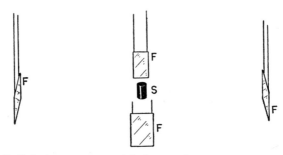

FIG. 17.2. *Relative positions of foils* F *undergoing activation and the source* S *mounted at the center of the tank.*

four riders simultaneously move in and out radially between the points r_1 and r_2. A detector foil is suspended from each rider by fine wire in the same horizontal plane with the center of the source, as indicated in Fig. 17.2. Four identical foils are used to reduce centering errors and to increase the activity available for measurement. Typical constants used by Walker for indium and manganese detectors in the calibration of a Ra-Be source are given in Table 17.1. As Table 17.1 reveals, it is possible to cover the range of mechanical integration in two steps by using a different cam for each portion. The integrator saves considerable time. Without its use, it would be necessary to expose foils at a number of radial distances from the source, and from the measured activities perform a numerical integration. Furthermore the mechanical integrator offers the possibility of more accurate measurements because many of the potential errors in measurements of lengths and activities are eliminated.

Because the integrator cannot cover the whole range from $r = 0$ to $r = \infty$, extrapolations must be made for the regions $r = 0$ to $r = r_1$ and

Table 17.1

CONSTANTS FOR THE MECHANICAL INTEGRATOR

Cam	Detector	Half-life (min)	r_1 (cm)	r_2 (cm)	T (min)	K
A	Indium	54	4.5	20	213	2.870×10^{-5}
B	Indium	54	5	20	120	2.381×10^{-5}
C	Indium	54	20	35	120	5.378×10^{-6}
D	Manganese	155	4.5	21	214	1.707×10^{-5}
E	Manganese	155	21	38	240	3.444×10^{-6}

$r = r_2$ to $r = \infty$. The contributions from these regions fortunately are small. The experimental curve of Fig. 17.3 shows the variation of the ratio

$$\int_0^\infty A_{th} r^2 dr \Big/ \int_0^r A_{th} r^2 dr$$

with r for a Ra-Be source. The curve indicates that 85 to 90 percent of the integral is included in the range $r = 4.5$ cm to $r = 35$ cm, covered by the mechanical integrator. For extrapolation in the region $r = 4.5$ cm to $r = 0$, advantage is taken of the fact that the neutron density here has a Gaussian distribution. Therefore we can write

$$A_{th} = A_0 e^{-r^2/r_0^2}$$

where A_0 is the activity at $r = 0$. Also we can represent A_0 by the relation $A_0 = c_1 A_{4.5}$, where $A_{4.5}$ is the activity measured at $r = 4.5$ cm. We can now express the contribution to the total volume integral from the region between $r = 0$ and $r = r_1$ as

$$4\pi \int_0^r A_{th} r^2 dr = 4\pi c_1 A_{4.5} \int_0^r e^{-r^2/r_0^2} r^2 dr$$

For a given value of r the above Gaussian integral is a constant $K(r)$ which can be evaluated from tables if r_0 is known. Hence we finally have

$$4\pi \int_0^r A_{th} r^2 dr = 4\pi c_1 K(r) A_{4.5} = C(r) A_{4.5} \tag{17.14}$$

The evaluation of $C(r)$ requires the determination of $c_1 = A_0/A_{4.5}$ and $K(r)$. This can be done experimentally if measured values of A_{th} in the interval are fitted to a Gaussian curve through the observed points. An example is shown in Fig. 17.4. Fortunately the value of $C(r)$ is not very sensitive to the form of distribution assumed for the neutron density, mainly because the contribution to the total integral in this region is small. For example, in a particular case the Gaussian distribution yields values $C(4.5 \text{ cm}) = 444$ and $C(5 \text{ cm}) = 581$. The corresponding figures for a

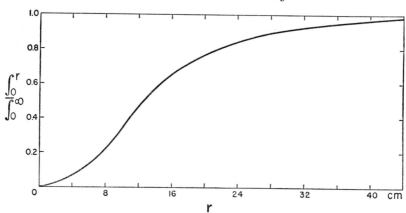

FIG. 17.3. *The ratio*

$$\frac{\int_0^r A_{th}\, r^2 dr}{\int_0^\infty A_{th}\, r^2 dr}$$

plotted as a function of r.

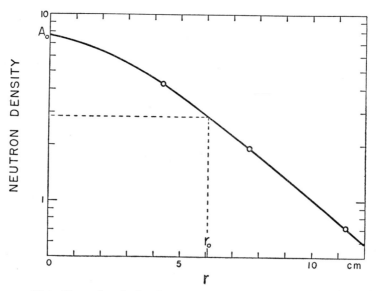

FIG. 17.4. *Example of the fitting of a Gaussian to three observed values of the neutron density near the source.* r_0 *is the value of* r *at which* $A = A_0/e$.

distribution assumed constant with r, that is, $A_{th}(r) = A_{4.5}$, are $C(4.5 \text{ cm})$ $= 382$ and $C(5 \text{ cm}) = 523$.

In the region $r = r_2$ to $r = \infty$ the distribution is, as we have seen in preceding chapters, exponential. Therefore it may be assumed that

$$A_{th}r^2 = ae^{-r/b} \qquad (17.15)$$

The constant a can be determined from the activity measured at a particular value of r, say $r = 35$ cm, so that

$$a = A_{35}(35)^2 e^{-35/b} \quad \text{or} \quad A_{th} = \frac{A_{35}(35)^2}{r^2} e^{-(r-35)/b} dr$$

and we have

$$4\pi \int_r^\infty A_{th}r^2 dr = 4\pi(35)^2 A_{35} \int_r^\infty e^{-(r-35)/b}$$

$$= A_{35}(1.539 \times 10^4)be^{-(r-35)/b} \qquad (17.16)$$

The value of b is obtained from special measurements of the activity in the region of $r = 35$ cm, using thick foil detectors to give sufficient activity for measurement. From Eq. 17.15

$$\ln(A_{th}r^2) = \ln(a) - r/b$$

Hence a semilog plot of Ar^2 versus r will have the slope $-1/b$. A graph of this relation for solutions with two different concentrations of boric acid, using manganese detectors, is shown in Fig. 17.5.

In determining the thermal activities, corresponding to A_{th}, the usual procedure of irradiating the detector foils with and without a cadmium sheath was followed. In the case of manganese detectors, the thermal activity was obtained by subtracting the activity obtained with the detector foil in the cadmium sheath from that obtained with the bare foil. In the case of indium this simple procedure was not adequate. The activity of the foil in the cadmium cover must be corrected for the indium resonance neutrons absorbed by cadmium. The correction is obtained in the usual way by measuring the activity of the indium foil in increasing thicknesses of cadmium. The data are plotted against the thickness of the cadmium and the graph is extrapolated to zero thickness of cadmium. The extrapolated value is the true resonance activity. In the case of indium it was found that $A_{res} = 1.038 \, A_{Cd}$ for the thickness of cadmium used in the calibration. The activities, as observed, must also be corrected for the depression of the neutron density produced by the presence of the foil. This correction, commonly called the drain correction, can be measured by determining the decrease in the activity of the foil when it is sandwiched between two similar foils as compared with the activity of a single isolated foil. The decrease represents the reduction in the neutron density produced by the outer foils

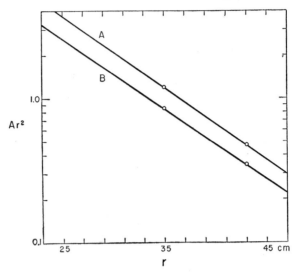

FIG. 17.5. *Determination of* b *in the equation*

$$A_{th} = \frac{a}{r^2} e^{-r/b}$$

by the use of thick foils at large values of r.

of the sandwich. The sandwich procedure is adequate only when the drain correction is small so that the introduction of the sandwich does not cause a considerable additional reduction of the neutron density in the vicinity of the sandwich. It is convenient to use the mechanical integrator to measure the drain correction over the region of the volume which can be covered by mechanical integration.

We now consider the quantity k appearing in Eq. 17.7. It is defined as a constant such that the rate of capture of fast neutrons at a distance r from the source is kn times the rate of capture of slow neutrons if n is proportional to the rate of capture of slow neutrons. The value of k may be determined experimentally, using a small ionization chamber lined with boron of the type shown in Fig. 17.6. Because k usually represents a small correction, about 3 percent, the depression of the neutron density near the ionization chamber when it is introduced into the capturing medium may be neglected. The absorbing element, boron, in the chamber is the same as that in the solution. Hence the number of neutrons captured above the cadmium cutoff can be determined by surrounding the chamber with cadmium during the measurement. We may write

$$\frac{C_{Cd}}{C_0} = \frac{k}{1+k} \tag{17.17}$$

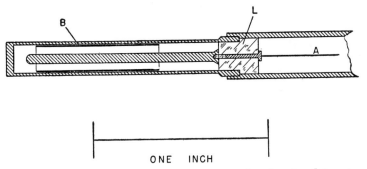

FIG. 17.6. *Small boron-lined pulse ionization chamber for determination of* k *by measurements with and without a cadmium shield.* B—*boron lining.* L—*insulator.* A—*connection to the amplifier.*

where C_{Cd} is the counting rate of the chamber surrounded by cadmium and C_0 is the counting rate with the bare chamber. The ratio represented by Eq. 17.17, when plotted as a function of r, yields a curve of the form shown in Fig. 17.7. The curve has a maximum near $r = 0$, where the ratio of fast to slow neutrons is largest. In the computation of the contribution of the capture of fast neutrons, an average value of k can be used, defined as

$$ k_{\text{av}} = \frac{\int_0^\infty k A_{\text{th}} r^2 dr}{\int_0^\infty A_{\text{th}} r^2 dr} $$

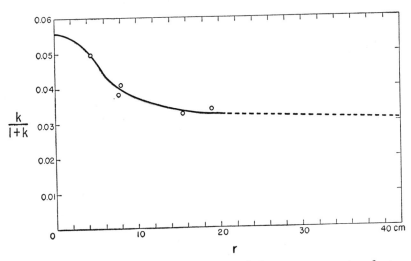

FIG. 17.7. *Curve showing the fraction of the neutrons captured at energies above the cadmium cutoff.*

The ratio of the integrals can be determined from the curve of Fig. 17.7 and that of Fig. 17.3. For Ra-Be source in a boron solution of 0.1883 mole per liter of H_3BO_3, Walker found k_{av} to be 0.0371. Hence the number of neutrons captured above the cadmium cutoff was 0.0371 times the number of thermal neutrons captured, or 0.0358 times the total emission Q from the source.

Finally we come to the most important factor in Eq. 17.7, namely the ratio I_B/A_B. We recall that I_B is the rate of disintegration per sec per mole of boron in a uniform reference flux. Similarly, A_B is the saturated activity of the detector foils used with the mechanical integrator when irradiated in the same reference flux. Therefore, the conversion of the observed foil activities to the rate of capture of neutrons in the solution is made by this ratio. I_B/A_B can be determined by irradiating a known quantity of BF_3 in a definite volume of a proportional counter tube and observing the counting rate. If the efficiency of the counting is practically 100 percent, the

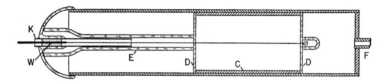

FIG. 17.8. *Demountable proportional counter for measurement of* I_B/A_B. *C—brass cylinder defining the counting volume, closed at ends by loosely fitting soft glass disks D. E—quartz insulator as a spacer to fix the position of the counting volume. K—kovar seal and guard ring. W—center wire.*

value of I_B can be computed from the counting rate and the moles of boron in the counting volume. The volume of the counter tube to contain the BF_3 is chosen with dimensions to accommodate the four detector foils used in the measurement of the thermal activity integral. The foils fit into this volume to form a cylindrical lining to just cover the inner surface of the barrel of the counter. The foils are then irradiated in the uniform reference flux in the same position as that at which I_B was determined. The activity of the foils is counted in the same arrangement as was used for counting their activity when irradiated in the boric acid solution. This measurement yields A_B, the saturated activity of the foils in the reference flux. A cross-sectional diagram of a demountable BF_3 proportional counter tube suitable for the measurement of I_B and A_B is shown in Fig. 17.8. The counting volume for determining I_B, when the tube is filled with BF_3 at a measured pressure, is the section between the two glass disks D,D, separated by the tube C. The glass disks D,D are made of a soft glass with a slight electrical conductivity to aid in making the counter nearly 100 percent efficient for the detection of disintegrations within the volume between the two disks. For measuring A_B, the detector foils just fit the inner surface of the tube C in the air-filled counter tube during irradiation in the reference flux. This flux may be produced by two neutron sources, each containing of the order of $\frac{1}{2}$ g of radium mixed with beryllium powder. The sources should be separated by a distance of 20 to 30 cm in a large block of paraffin. A well for the introduction of the counter tube is located midway between the sources.

Referring again to Eq. 17.7, we can now give a typical set of figures, from the measurements by Walker, for the factors entering into the computation of Q. These data are for a Ra-Be source in a boric acid solution of 0.1883 mole of boron per liter.

$$\left(M_B + M_H \frac{\sigma_H}{\sigma_B}\right)\left(\frac{I_B}{A_B}\right)\left(4\pi \int_0^\infty A_{th}(1 + k)r^2 dr\right) = Q$$

$(6.762 \times 10^{-5})\ (590.4)\ (14.56 \times 10^7) = 5.81 \times 10^6$ neutrons per sec

The data entering into the evaluation of the integral $4\pi \int_0^\infty A_{th}(1 + k)r^2 dr$ in the example above were obtained in the form given in Table 7.2.

Table 17.2

EVALUATION OF THE INTEGRAL OF FOIL ACTIVITY
WITH A MECHANICAL INTEGRATOR USING THIN
INDIUM FOIL DETECTORS

Foil Position (cm)	Activity Without Cadmium	Resonance Activity	Thermal Activity	$r_1 - r_2$ (cm)	$4\pi \int_{r_1}^{r_2} A_{th} r^2 dr$	
4.5	$30\,520 \pm 570$	8553 ± 170	$21\,967 \pm 600$	0–5	$C(5) = 581$	1.276×10^7
5–20	2941 ± 32	635 ± 14	2306 ± 35	5–20	$K = 2.381 \times 10^{-5}$	9.685×10^7
20–35	178 ± 7	39.8 ± 8	138 ± 8	20–35	$K = 5.378 \times 10^{-6}$	2.567×10^7
35			44.3 ± 1	35–	$b = 9.02$ cm	0.614×10^7
		Drain correction = 1.9 percent				0.269×10^7
		Captured at energies above thermal = 1.01 percent				0.145×10^7
		$4\pi \int_0^\infty A_{th}(1 + k)r^2 dr =$				14.56×10^7

17.2. Source Calibration by Physical Integration

The $r^2 dr$ integral of the preceding section is a method of adding up the total rate of neutron capture in the volume surrounding the source. The same result is achieved if the capturing element in the solution becomes activated with a half-life convenient for measurement of the activity. After irradiation to saturation, the solution can be stirred and the absolute disintegration rate per unit volume determined. This average disintegration rate, multiplied by the volume of the solution, is equal to Q, the total rate of emission of neutrons from the source used for the irradiation. The chief obstacle to the use of the method of physical integration is the small activation cross sections of elements suitable for use in the integrating solution. Because the method requires an absolute determination of the disintegration rate of the activated element, serving simultaneously as absorbing material and detector, thick samples cannot be used for measurement of the activity. Another requirement, of course, is that the absorber must follow the $1/v$ law.

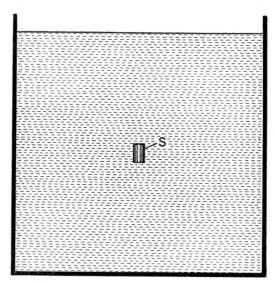

FIG. 17.9. *Tank of manganese sulfate containing source S for measurement of the source strength by physical integration.*

O'Neal and Scharff-Goldhaber (2) describe a modification of the method of physical integration, using a solution of manganese sulfate to absorb the neutrons. The experimental arrangement takes the simple form of the diagram in Fig 17.9. The tank containing the manganese sulfate solution has a volume sufficient to absorb practically all neutrons from the source S located at its center. The procedure for obtaining Q consists of two principal steps to obviate the difficulty of measuring directly the absolute specific disintegration rate of the irradiated manganese in the solution. In the first step, the solution is irradiated to saturation and stirred. The activity of the solution is measured by lowering a thin-walled Geiger-Müller counter into the tank to yield a counting rate R_1. The irradiation process is then repeated with a quantity of finely divided manganese powder suspended in the solution. This powder, called the absorber, is removed after the irradiation but before the activity of the solution is measured as before, to give the counting rate R_2. The ratio $R_2/R_1 = R$ is that fraction of Q absorbed in the solution in the second irradiation. The next step is to determine the rate of absorption of neutrons in the absorber. Here again the activity is too small to permit direct absolute measurement of the disintegration rate. Therefore a thick sample is exposed to a counter and a counting rate R_3 observed. The desired specific disintegration rate, D_1, of the sample can be expressed as

$$D_1 = C \frac{R_3}{w_1} \tag{17.18}$$

where w_1 is the weight of the sample and C is a conversion factor to give the absolute disintegration rate. To determine C, a quantity of manganese powder, similar to that used as the absorber, is irradiated in a reactor to a high specific activity. A weighed sample of this highly activated powder is measured for activity in the same counter geometry used to measure the activity of the thick sample of the absorber. The observed counting rate for this highly activated sample is represented by R_4. A thin sample of this highly activated powder is also used to determine its specific disintegration rate D_2—say, by counting in a 4π-counter. Then we have

$$D_2 w_2 = C R_4 \quad \text{or} \quad C = \frac{D_2 w_2}{R_4} \tag{17.19}$$

where w_2 is the weight of the thick sample of the highly activated powder. Introducing the value of C from Eq. 17.19 into Eq. 17.18 we can compute D_1, the specific disintegration rate of the absorber. Finally N_a, the rate of absorption of neutrons in the absorber, is given by $N_a = D_1 W$, where W is the total weight of the absorber in the solution during the second irradiation. The total rate of emission Q from the source is the sum of N_a plus RQ, the fraction of the neutrons absorbed in the solution in the second irradiation. Hence

$$Q = N_a + RQ = \frac{N_a}{1 - R} \tag{17.20}$$

Another modification of the method of source calibration by absorption of neutrons in a solution of manganese sulfate is described by De Juren and Chinn (3).

17.3. Use of a Reactor in Absolute Calibration of Neutron Sources

When a source of neutrons is introduced into a reactor running at a uniform power level, the net result is an increase in the effective multiplication factor of the reactor. This causes the power level of the reactor to rise exponentially, unless checked by a change in the position of the control rod. The required change of the control rod to bring the reactor back to the original power level is a measure of the additional neutrons supplied by the source. Under otherwise constant conditions, it would be possible, in principle at least, to calibrate the position of the control rod in terms of the intensity of sources of neutrons introduced into the reactor.

Littler (4) describes a different method for using a low-power graphite reactor in the absolute calibration of neutron sources. He uses the reactor as a device for relating the rate of capture of neutrons in an absorber introduced into the reactor to the number of neutrons emitted by the source by means of the change in the multiplication factor k of the reactor in the two cases. The rate of capture of neutrons in the absorber, which is activated by neutron capture, is obtained from absolute beta-counting of the induced activity. Therefore, in reality, the reactor is used to convert the problem of counting the number of neutrons emitted by the source to the problem of determining the number of beta particles emitted from the absorber after irradiation in the reactor.

The principle of the method can be explained in terms of the effect of the source and of the absorber on the multiplication constant k of the reactor. The constant k is defined as the number of thermal neutrons generated and remaining in the reactor for each thermal neutron absorbed in the reactor. When the source is introduced into the reactor, two opposing processes are set up. A certain number of thermal neutrons are absorbed in the materials of the source. On the other hand, fast neutrons are supplied to the reactor by the source. At a uniform power level, k is unity. When k becomes greater than unity the reactor becomes divergent, the power level increasing exponentially; and when k is less than unity the reactor becomes convergent, the power level decreasing exponentially. By use of diffusion theory, Littler establishes that the change in k, represented by δ, can be expressed as

$$\delta = A\left(\frac{\omega Q}{\rho_s} - B\right) \tag{17.21}$$

where A is a constant for a specific location in the reactor, B is another constant proportional to the neutron absorption cross section of the source, Q is the strength of the source in neutrons per sec, ρ_s is the thermal neutron density at the position of the source when the source is not present, and ω is a combination of reactor constants. In the measurements made by Littler, ω had a value of 0.875 for a Ra-Be source. However, ω does not depend very critically on the energy of the neutrons emitted by the source. The most important characteristic of the reactor in the evaluation of ω is the value of the resonance escape probability, that is, the probability that a neutron escapes resonance capture in U^{238} and eventually becomes a thermal neutron.

The power level of the reactor is measured by a neutron-sensitive ionization chamber so that the ion current is always proportional to ρ_s. Because the ion current is measured in terms of the voltage V across a resistor in the ion-current circuit

$$\rho_s = CV$$

where C is a constant and Eq. 17.21 becomes

$$\delta = A\left(\frac{\omega Q}{CV} - B\right)$$

Therefore if a source is used to determine the values of δ as a function of $1/V$ at a number of power levels, the graph will be a straight line with a slope m given by

$$m = \frac{A\omega Q}{C} \tag{17.22}$$

To establish the relation between δ and the number of neutrons absorbed in a calibrating absorber, on the other hand, first the absorber is introduced into the reactor at the same position which the source under calibration occupied in observing δ. Designating the value of δ produced by the absorber by δ^*, we have

$$\delta^* = -A\alpha \tag{17.23}$$

where α represents the absorption cross section of the element in the absorber. Hence the rate of neutron absorption is $\alpha\rho_s$. Next, the absorber is irradiated at a power level corresponding to V_0 where ρ has the value ρ_0, and N, the rate of neutron capture by the calibrating absorber, is determined by absolute beta counting. N can be represented by

$$N = \alpha\,\rho_0 = \alpha CV_0 \tag{17.24}$$

On combining Eq. 17.22, Eq. 17.23, and Eq. 17.24 we obtain

$$Q = \frac{Nm}{\omega|\delta^*|V_0} \tag{17.25}$$

Thus the value of the source strength has been obtained in terms of the rate of absorption of neutrons in a calibrating absorber which, in turn, is obtained from absolute measurements of the rate of beta-disintegration in the absorber. Both N and δ^* are constants of the reactor which need be measured only once. Successive calibrations of neutron sources then require only the determinations of the corresponding values of m.

Experimentally, the values of δ for a number of power levels of the reactor were measured with a pile oscillator. In this case the pile oscillator consisted of a mechanical device by which the source, mounted in a block of graphite, could be moved back and forth from a position outside the reactor to the center of the reactor. The source remained in the terminal positions for 20 sec and moved from one point to the other in 2 sec. The motion of the source produced a periodic modulation of the reactor which could be observed in the ion current of the neutron-sensitive ion chamber. An electrical circuit analyzed the current wave thus set up to yield a signal proportional to δ. The observations on δ for two experimental series are plotted in Fig. 17.10. As expected, the points fall on a straight line. The precision of the measurements is indicated by the extremely small deviation of any point from the straight line as drawn.

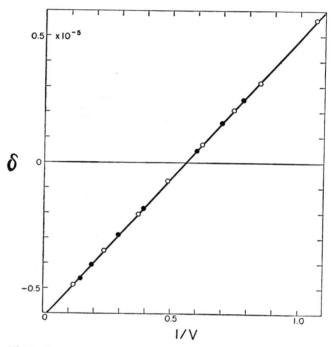

Fig, 17.10. *Experimental curve for δ, the change in the multiplication constant of the reactor, as a function of 1/V, where* $CV = \rho_s = the$ *thermal neutron density at the source position in the reactor.*

The calibrating absorber was placed in the oscillator and the value for δ* determined. The absorber was irradiated to saturation at the center of the reactor at a power level V_0. The disintegration rate of the irradiated absorber was measured to yield N, the rate of absorption of neutrons at the power level V_0. As has been mentioned, the ratio

$$\frac{N}{|\delta^*|V_0}$$

is a constant of the reactor and need only be determined once. The ratio was measured with absorbers of sodium and of phosphorus. These elements were selected because they are monoisotopic and the activation cross section is equal to the absorption cross section. Also the activities induced in them can be measured conveniently by absolute beta-counting. The values obtained are

$$\frac{N}{|\delta^*|V_0} \text{ (sodium)} = 7.51 \times 10^{10}(\pm 3\%)$$

$$\frac{N}{|\delta^*|V_0} \text{ (phosphorus)} = 7.24 \times 10^{10}(\pm 5\%)$$

and are the same within the experimental accuracy. The value of m from Fig. 17.10 is 10.84×10^{-5} volts. Combining this figure with the value of $\omega = 0.875$, we have

$$\frac{m}{\omega} = \frac{10.84 \times 10^{-5}}{0.875} = 12.39 \times 10^{-5}$$

Following Eq. 17.25 we thus have for the source strength $Q = (7.51 \times 10^{10})$ $(12.39 \times 10^{-5}) = 9.3 \times 10^{6}(\pm 4.5\%)$ neutrons per sec.

The main argument in favor of the above procedure for use of a reactor in the absolute calibration of neutrons sources is the saving in time. Once the reactor has been calibrated, any number of sources may be calibrated by determining the value of m for each. This measurement requires a few hours. A disadvantage of the reactor method of source calibration is that the precision is not quite as good as for volume integration methods. Furthermore the precision falls off rapidly as the rate of emission from the sources decreases below 10^7 neutrons per sec. This limitation arises from the fact that the precision for each individual value of δ in Fig. 17.10 is chiefly determined by statistical fluctuations in the reactor. As the strength of the source becomes comparable with these fluctuations, the values of δ also fluctuate widely. It is important to note that the absorbing elements must be of high purity and that corrections must be made for (n,p) and (n,α) reactions produced by fast neutrons. These corrections were not large for the sodium carbonate used as an absorber, even including the corrections for the absorption of neutrons in the carbon and oxygen, which have very small absorption cross sections. In the case of the red phosphorus, impurities were encountered for which larger corrections were made.

17.4. Calibration of Neutron Sources in Terms of the Production of Helium

A number of nuclear reactions in which neutrons are either absorbed or released have helium as one of the products of the reaction. This suggests that the measurement of the amount of helium produced in a measured time could be used to determine the number of neutrons from a source. For example, in photoneutrons sources containing beryllium, the neutrons result from the reaction

$$Be^9 + h\nu \rightarrow 2He^4 + n^1$$

and two helium atoms are produced for each neutron. The complete recovery of the helium from the beryllium metal is difficult without dissolving the beryllium and destroying the source. In any case this method of calibration is limited to photoneutron sources.

In another common nuclear reaction

$$B^{10} + n^1 \rightarrow He^4 + Li^7$$

a helium atom is produced for each neutron absorbed. However the volume of helium accumulated in a convenient time for sources emitting of the order of 10^7 neutrons per sec is of the order of 10^{-6} cm^3. To avoid the difficulty of measuring such small volumes, Seidl and Harris (5) have tested an indirect procedure. A composite solution containing manganese sulfate and boric acid was prepared. The proportions of manganese and boron were chosen so that the majority of the slow neutrons would be absorbed in the boron when the solution of large volume was irradiated by a source of neutrons at the center of the solution. The determination of the volume of helium produced was carried out in two steps. First the ratio of the gamma-ray activity of a portion of the irradiated solution to the production of helium in it was measured. To do this, a small amount of the solution was strongly irradiated in a reactor. About 4×10^{-4} cm^3 of helium was recovered from this irradiated solution and its volume was measured under standard conditions of temperature and pressure. Also the specific activity of this irradiated sample of the solution was measured. The next step was to irradiate the large volume of solution by the Ra-Be source to be calibrated. The specific gamma-ray activity of this large solution was measured in the same geometry used to measure the gamma rays from the small pile-irradiated sample. From the specific gamma-ray activity of the large solution and the ratio of gamma-ray activity to helium production in the pile-irradiated sample, the amount of helium produced in the large solution by the source under calibration could be computed. In the actual experiment, the specific gamma-ray activity of the pile-irradiated solution was adjusted to be equal to the specific activity of the source-irradiated solution by dilution with inactive solution. The diluted solution had the fractional composition m/M, where m is the weight of the pile-irradiated component and M is the total weight of the diluted solution. Then in consistent units

$$Q = \frac{V}{t} \frac{m}{M} \frac{1}{f} \frac{\Sigma_t}{\Sigma_B} \tag{17.26}$$

where V is the measured volume of helium, t is the time of irradiation both by the source and the reactor, f is the fraction of the neutrons from the source absorbed in the large solution, and Σ_t/Σ_B is the ratio of the total neutron capture to capture by boron. This ratio may be computed from macroscopic cross sections which, in turn, may be calculated from values of atomic cross sections to be found in published tables of cross sections.

17.5. Counting Beta-Gamma Coincidences in Source Calibrations

When thin foil detectors are used to obtain the data for the volume integral in the determination of Q, the activity of the foils is usually measured in a fixed geometry of unknown efficiency. The same fraction of the total radiation is included in each foil measurement. An auxiliary calibration is required to convert the data to an absolute rate of emission of neutrons from the source. This type of measurement is satisfactory in most cases as, for example, in the procedure described in § 17.1. Larsson (6) has described a method of using gold foil detectors in pure water for the volume integration of the neutrons emitted by the source. By using coincidence counting to determine the actual disintegration rates of the foils irradiated by the source to saturation, the integration becomes relatively simple and an auxiliary calibration is avoided. Neglecting the required corrections for resonance activation, capture above thermal energies, and the depression of the neutron density by the presence of the source, to simplify the explanation, the expression for Q may be written as

$$Q = 4\pi \frac{\sigma_H}{\sigma_{Au}} \frac{M_{Au}}{M_{H_2O/2}} \int_0^\infty C(r) r^2 dr \qquad (17.27)$$

Here $C(r) = n/m$, where n is the saturated disintegration rate of the gold detector at distance r from the source, and m is the mass of the detector in grams. Hence n is also equal to the absolute rate of capture of neutrons by the foil. The ratio

$$\frac{\sigma_H}{\sigma_{Au}} \frac{M_{Au}}{M_{H_2O/2}}$$

in Eq. 17.27 converts the measured rate of neutron capture in the gold to the rate of capture that would occur in the volume occupied by the foil if this volume were occupied by water. In this fraction, σ_H is the thermal neutron capture cross section of hydrogen, σ_{Au} is the corresponding cross section for gold, M_{Au} is the atomic weight of gold, and $M_{H_2O/2}$ is one-half the molecular weight of water. Hence the quantity obtained for Q in Eq. 17.27 is the integrated rate of capture of neutrons in the hydrogen of the water.

The value of n can most conveniently be determined by counting coincidences between beta and gamma rays emitted by the activated gold foil. The disintegration rate N_0 of the foil at the beginning of the coincidence measurements is given by

$$N_0 = \frac{N_\beta N_\gamma}{N_{\beta\gamma}} \frac{\lambda}{1 - e^{-\lambda T}} \qquad (17.28)$$

where N_β is the number of beta pulses, N_γ the number of gamma pulses, $N_{\beta\gamma}$ the corresponding number of coincidences, all observed in time T, and λ is the disintegration constant of the radioactive isotope in the activated foil. The value of N_0 after a period of irradiation t, at the end of this period, is also given by

$$N_0 = n(1 - e^{-\lambda T}) \qquad (17.29)$$

Combining Eq. 17.28 and Eq. 17.29, we have for n

$$n = \frac{N_\beta N_\gamma}{N_{\beta\gamma}} \frac{\lambda}{(1 - e^{-\lambda T})(1 - e^{-\lambda t})} \qquad (17.30)$$

Eq. 17.30 assumes a simple decay scheme for the radioactive isotope. In Au^{198}, the radioisotope involved in the present example, there is a branching in the beta decay. However, this branching is of the order of 1 percent and may be neglected in most measurements. There is also a correction for internal conversion of the gamma rays which is more important. By indirect methods it was ascertained that the correction for internal conversion could be made by dividing the experimental values of n by 1.04.

Larsson used scintillation counters to measure N_β, N_γ, and $N_{\beta\gamma}$. The greater sensitivity of scintillating crystals for gamma rays, compared with counters, partly compensated for the low activities induced in gold by neutron sources with rates of emission in the range of 10^6 to 10^7 neutrons per sec. The relative positions of the crystals and the gold foil in the counting process are sketched in Fig. 17.11. The thin stilbene crystal C_1 detected mainly beta rays from the foil F. The thick sodium iodide crystal C_2, covered with a metallic absorber to reduce beta-ray response, detected gamma rays from the foil. The efficiency of the stilbene crystal for the beta rays was estimated at 30-35 percent whereas its gamma-ray efficiency was about 1 percent. The gamma-ray efficiency of the sodium iodide crystal was about 8 percent. The pulses from the photomultiplier tubes were fed into a coincidence-detecting circuit for which Fig. 17.12 is a block diagram.

18.1. Absolute Determination of Neutron Flux

The measurement by De Juren and Rosenwasser (7) is an example of a procedure which successfully determines the absolute value of a thermal neutron flux. The geometrical arrangement for producing the uniform thermal flux is shown in Fig. 18.1. This flux was set up as a standard for absolute calibration of activation foils, small neutron detectors, and neutron dosimeters. A slot 2×4.5 inches penetrated to the center of the graphite moderator for the introduction of detectors. The sources which generated the flux each contained approximately 1 g of radium mixed with beryllium

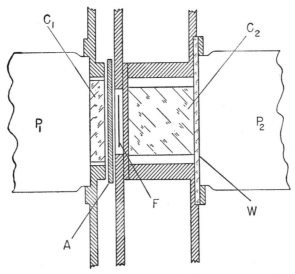

FIG. 17.11. *Scintillation counters for absolute counting of gold foil deuteron detectors by the coincidence method.* C_1—*thin stilbene crystal.* C_2—*thick sodium iodide crystal.* F—*gold foil.* W—*transparent window.* A—*absorber.* P_1, P_2—*photo multipliers.*

powder. The moderator consisted of paraffin, except in the region near the slot. Here graphite was used to reduce the depression in the neutron density by the detectors. This advantage of graphite, compared with paraffin, is the result of the larger value of λ_{tr} for graphite. The moderator of the di-

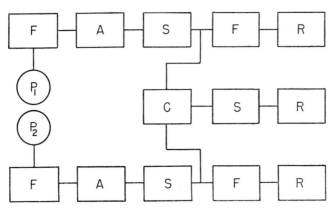

FIG. 17.12. *Block diagram of the electronic circuit used with the scintillation detectors of Fig. 17.11.* P_1, P_2—*photomultipliers.* F—*cathode followers.* A—*amplifiers.* S—*pulse shapers.* C—*coincidence circuit.* R—*scalers and registers.*

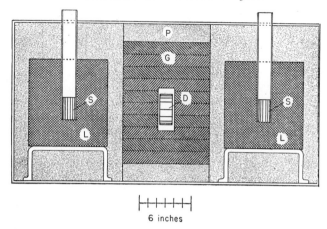

6 inches

FIG. 18.1. *Geometry of a uniform thermal neutron flux.* S_1S—*Ra-Be neutron sources.* g—*graphite.* L—*lead.* P—*paraffin.* D—*proportional counter.*

mensions shown does not produce a true Maxwellian distribution of velocities. In such a flux the rate of neutron capture dn/dt is given by

$$dn/dt = \sum_i n_i v_i \sigma_i N$$

where the subscripts refer to a particular velocity v_i. N is the number of capturing nuclei, σ_i is the capture cross section and n_i the number of neutrons with the velocity v_i. Because $\sigma_i v_i$ is a constant for a detector obeying the $1/v$ law, we may write

$$dn/dt = nNC = nN\sigma_0 v_0 \tag{18.1}$$

where, as in Table 9.1, σ_0 and v_0 refer to the most probable velocity in the Maxwell distribution. Moreover v_0 is the velocity for which thermal neutron cross sections are usually tabulated. The activation rate of a monoisotopic detector foil, obeying the $1/v$ law, thus gives the neutron density n, and nv_0 can be taken to represent a flux in which all neutrons have the most probable velocity. This hypothetical flux will be equivalent to the actual flux for the activation of foils which follow the $1/v$ law.

The neutron density in the air-gap of the flux standard was determined with a pulse ionization chamber. The chamber had the form of a short circular cylinder with an internal diameter of 2.625 in. and a depth of 1.125 in. A boron film was attached to the inside of the cover plate. Neutrons ejected alpha particles from the boron and these particles ionized the gas of the chamber. Electrons from this ionization were collected on an insulated, centrally located electrode. The boron films were deposited by evaporation in a vacuum of natural boron on quartz wafers coated with platinum or, in some instances, directly on platinum foils. Measurements were made to determine the cadmium difference counting rate as a function of the settings of a discriminator connected to the amplifier for the ion chamber. As we have seen from previous discussions, the cadmium difference counting rate results from the capture of neutrons with energies less than about 0.4 ev. Corrections for alpha particles multiply scattered into the sensitive volume of the chamber were avoided by choice of the discriminator setting. The level was selected between two-thirds and three-fourths of the maximum pulse-height of the 1.473-Mev alpha particles from the

$$n + B^{10} \rightarrow Li^{*7} + He$$

reaction. These particles are ejected in 93.5 percent of the neutron captures. The remainder of the alpha particles have an energy of 1.778 Mev.

The data obtained by the procedure just described requires correction for the alpha particles released in a disintegration which lose energy in the boron film to reduce their emergent energy below the discrimination level. In the region of alpha particle energies encountered here, it was assumed that the emergent energy E can be computed from

$$E = E_0 \frac{1 - x}{R \cos \theta} \tag{18.2}$$

where x is the perpendicular distance from the point of origin of the particle to the surface of the film, θ is the angle of the direction of the alpha particle with respect to this normal, R is the range of the particle in the material of the film, and E_0 is the initial energy of the particle. Corrections were calculated on the basis of Eq. 18.2 giving N_0, one-half the total number of disintegrations per second, in terms of the observed counting rate N from the boron films, as a function of t/R. Here t is the thickness of the boron film. Typical data are given in Table 18.1. To compute the neutron flux

Table 18.1

DATA FOR COMPUTATION OF STANDARD NEUTRON FLUX

Film	Boron content (moles)	t/R	N_0 (counts/sec)	$I_b = 2N_0$ per mole of boron (dis/sec/mole)
1	1.416×10^{-3}	0.050	12.57	1.775×10^6
2	1.012	0.0505	8.89	1.755
3	1.751	0.102	15.29	1.753

from the data of Table 18.1, we note that $I_b = nv_0\sigma_0 L_0$ in which $L_0 = 6.025 \times 10^{23}$ atoms per mole and σ_0, the capture cross section for boron at v_0, is 746 barns. Hence $nv_0 = 3918$ neutrons per cm² per sec.

18.2. A Readily Reproducible Standard of Neutron Density

Cohen and Barloutaud (8) have proposed a standard of thermal neutron density defined as the termal neutron density in which a disk of copper 15.00 mm in diameter and a thickness of 500 mg/cm² acquires at saturation an activity of Cu^{64}(12.8 hr) which will give one count per second in a 4-π counter. Actually the procedure represents a calibrated, reproducible method for the measurement of absolute neutron density. In the definition, the 4-π counter is merely a reproducible geometry for the measurement of the activity of the copper disk. No attempt at measuring absolute disintegration rates is to be made. The only corrections to the observed counting rate are those required by the decay of the activity of the Cu^{64}, the dead time of the counter, and for the slope of the plateau of the counter. It is assumed, of course, that the cadmium difference is taken in arriving at the density of the thermal neutrons. Also this standard relies on the fact that the activation cross section of copper is inversely proportional to the velocity of the neutrons in the thermal region. The authors estimate the thermal neutron density represented by this definition as (5.70 ± 0.19) × 10^{-3} neutrons per cm³.

In regard to the reproducibility of the standard, because the activity of the copper disk is proportional to its area, it is easy to calculate the correction for a disk not exactly 15.00 mm in diameter. Copper foil can readily be made with a thickness of 500 ± 10 mg/cm² which represents an error of less than 0.2 percent in the standard. This conclusion is based on the experimental fact that a change from 450 to 550 mg/cm² causes the activity of the disk to increase by less than 2 percent. Furthermore the copper need not be of greater purity than that of commercial electrolytic copper as long as the measurements of activity are restricted to that from Cu^{64}. During activation, the disk is suspended by fine threads which may even be passed through holes, about 0.3 mm in diameter, in the disk without introducing an error of more than 0.2 percent. The authors regard the standard as definitely reproducible to better than 1.5 percent.

Some remarks are in order regarding this standard of neutron density. It is important to note that the standard copper disk must conform within the specified limits to the description for strict validity. Because the activation cross section for Cu^{63} is only about 4 barns, there is no screening correction for the absorption of neutrons in the copper. Hence the disk is chosen to have a thickness, 0.5 g/cm², which gives a saturation thickness for the emergence of beta particles from Cu^{64}. Therefore, as indicated above, the exact thickness of the copper is not critical, in part because the maximum energy of the beta particles from Cu^{64} has the moderate value of about 0.6 Mev. However, because the disk is thick enough to have a rim which contributes significantly to the measured activity, it is necessary to control the diameter of the disk within narrow limits to the 15 mm specified in the definition. As the diameter of the disk changes, the ratio of the effect from the rim to that from the plane surfaces also changes. Hence the over-all effect is not linear with the area of the face of the disk. A difference of the order of 1 percent or more would be introduced by doubling the diameter of the disk.

It also should be noted that the beta counting in the 4-π counter is quite inefficient, of the order of 0.5 percent. This inefficiency results from the choice of a saturation thickness for the copper disk. However, the low efficiency does not impair the accuracy or reliability of a standard which complies with the specifications which have been outlined.

18.3. Absolute Measurements of Fast Neutron Flux

The difficulties in the absolute measurement of a fast neutron flux are more numerous and complicated than those encountered in the corresponding measurements of thermal fluxes. In spite of the importance of the standardization of fast neutron fluxes—for example, in the determination of neutron cross sections of nuclear processes induced by fast neutrons—no entirely satisfactory method has been developed for the absolute measurement of fast neutron flux. Allen, Livesey, and Wilkinson (9) have made experimental comparisons of some of the methods which have been used in the absolute measurement of fast flux and examined the validity of the assumptions underlying them. In order to make the intercomparisons under conditions as nearly identical as practicable, the monoenergetic neutrons used in the study were produced by the disintegration of deuterium by deuterons in the reaction

$$H^2 + H^2 \rightarrow He^3 + n$$

The energy-release in this reaction is single-valued and known to have the value $Q = 3.23$ Mev. The distribution of neutron energy as a function of the laboratory angle θ between the direction of the deuteron beam and the direction of the emitted neutrons is shown in Fig. 18.2. The solid line represents values computed for a thin target and the dotted line corresponds to the mean energies of neutrons from a thick target. The intersection of the solid and dotted curve at $\theta = 120°$ indicates that the neutron energy is relatively independent of target thickness at this angle. Therefore the most precise measurements for the purpose of intercomparison of methods can be made at $\theta = 120°$. Comparisons were made of four practical methods for the absolute measurement of fast neutron flux.

(1) *The Homogeneous Ionization Chamber*. It has been pointed out by Gray (10) that one difficulty encountered in the absolute interpretation of

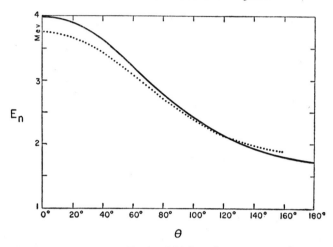

FIG. 18.2. *Neutron energy* E_n *for 930-kev deuterons on deuterons as a function of* θ, *the angle with respect to the accelerator beam in the laboratory system. The solid curve is for a thin target and the dotted curve is the mean energy for a thick target.*

the ionization current in a simple ionization chamber can be obviated. This difficulty concerns the fraction of the recoiling protons, produced by fast neutrons, which reach the walls of the chamber before the end of their range. The calculation of this fraction requires simplifying assumptions which may not always be valid. To eliminate the necessity for this computation, Gray suggested that the walls of the ionization chamber should have the same molecular composition as the gas used to fill it. Furthermore the chamber walls should have a thickness greater than the range of the recoiling protons. Then the ionization per unit volume in the filling gas of the chamber is the same as that which would be produced in a gaseous medium of infinite volume. The walls, in effect, have disappeared. The underlying assumption here is that W, the energy required to form an ion pair, is the same in the gas phase as in the solid state for the molecular compound involved. In a chamber lined with polyethylene and filled with ethylene gas, Gray has shown that the ionization current i is given by

$$i = \phi(E) \frac{eV}{W} (N_H \sigma_H \bar{E}_H + N_C \sigma_C \bar{E}_C) \qquad (18.3)$$

where $\phi(E)$ is a monoenergetic neutron flux of energy E, e is the electronic charge, V is the volume of the chamber, W the energy in electron volts required to form an ion pair in ethylene or polyethylene, N_H is the number of hydrogen nuclei per cm^3, N_C the number of carbon nuclei per cm^3, σ_H is the neutron-proton scattering cross section for neutrons of energy E, σ_C is the scattering cross section of carbon for neutrons of energy E, $\bar{E}_H$ is the

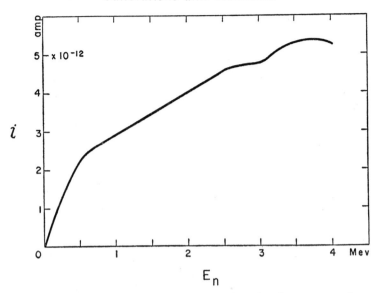

FIG. 18.3. *Ionization current* i *in a polyethylene-lined ionization chamber filled with ethylene at atmospheric pressure as a function of neutron energy* E_n *for θ flux of 10^4 neutrons per cm² per sec.*

mean energy of a hydrogen recoil, and $\bar{E}_C$ is the mean energy of a recoiling carbon nucleus. $\bar{E}_H$ can be calculated by assuming isotropic scattering of neutrons by protons. The term $N_C \sigma_C \bar{E}_C$ in Eq. 18.3, representing the contribution of carbon recoils to the ion current, is about 10 percent of the contribution from hydrogen recoils. Inaccuracy of information regarding $\bar{E}_C$, therefore, does not greatly impair the over-all accuracy. Eq. 18.3 can be generalized to the case of an energy spectrum if the spectral distribution of the neutrons is known. The values of i in units of 10^{-12} amperes obtained in a chamber with $V = 200$ cm³ and a neutron flux of 10^4 neutrons per cm² per sec are plotted in Fig. 18.3 as a function of E_n, the neutron energy. A practical difficulty with the homogeneous ionization chamber is its sensitivity to gamma rays. The effect of gamma rays can be compensated by measuring the difference in the ion currents in two otherwise identical chambers of which one uses ordinary hydrogen compounds and the other deuterated hydrogen compounds. The ion current produced by gamma rays would be the same in each chamber. The difference between the ion currents would be a measure of the neutron flux.

(2) *Triple-Coincidence Counter.* Kinsey, Cohen, and Dainty (11) have used a triple-coincidence counter telescope to detect proton recoils ejected by fast neutrons from an hydrogenous radiator. The counter tubes were mounted coaxially as sketched in Fig. 18.4. The principle of triple coinci-

dences was adopted to reduce background effects and to permit recording of only the recoil protons in a solid angle well-defined by the aperture in the guard ring of the third counter. The narrowness of the cone of protons thus selected makes the accuracy of the measurement depend strongly on the angular distribution of the scattered protons. The scattering is effectively isotropic in the center-of-mass sytem for neutrons with energies less than about 10 Mev. Hence impairment of accuracy resulting from the narrow cone of protons becomes serious at higher energies. Neutrons of all energies producing recoil protons energetic enough to penetrate the three counters may be measured in the triple-coincidence counter. The only dependence on neutron energy is that resulting from the variation of the neutron proton scattering cross section with energy in the region where the angular distribution of the protons is independent of the energy of the neutrons. The number of protons N_p per second ejected into a small solid angle Ω from a thin hydrogenous layer containing N_H hydrogen nuclei per cm³ irradiated by a neutron flux ϕ is

$$N_p = \phi N_H \sigma_H \frac{\Omega}{4\pi} V \qquad (18.4)$$

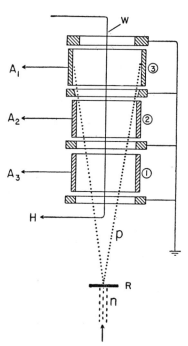

FIG. 18.4. *Triple coincidence recoil counter. n—neutron beam. P— proton recoils* A_1, A_2, A_3 *to separate amplifiers. H—to high voltage. W—center wire.*

where V is the volume of the radiator. For a flux $\phi = 10^4$ neutrons per cm² per sec of 2-Mev neutrons, with $\sigma_H = 3$ barns, and $\Omega = 4\pi/100$, the counting rate N_p is 1.5 per minute. This low counting rate is the chief disadvantage of the triple-counter method.

(3) *The Counting Pressure Chamber.* The problem of correcting for recoil protons which strike the wall of an ionization chamber before losing all of their energy can also, under special conditions, be avoided by increasing the gas pressure in the chamber. At higher pressures, the ranges of the protons are reduced to lengths small in comparison with the dimensions of the chamber. It is advantageous to use hydrogen in an ionization chamber when making absolute measurements. With hydrogen as the filling gas, which also serves as the source of recoil protons, the rate of generation of

protons N_p with energies greater than E in a chamber of volume V, containing N_H atoms of hydrogen per cm³, when irradiated with monoenergetic neutrons of energy E_n is given by

$$N_p = \phi N_H \sigma_H V \left(1 - \frac{E}{E_n}\right) \qquad (18.5)$$

where ϕ is the neutron flux. If $E_n = 2$ Mev, $E = 1$ Mev, $\phi = 10^4$ neutrons per cm² per sec, $V = 10$ cm³, $\sigma_H = 3$ barns and $N_H = 5.4 \times 10^{19}$, corresponding to 1 atmosphere of hydrogen, we obtain $N_p = 485$ counts per

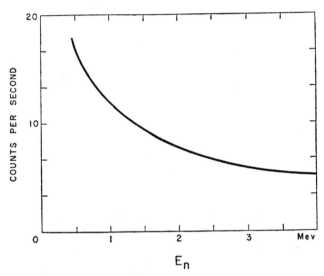

FIG. 18.5. *Counting rate as a function of neutron energy* E_n *in a pressure counting chamber at a flux of* 10^4 *neutrons per cm² per sec with* $E/E_n = 0.5$ *where* E *is the lower limit of the energy of the recoil protons. Volume of the chamber is 10 cm³ filled with hydrogen at atmospheric pressure.*

minute. The counting rate in a pressure chamber as a function of the neutron energy is plotted in Fig. 18.5, which shows the increase in efficiency at low neutron energies. The main drawback to the pressure chamber is that its use is limited to the measurement of neutrons of comparatively low energies. At higher energies, wall corrections must be calculated, and as the neutron energy increases, the magnitude of these corrections becomes too large to be reliable.

(4) *The Thick Radiator with an Ion Pulse Chamber.* A thick radiator for the purpose of this discussion is defined as a layer of hydrogenous material having a thickness at least equal to the range of the most energetic recoil protons released in it. The radiator must still be thin enough to produce

negligible attenuation of the neutron beam. The thick radiator will yield a high proton counting rate relative to the background. Another advantage is that the probability of detecting a neutron incident perpendicularly to the surface of the radiator increases with the energy of the neutron, the result of the rapid increase in the range of the recoil protons as the neutron energy increases. The probability of detecting 10-Mev neutrons is about nine times greater than that for detecting 1-Mev neutrons. The sensitivity of the detector thus increases almost linearly with the neutron energy. Because of the comparatively high sensitivity of the method, a simple pulse ionization chamber can be used to detect the protons.

Theoretically the probability $P(fE_n)$ of the release from the radiator of a proton with an energy gE_n greater than fE_n, where f has some value between zero and unity and gE_n is an energy between fE_n and E_n, by a neutron with an energy E_n in a thick radiator of area A and containing N_H hydrogen atoms per cm^3 is given by

$$P(fE_n) = AN_H\sigma_H \int_f^1 \frac{1-g}{2\sqrt{g}}\Big[R(gE_n) + 2gER'(gE_n) - R(fE_n)\Big] dg$$

(18.6)

where $R(fE_n)$ is the range in the radiator of a proton having energy fE_n and $R(gE_n)$ is the range for a proton of energy gE_n and $R'(gE_n)$ is $dR(gE_n)/d(gE_n)$. If it is assumed that

$$R(fE_n) = R(E_n)\, f^{3/2}$$

(18.7)

Eq. 18.6 can be simplified to read

$$P(fE_n) = \tfrac{1}{3} AN_H\sigma_H(E_n)R(E_n)(1 - f^{3/2})^2$$

(18.8)

With this approximation, the shape of the curve for $P(fE_n)$ versus f is independent of the neutron energy. The change in the shape of the curve introduced by the simplification is shown in Fig. 18.6. The dotted curve represents Eq. 18.8 and the solid curve was obtained by numerical integration of Eq. 18.6. The two curves are fairly close together, but the difference introduces an error of about 6 percent in the estimation of the neutron flux. The curves of Fig. 18.6 may be interpreted as bias curves. In a circuit containing an amplifier with discriminator for the ion pulses from the chamber, there is, for each value of f, a corresponding setting of the discriminator bias. An experimental test revealed that the solid curve of Fig. 18.6 agrees with the observations. Assuming, for convenience, that the range-energy relation for protons in the radiator follows approximately the relation in Eq. 18.7, then in a monoenergetic neutron flux ϕ of energy E_n the proton recoil counting rate N_p becomes

$$N_p = \tfrac{1}{3} \phi AN_H\sigma_H R_m(1 - f^{3/2})^2$$

(18.9)

where $R_m = R(E_n)$ is the maximum range in the radiator for the recoil protons.

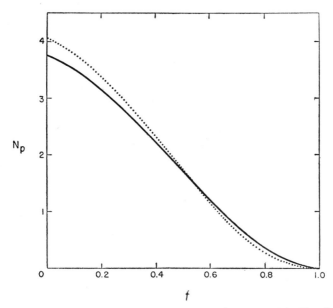

FIG. 18.6. N_p, *the proton counting rate as a function of* t. *The dotted curve represents Eq. 18.8 and the solid curve was obtained by numerical integration of Eq. 18.6.*

The ionization chamber for use with a thick radiator can be quite simple. The requirement that the size of the pulses appearing on the collecting electrode be proportional to the energy lost by individual protons in the chamber can also be readily fulfilled. By using a thin wire as collecting electrode, about 40 microns in diameter, and a pure gas with low electron affinity to insure that negative ions are predominantly electrons, a collection time for negative ions of the order of microseconds can be achieved. This short collection time not only simplifies the design of the amplifier but also provides quantitative collection of the negative ions. A pulse ionization chamber meeting the requirements is described by Allen and Wilkinson (12). Best results were obtained with the form of chamber shown in cross section in Fig. 18.7. The chamber consists of a cylindrical brass tube with its axis vertical. The diameter of 10 cm also equals the height. The collecting wire W is mounted horizontally midway up the chamber. The radiator R is mounted in the center on the inside of the removable base plate. An internal shutter, not shown, could be operated by tilting the chamber and permitted the proton beam to be cut off at will. The chamber contained argon at a pressure of 1 atmosphere. Fig. 18.8 gives the counting rate per cm² from a thick polyethylene radiator as a function of the neutron energy for $\phi = 10^4$.

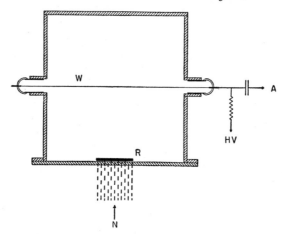

FIG. 18.7. *Thick radiator pulse chamber.* W—*center wire,* R—*radiator.* N—*neutron beam.* HV—*to high voltage.* A—*to amplifier.*

18.4. Comparative Measurements of Absolute Methods for Measuring Fast-Neutron Flux

The four methods of absolute measurement of fast neutron flux, described above, were compared experimentally by Allen and his co-workers (9).

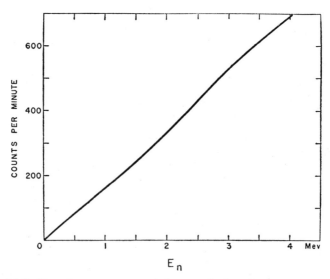

FIG. 18.8. *Counting rate per cm² from a thick polyethylene radiator as a function of the neutron energy for a flux of 10^4 neutrons per cm² per sec.*

The measurements were made by comparing the homogeneous ionization chamber with the triple counter and with the counting pressure chamber and then comparing the counting pressure chamber with the thick-radiator chamber. Magnetically resolved deuterons of 930-kev energy were used to bombard a deuterium target to produce monoenergetic neutrons. The neutrons were accepted at 120° to the direction of the beam of deuterons. In comparing the homogeneous chamber with the triple counter, a preliminary test of the homogeneous chamber was made. This test included

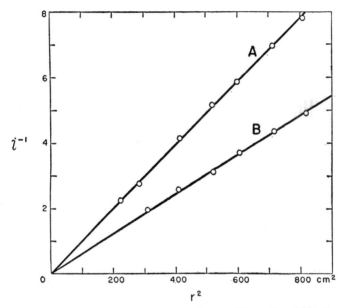

FIG. 18.9. *Inverse square graph at 45° (curve A) and at 150° (curve B) observed with homogeneous ionization chamber. r—distance of source of neutrons from the center of the chamber. i—ion current in the chamber.*

a determination of the angular distribution of the neutrons. The possible errors introduced by background effects were also investigated, by measuring the ionization current for different distances between the target of the accelerator and the chamber. Two typical inverse-square plots of these measurements are shown in Fig. 18.9.

Spurious effects arising from gamma rays and neutrons generated in parts of the accelerator other than the target and neutrons scattered into the chamber from the walls of the room would cause the observations plotted in Fig. 18.9 to deviate from the straight lines. The absence of any large deviations indicates that background effects were negligible. Furthermore, at the usual working distance of 20 cm, the background was always less than 1 percent of the ionization produced by neutrons from the target. When the homogeneous ionization chamber and the triple counter were set up on opposite sides of the target assembly at 120° to the deuteron beam it was found that the measurements in the triple counter were not consistent. The disagreement with the homogeneous chamber was as high as 20 percent, when different thicknesses of radiator were used for the triple counter. The discrepancy appeared to be the result of errors in the determination of the amount of hydrogen in the polyethylene radiators. However Kinsey, Cohen, and Dainty (11), using a different type of radiator, have obtained results with the triple counter that were consistent to within 10 percent. After taking all measurements into account it was decided that the flux under measurement, as measured by the triple counter, was 0.95 ± 0.07 of the value obtained with the homogeneous ionization chamber.

Because the counting pressure chamber at low bias is more sensitive to scattered neutrons than the other detectors under comparison, measurements were also made with it to detect background effects. The inverse-square law test revealed the counting rate to be accurately proportional to the inverse square of the distance from the accelerator target to the center of the chamber. Fig. 18.10 is a typical plot of the inverse-square observations made at a bias setting of 10 volts.

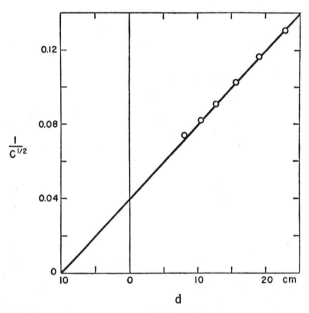

FIG. 18.10. *Inverse square test at 120° with counting pressure chamber at a bias setting of 10 volts. C—counting rate. d—distance from the target to the center of the chamber.*

In the comparison test with the homogeneous chamber, the counting chamber was set up on the opposite side of the target from the homogeneous chamber, each at 20 cm from the target. Several comparison measurements resulted in an evaluation of the counting chamber response as 0.95 of that obtained from the homogeneous chamber.

Fig. 18.11 is a plot for the counting rate for the pressure chamber versus the discriminator bias in volts. It was estimated that the error, excluding the uncertainty in the value for the neutron-proton scattering cross section, in the measurement of the flux by the homogeneous chamber was about

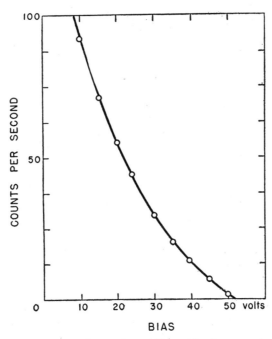

FIG. 18.11. *Bias curve obtained at 120° with the counting pressure chamber.*

4 percent. Lack of information regarding the energy required to form an ion pair in ethylene and regarding the average energy of carbon recoils contributed to this error for the homogeneous chamber. In the case of the pressure chamber, an error of 5 percent was anticipated in the flux measurement. Errors in measuring the hydrogen pressure, in interpreting the bias curve, and in the determining the volume of the chamber contributed to the error of measurement with the pressure chamber. Combining the various estimated errors gives the ratio of the flux as measured by the homogeneous chamber to the value measured by the pressure chamber as 0.95 ± 0.06,

In the final comparison, the counting pressure chamber was mounted opposite the thick-radiator chamber with the target midway between. No additional error was introduced by this indirect comparison of the thick-radiator chamber and the homogeneous ionization chamber. The experimental bias curves, of the type shown in Fig. 18.6, for the thick-radiator chamber were accurately reproducible, and the only error arose from their interpretation. From this last comparison it was decided that the flux as measured by the thick-radiator chamber was 1.01 ± 0.05 times the value obtained with the homogeneous chamber. The error was made up of the 4 percent uncertainty in the value from the homogeneous chamber plus a 3 percent error for the thick-radiator chamber. This 3 percent was the result of uncertainties in the range-energy relation for protons in polyethylene and in the interpretation of the bias curve. Table 18.2 is a summary of the comparison.

Table 18.2

COMPARISON OF FOUR METHODS FOR THE ABSOLUTE MEASUREMENT OF FAST NEUTRON FLUX

Method	Value for reference flux
Homogeneous ionization chamber	1
Triple counter	0.95 ± 0.07
Counting pressure chamber	0.95 ± 0.06
Thick-radiator chamber	1.01 ± 0.05

19.1. Comparisons of the Rate of Neutron Emission from Sources

The comparison of the strengths of neutron sources is a simple matter if the sources to be compared emit neutrons with the same distribution of energies. Any detector may then be used at the same distance from each source, and the ratios of the responses of the detector will be the ratios of the source strengths. Because most sources do not have a uniform distribution of neutrons in all directions about the source, it is often desirable to rotate the sources about an axis perpendicular to the direction to the detector to obtain an average reading. The comparison of sources which emit neutrons with different distributions of energy is complicated if an accuracy of better than ±10 percent is expected in the ratio. A few of the methods which have been used or proposed for the intercomparison of sources with different energy distributions are discussed below.

19.2. The Long Counter

This counter, described in §10.6 of Chapter IV, has an efficiency for the detection of neutrons which is independent of the neutron energy over a wide range of energies. The efficiency as a function of neutron energy is plotted in Fig. 10.7. For many purposes, therefore, the long counter can be used to compare sources of different energies with accuracies limited chiefly by errors inherent in counting techniques.

19.3. The Use of Moderators in Comparing Sources of Different Energies

Instead of using a detector with the same sensitivity for neutrons of all energies, the comparison of the sources may be made by first reducing the energies of the neutrons to a thermal distribution and using detectors for thermal neutrons to determine the density of thermal neutrons in the moderating medium. It is equally possible to use detectors of resonance neutrons to measure the slowing-down density as the moderated neutrons pass through the energy region corresponding to the resonance level of a detector. The moderation of the neutrons can be accomplished conveniently in a rectangular graphite column, 5 to 6 feet square on the base and 8 to 10 feet in height. For the measurements, one of the sources to be compared is placed on the centerline 2 or 3 feet from the base of the column, as indicated at S in Fig 19.1. Detecting foils are placed in slots F, also on the centerline of the column, at various distances above the source. A common method for using the graphite column is to measure A_{res} at a number of distances r from the source. A_{res} is the saturated activity of a foil having a large resonance activation cross section at some low neutron energy. Three elements suitable for the determination of A_{res} are indium, with a resonance at 1.458 $\pm$ 0.003 ev; gold, with a resonance at 4.906 $\pm$ 0.01 ev; and manganese, with a resonance at 3.37 $\pm$ 6 ev. The slowing-down density $q(r)$ at each distance r from the source is proportional to A_{res}. So we may write for two different sources, a and b, under comparison

$$\frac{q_{(a)}}{q_{(b)}} = \frac{A_{res(a)}}{A_{res(b)}} \tag{19.1}$$

The ratio of the source strengths can be written

$$\frac{Q_{(a)}}{Q_{(b)}} = \frac{\int_0^\infty q_{(a)} r^2 dr}{\int_0^\infty q_{(b)} r^2 dr} \tag{19.2}$$

The integral for each individual source can be obtained if the value of $A_{res}(r)$ is expressed as the sum of three Gaussian curves which fits the series of observations, as represented by

$$A_{res} = \sum_{i=1}^{i=3} A_i e^{-r^2/r_i^2} \tag{19.3}$$

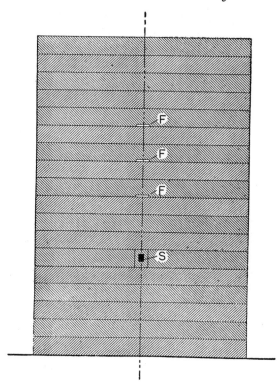

FIG. 19.1. *Cross section of a graphite column. F—foil slots. S—source to be calibrated.*

Three Gaussian curves are usually sufficient for this purpose. Each integral in Eq. 19.2 then takes the form

$$\sum_{i=1}^{i=3} A_i \int_0^\infty e^{-r^2/r_i^2} r^2 dr$$

which when integrated becomes

$$\sum_{i=1}^{i=3} A_i \frac{\sqrt{\pi}}{2} r_i \qquad (19.4)$$

Therefore Eq. 19.2 becomes

$$\frac{Q_{(a)}}{Q_{(b)}} = \frac{\sum\limits_{i=1(a)}^{i=3} A_i r_i}{\sum\limits_{i=1(b)}^{i=3} A_i r_i} \qquad (19.5)$$

Six or more measurements of A_{res} as a function of r are required to plot the experimental curve to which the three Gaussian curves, each with a different value of A_i and r_i, are to be fitted.

Walker (13) has suggested a procedure with the graphite column which permits the comparison of sources of different energies with a single measurement of an activated foil for each source. The method depends on the selection of a value of r for the activation in a region where the thermal flux is proportional to the strength of the source. For a point source of strength Q of monochromatic neutrons in a moderator, the slowing-down density q, as the neutrons just become thermal, is given approximately by

$$q(r) = \frac{Q}{(4\pi\tau)^{3/2}} e^{-r^2/4\tau} \qquad (19.6)$$

where τ is the age of the neutrons. For convenience we put $4\tau = r_0^2$ so that Eq. 19.6 becomes

$$q(r) = \frac{Q}{\pi^{3/2} r_0^3} e^{-r^2/r_0^2} \qquad (19.7)$$

In the Gaussian of Eq. 19.7, r_0 increases with the energy of the neutrons emitted by the source. The neutrons represented by $q(r)$ form a distributed source of thermal neutrons which then proceed to diffuse in the graphite. Introducing this source of thermal neutrons into the diffusion equation for a steady state we have

$$-D\nabla^2 n(r) + \frac{n(r)}{T} = q(r) \qquad (19.8)$$

where D is the diffusion coefficient, T is the mean life of thermal neutrons in graphite, and $n(r)$ is the neutron density at a distance r from the source. The boundary conditions require $n(r)$ to vanish at the effective edges of the column. Eq. 19.8, when solved with the value of $q(r)$ given in Eq. 19.7, yields the thermal neutron density throughout the graphite as a function of r_0. Walker has made such calculations for four different values of r, and his curves are reproduced in Fig. 19.2. The significant feature of the graph is that as r becomes greater, the range where nv/Q is approximately independent of the value of r_0 becomes longer. In this region, nv/Q is also correspondingly independent of the energy of the neutrons emitted by the source. Therefore a foil exposed to the thermal neutrons at a distance r where the curve of nv/Q versus r_0 is relatively flat should yield an approximately absolute calibration of the source in a single measurement. The reliability of the estimate of the source strength is indicated by the single observation for a Ra-Be(α,n) source at $r = 55.6$ cm. This observation should fall on the curve C, which is also for $r = 55.6$ cm. Actually the point is 10 to 15 percent below curve C. However, for the intercomparison of sources this discrepancy becomes less important and the accuracy of the determination of the ratio of two sources should be somewhat better.

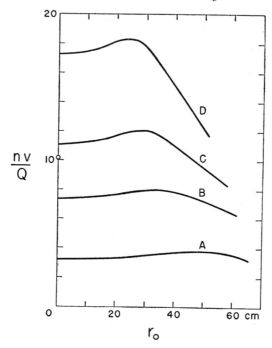

$\dfrac{n\,v}{Q}$

FIG. 19.2. *Flux of thermal neutrons as a function of the parameter* r_0
for different distances of the source from the detector in a graphite
column. These distances are, curve A—86.1 cm, curve B—65.7 cm,
curve C—55.6 cm, curve D—45.4 cm.

A manganese sulfate solution in a large tank can also be used in the comparison of sources of different energies. The procedure is simply to irradiate
the manganese to saturation activity successively with each source. At the
end of each irradiation the solution is stirred and the activities of either
identical aliquots of the solution, or of the whole solution with a dipping
counter, are measured. The ratio of the activities is the ratio of the source
strengths. The manganese method has the advantage over all other methods, described here for source comparisons, that the measurements are independent of the angular distribution of the neutrons around the source.

20.1. Calibrated Counter for Measurement of
Neutrons

Harding (14) describes a coincidence method for determining the absolute efficiency of a neutron counter for neutrons in a specific energy range.
The calibration of counters with standardized Po-Be(α,n) sources, for example, encounters difficulties because of the complexity of the neutron
spectrum from these sources and because of the inaccuracies inherent in

the standardization of neutron sources. However, if a coincidence circuit containing a gamma-ray detector and a neutron counter is adjusted to permit the neutron counter to respond only to those neutrons in coincidence with the well-known 4.43-Mev gamma rays from Po-Be sources, the counter can be calibrated without knowing the strength of the Po-Be source. The greater fraction of the neutrons from a Po-Be source are produced in the reaction $Be^9(\alpha,n)C^{12}$, according to the energy-level scheme of Fig. 20.1. A gamma-ray scintillation counter, with a bias which allows it to respond only to gamma rays of energy 4.43 Mev and higher, may be used in the coincidence circuit. Then only those neutrons which excite either the 7.59-Mev or the 4.43-Mev level will be recorded as coincidences. The

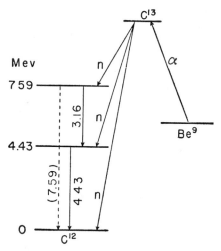

average efficiency of the neutron counter for the two neutron energies involved will be the ratio of the coincidence counting rate to the gamma-ray counting rate in the coincidence circuit. This value of the efficiency follows from the fact that the 4.43-Mev gamma ray is emitted only after neutron emission. The efficiency would be in error if the 7.59-Mev level were to lose its excitation energy by a single gamma ray, as indicated by the dotted arrow in Fig. 20.1. Experimental evidence exists, however, to show that this 7.59-Mev gamma ray, if emitted at all, has an intensity of less than 0.04 percent of the 4.43-Mev gamma ray.

FIG. 20.1. *Energy level scheme for the reaction* $Be^9(\alpha,n)C^{12}$.

If, on the other hand, the 7.59-Mev level were deexcited by internal pair formation, the electron pairs would not be recorded by the gamma-ray detector, nor as coincidences, and the calibration would not be impaired. The net result of the pair-formation possibility would be a slight reduction in the lower-energy component of the neutron spectrum.

Although no evidence is yet available regarding an angular correlation between the gamma rays and the neutrons, such an effect may exist. If discovered, angular correlation effects would need to be taken into account in the calibration. Care must be taken also to avoid the simultaneous detection of the 3.16-Mev and the 4.43-Mev gamma rays with an efficiency greater than that for the 4.43-Mev gamma ray alone. Because the 3.16-Mev gamma ray has only about 3 percent of the intensity of the 4.43-Mev gamma ray, the effect cannot be large. False coincidences, produced by neutrons scattered by the neutron detector back into the beryllium, where they may generate gamma rays detected by the gamma-ray counter, must also be eliminated.

21.1. Standard Sources

The absolute calibration of a neutron source is a tedious and complicated task even under the most favorable conditions. Therefore it has become the practice to standardize a few sources by absolute methods and to calibrate other sources used in actual measurements by comparison with a standard. The earlier neutron standards were all of the Ra-Be(α,n) type. This choice was influenced by the relatively high yield of neutrons and the long half-life of radium. Ra-Be standards have found many uses in spite of the hazards involved in their manufacture and their occasional leakage of radon, with disastrous effects on the laboratory in addition to the impairment of the standard. One puzzling aspect of neutron sources prepared by mixing a radium salt with beryllium powder has been an absence of reproducibility. Mixing the same amount of radium salt with the same amount of beryllium powder of the same fineness, under as identical conditions as practicable, does not produce sources of equal strengths. The variation may be as high as 15 percent. Compressing the mixture of radium and beryllium into pellets of the same density produces slight improvement. The opinion became prevalent that the lack of reproducibility of mixed radium and beryllium sources could be taken as an indication of the possible instability of the subsequent rate of neutron emission. Little evidence has come to light, however, to show that properly sealed mixed sources exhibit unaccountable fluctuations in neutron strength.

When, in 1947, the National Bureau of Standards undertook the preparation of a national standard neutron source, factors affecting the permanence of the source and the stability of the rate of emission of neutrons were taken into consideration. After consultation with a number of experienced users of neutron standards, a Ra-Be photoneutron source was constructed to be calibrated as a standard. The lower neutron yield, about 10^6 neutrons per gram of radium, and the lower neutron energy, both compared with Ra-Be(α,n) sources, were disadvantages that were accepted for the benefit of reproducibility and long-time reliability. The reproducibility was tested by making two photoneutron sources as nearly identical as possible. The sources consisted of solid beryllium spheres, 4 cm in diameter, with a central cavity into which a compressed pellet of radium salt, sealed in a metal capsule, fitted closely. Each capsule contained approximately one gram of radium. A cross section of one of the sources is shown in Fig. 21.1. Comparative measurements were made by Curtiss and Carson (15) of the neutron emission from the two sources, of the gamma-ray emission from the two radium capsules, and of the mass of the beryllium in the two

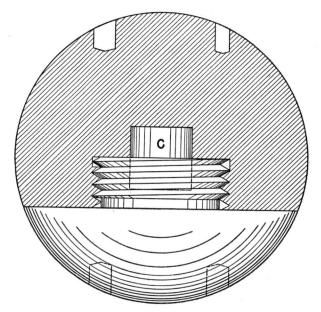

FIG. 21.1. *Photoneutron standard. C—capsule containing 1 g of radium in a compressed pellet of radium bromide at the center of a beryllium sphere 4 cm in diameter.*

spheres. These measurements revealed an equal rate of emission of neutrons from the sources after small corrections for differences in the radium content of the capsules and in the masses of the beryllium in the spheres.

The absolute rate of emission of neutrons from one of these sources, designated as NBS1, has been measured by determining the volume integral of the neutron absorption rate in water (1) and by measuring the rate of absorption of the neutrons in a manganese sulfate solution (3). The integral method yielded $Q = (1.26_5 \pm 0.03_8) \times 10^6$ neutrons per sec and the manganese solution method $Q = (1.25_0 \pm 0.02_5) \times 10^6$. The average of these values is $Q = (1.25_7 \pm 0.02_2) \times 10^6$. NBS1 has served as the fundamental reference standard for comparison of neutron sources at the National Bureau of Standards. The uncertainty in the measured rate of emission of neutrons from this standard, of the order of ± 2 percent, may be compared with uncertainties in the values of other national standards. A survey of the situation was made by Hughes (16) in 1954, just prior to the completion of the standardization of NBS1. The data collected by Hughes indicated a 30 percent disagreement among the various national standards. More significant in this connection, is the comparison of absolute measurements made at Los Alamos of the Los Alamos source No. 40, a Ra-Be(α,n) source, with a measurement made on the same source at the

National Bureau of Standards. The measurement at the Bureau consisted in comparing source No. 40 with NBS1 in a manganese sulfate solution. The divergence between the two values for the rate of emission of neutrons from source No. 40 was 1.1 percent.

Any neutron source containing radium is difficult to handle with safety for the operator because of the strong gamma radiation emitted by the radium. This handicap is absent in $PuBe_{13}(\alpha,n)$ neutron sources, as mentioned in § 7.4. Consequently plutonium-beryllium sources are more suitable for neutron standards. Additional advantages are that they do not evolve a radioactive gas like radon which can cause trouble, and they do not require massive lead shields for shipment. Therefore $PuBe_{13}$ standards could be more conveniently interchanged among laboratories for intercomparisons than Ra-Be sources.

SYMBOLS FOR CHAPTER VII

A	activity induced in nuclei by neutron capture
A_{th}	activity induced in nuclei by capture of thermal neutrons
E, E_n	neutron energy
$h\nu$	energy of a photon
k	multiplication constant of a reactor
L	neutron diffusion length
L_0	Loschmidt's number
N	rate of neutron capture
N	rate of emission of radiation
N	number of nuclei or atoms per cm^3
n	neutron density
nv	neutron flux
Q	source strength in neutrons per second
q	slowing-down density of neutrons
r	radial distance from a source
v	velocity of a neutron
α	an alpha particle
α	neutron absorption cross section
β	beta particle
γ	gamma radiation
Σ	macroscopic neutron cross section
Σ_t	total macroscopic neutron cross section
σ	atomic neutron cross section
τ	neutron "age"
ϕ	neutron flux $= nv$
Ω	a solid angle

PROBLEMS FOR CHAPTER VII

1. Compute the volume of helium at 20°C and 760 mm Hg pressure produced per hour by the absorption in B^{10} of 10^7 neutrons per sec.

2. A proportional counter tube having an active counting volume of 30.25 cm³ is filled with BF_3 to a pressure of 16.5 cm of Hg. If the efficiency is 98.5 percent and the counting rate in a steady neutron flux is 4565 counts per min, compute the number of disintegrations per sec per mole of boron.

3. The induced thermal activities of a manganese foil detector, in terms of the counting rates of the saturated foil, as a function of the distance r from the source in a large tank of boric acid solution are tabulated below. The solution contains 0.2 moles of H_3BO_3 per liter and the fraction of the thermal neutrons represented by the neutrons captured above the cadmium cutoff is 0.03. The ratio of the rate of capture of neutrons per sec per mole of boron to the counting rate of the foil in a given thermal flux is 1240. Compute the value of Q for the source.

r (cm)	A_{th} (counts per sec)
4	80,000
8	20,000
12	13,000
16	10,000
25	6,400
40	4,000

4. A source immersed in a tank containing a solution of manganese sulfate imparted a saturated disintegration rate to the manganese of 3.5 disintegrations per ml per sec, when the solution was stirred immediately after completion of the irradiation. Compute the number of neutrons emitted per sec by the source.

5. Compute the rate of generation of protons with energies greater than 1.5 Mev in a chamber filled with hydrogen at atmospheric pressure and having a volume of 8.5 cm³ when placed in a flux of 5×10^6 neutrons per cm² per sec having an energy of 3 Mev.

REFERENCES FOR CHAPTER VII

1. R. L. Walker. *Report MDDC 414.* J. A. De Juren, D. W. Padgett, and L. F. Curtiss. *NBS J. Res.* **55,** 63 (1955).
2. R. D. O'Neal and G. Scharff-Goldhaber. *Phys. Rev.* **69,** 368 (1946).
3. J. A. De Juren and J. Chin. *NBS J. Res.* **55,** 311 (1955).
4. D. J. Littler. *Proc. Phys. Soc.* **64A,** 638 (1951).
5. F. G. P. Seidl and S. P. Harris. *Rev. Sci. Inst.* **18,** 897 (1947).
6. K. E. Larsson. *Ark. Fys.* **7,** 323 (1954).
7. J. A. De Juren and H. Rosenwasser. *NBS J. Res.* **52,** 93 (1954).
8. R. Cohen and R. Barloutaud. *C. R.* **238,** 2413 (1954).
9. K. W. Allen, D. L. Livesey, and D. H. Wilkinson. *Proc. Camb. Phil. Soc.* **46,** 339 (1950).
10. L. H. Gray. *Proc. Camb. Phil. Soc.* **40,** 72 (1944).
11. B. B. Kinsey, S. G. Cohen, and J. Dainty. *Proc. Camb. Phil. Soc.* **44,** 96 (1948).
12. K. W. Allen and D. H. Wilkinson. *Proc. Camb. Phil. Soc.* **44,** 581 (1948).
13. R. L. Walker. *Phys. Rev.* **76,** 244 (1949).
14. G. N. Harding. *Proc. Phys. Soc.* **68A,** 52 (1955).
15. L. F. Curtiss and A. Carson. *Phys. Rev.* **76,** 1412 (1949).
16. D. J. Hughes. *Nucleonics* **12,** 26, Dec. (1954).

Chapter VIII

NEUTRON SHIELDING AND PROTECTING OF PERSONNEL

22.1. Health Physics

In experiments utilizing neutrons it is necessary to use neutron-absorbing shields to confine the neutrons to the regions required by the experiment. The shields are provided with channels in the limited directions in which neutron beams are desired. After the beam has traversed the apparatus it must be obliterated so that neutrons are not scattered back to disturb the effects under study or interfere with some nearby experiment. The experimental shielding is a direct problem of the investigator. The success of the experiment may depend to a great extent on the care and skill with which the experimental shield are designed. The investigator is usually in a position to test the efficiency of his shielding assembly as a part of the experimental operation.

In addition to shielding demanded by the experiment, the investigator requires protection from the effects of neutrons and other radiations at all sites where he may need to work. Wherever neutrons are generated in measurable intensities, there is also production of radioactive radiations. Therefore attention must be given to shielding personnel from beta and gamma rays as well. Because of its great penetration, gamma radiation creates the more important problem. The composite shielding for health protection in an operation involving neutrons consequently is designed to reduce neutron and gamma-ray intensities in working areas to acceptable values for safety.

As more powerful sources of neutrons, notably nuclear reactors, have been developed, the intensities of the accompanying radioactive radiations have increased. The required shields are also more ponderous and cumbersome. Fortunately the most important and heaviest shields are incorporated in the reactor or accelerator serving as a source of neutrons. They are part of the construction and need not concern us here. However, these devices must have exit ports which may be opened to permit the neutrons

338

to reach the apparatus. The shielding used to control the beam of radiation after emerging from the exit port will be partly experimental, and partly biological to protect the workers.

The biological shielding is commonly assembled under the watchful eye of a health physicist. It is his responsibility to see that the shield provides adequate protection. He also supervises all operations where dangerous amounts of radiations are present to insure that the work is performed without excessive exposure. This assumes, of course, that one or more health physicists are on the staff of the laboratory. This is now the case in all the larger nuclear laboratories of the country. It is unlikely that any installations of generators of strong neutron beams will be without health physicists in the future. Health physicists are trained in the techniques of the measurement of the different types of radiation in units which can be interpreted in terms of potential injuries to humans. They are also cognizant of tolerance regulations for radiation exposure. Therefore the health physicist can quickly ascertain whether radiation escaping through shields constitutes a health hazard in the light of current knowledge on the subject.

Although most experimenters in neutron physics will thus find themselves surrounded with safeguards against hazardous exposure to radiations, it is also desirable that the experimenter himself know something of the principles and methods of radiation protection. It is in this limited sense that the problems of protection from radiation will be discussed here.

22.2. Ionization as a Cause of Injury

Undesirable effects are produced in the human body whenever radiant energy is absorbed in excess of amounts to which the human organism has become accustomed in its natural surroundings. The damage inflicted from excessive amounts of radiation has been traced to the ionization produced in the living cells of the tissues. The injury has been found, for a specific type of radiation, to be proportional to the ionization produced, that is, to the amount of radiant energy absorbed, in the tissues. Therefore high-energy radiation, with low coefficient of absorption, produces comparatively less damage than low-energy radiation of the same type.

One of the consequences of the localization of the primary injury in the individual cells is the well-known latent period for the appearance of recognizable symptoms of the damage. Even in the case of very severe overexposures, the impairment of tissue functions does not become strongly evident until about ten days after the exposure. This time is required for the reactions within the tissue to the presence of dead cells to develop into obvious evidences of malfunction. For lesser exposures, requiring many repetitions to produce serious effects, the development of discomfort or disability is much slower. The importance of the situation to the experimenter is that his own sensations do not in any way warn him of the presence of harmful amounts of radiation. He is completely dependent on the indications of devices designed to measure his exposure to radiation for a knowledge of the hazards which he encounters.

Another important consequence of the cellular function in radiation injury is the ability of the tissues to recover from mild doses of radiation. If a very small fraction of the cells are affected, in most tissues restorative reactions are set up which lead to the repair of the damage. Some tissues of the body do not have this ability. For example, parts of the eye, the brain, and most muscular tissues are unable to replace damaged parts by new. However, for low levels of radiation on a biological scale the restoration of damaged cells is sufficiently effective to remove evidences of impairment of health. It is on this basis of the natural restorative powers of the body that the principle of radiation tolerance is largely based.

A third consequence of the role of the individual cells in exposures to radiation is the effect of ionizing density in the radiation on the amount of the damage. It is easy to see that the destruction of a number of adjoining cells can produce a more severe localized injury to the tissue than the destruction of the same number of cells at widely spaced sites. Thus the absorption of a given amount of radiant energy by a tissue depends on how the energy is absorbed, whether in concentrated amounts in small areas or more or less evenly distributed over the tissue. This aspect of the radiation problem has resulted in the establishment of a factor, called the relative biological effectiveness, for different types of radiation. The absorbed energy is multiplied by this factor, abbreviated "rbe," to estimate the ultimate potential injury. On this scale, alpha particles and protons have a higher rbe than electrons because the ionization density along the path of a heavy particle is much greater than that along the path of an electron.

22.3. Tolerances for Radiation

The principle of radiation tolerance, in the sense that the tolerance dose is that which the human body can accept without permanent injury, grew gradually out of the early experiences with penetrating ionizing radiation, as represented by x-rays and gamma rays. The determination of the tolerance dose was also a somewhat haphazard procedure based on gradually accumulating information regarding the relatively few individuals habitually exposed to x-rays and gamma rays. As records of exposure began to be kept methodically with a parallel history of the health of the workers, no impairment of health was evident over a period of about ten years for individuals who were exposed to doses of about 0.1 reontgen for each working day.

In the examination of the workers at that time great reliance was placed on the count of the blood cells. A short excessive exposure was known to produce a prompt leucopenia from which the subject recovered on absence of further exposure. This and related facts led to the choice of the relative counts of blood cells as an indicator for overexposure. However, it is now known that bodily damage can be produced by radiation without detectable change in the blood picture. Hence protective measures are based on careful measurements of radiation exposures.

Since 1943, following the development of the nuclear reactor, an extensive program of experiments with radiations on animals has been in progress. Much more has been learned about the mechanisms of injury and the amounts of radiation which can be dangerous. One result of this is that the maximum tolerance dose has been reduced to 0.3 roentgen per week. In this change both the tolerance level and the period for which exposure is measured are significant. As more information becomes available regarding bodily effects of radiation, further downward revisions may be expected in the tolerance dose. It is well to point out that recommended values are the maximum values for any individual within the specified time. It is expected that the average exposure over longer periods for each individual will be considerably less than the maximum.

22.4. Genetic Effects of Radiation

The preceding discussion of health hazards from radiation has been based entirely on estimates of possible injury and recovery of somatic tissue. When we turn to the effect of radiation on germ cells an entirely different picture is found. The reproductive cells show no recovery, during interruptions of exposure, from the effects of radiation. The injuries are cumulative throughout the genetic life of the individual. The end result of the injury, moreover, may not come to light until several generations following the exposed individual. The estimation of a tolerance level to prevent or reduce genetic injury is far more difficult than for bodily injury.

In genetic injuries, the damage is considered to be inflicted on the genes. These units within the chromosomes, on the view of some workers in the field, partake of the nature of giant chemical molecules. They are differentiated from ordinary molecules by an ability in general to faithfully reproduce their own structure in another molecule. The genes are believed to control the hereditary characteristics passed on from parent to offspring. When genes fail to duplicate themselves exactly, the situation is described as a mutation. The rate at which such events occur is the mutation rate. A small mutation rate exists in any population. However, the present genes have acquired their form over a long period of natural selection and are regarded as best adapted to our present environment. On this view any mutations can be regarded as deleterious. The well-known genetic studies with x-rays on fruit flies and other organisms have shown that radiation can greatly increase the mutation rate.

The problem of genetic injury from radiation thus resolves itself into the question of how great an increase in the mutation rate from radiation the population can endure. The fraction of the total population exposed to unusual amounts of radiation is an important factor in determining the answer. Qualified geneticists seem inclined to the view at present that, as far as workers in nuclear laboratories are concerned, they are genetically protected within the current maximum permissible dose. Evans (1) concludes from numerical calculations with available data that small fractions of the population can be exposed to radiation doses up to 0.1 roentgen per day with no detectable increase in hereditary abnormalities in succeeding generations.

22.5. Biological Units for Radiation

The physical units in which radiation is usually measured in terms of intensity and energy do not give directly the magnitude of bodily injury to be expected from it. The important factors in estimating injury are the amounts of energy absorbed in the body from the radiation and the manner in which this energy is absorbed. The site of the absorption may also be important.

In a search for a biological unit in which to measure radiation in units directly proportional to the injury, the roentgen was devised. The roentgen was originally defined for use with x-rays at a time when the highest energy of x-rays in common use was 200 kev. The definition of the roentgen is based on the absorption of energy from the radiation by air. Ionization chambers containing air thus can be conveniently used to measure radiation in roentgens. The original definition stated that a roentgen represented the amount of radiation which, on utilization of all secondary particles, produced ions of either sign in 0.001293 g of air equal to 1 electrostatic unit of charge. This turns out to be the absorption of about 83 ergs per gram of air.

The roentgen, as defined relative to air, does not immediately apply to tissues of the body. Absorption in tissues from the same intensity and energy of radiation varies greatly with the nature of the tissue. Hence for convenience in estimating tissue dosage, another unit, roentgen-equivalent-physical abbreviated "rep," has been introduced and defined as the amount of radiation which on the average delivers 93 ergs per gram of tissue in the body. For practical purposes, still an additional unit, the roentgen-equivalent-man, abbreviated "rem," has been defined as the amount of radiation which on absorption in human tissues produces the same biological effect as 1 roentgen.

This system of units based on tissue absorption has led to a complexity which introduces difficulties of interpretation in trying to avoid them. The intensity and the energy of the radiation are the two physical attributes which can be measured unambiguously. What is needed to complete a clear picture of biological effects is, for example, curves showing the amount of biological injury as a function of the intensity and the energy for different types of radiation.

For the guidance of the experimenter, the matter of permissible exposure can actually be handled much more simply. The variation of biological effects of radiation with energy is gradual enough that the tolerances can be expressed as intensities for a number of ranges of energy. Two or three ranges would cover most situations. The tolerance table would then become very simple and immediately intelligible to all physicists. The concept of the roentgen fails completely for radiation of energies above about 10 Mev. In this region of high energies the complete absorption of the secondary corpuscular radiation becomes impossible in any conceivable ionization chamber. Even if this were possible, the measurements made in such a chamber would have little relation to the biological effects of the radiation.

22.6. Injuries from Radioactive Materials Taken Internally

Most of the fatal results of exposure to radioactive radiation occurred in the radium dial painting industry during World War I. The deaths were caused by the ingestion of radium salts when the brushes used in applying radioactive luminous compound containing radium were pointed by use of the lips. Ingested radium gradually accumulates in the bone structure, where it is retained over long periods. The victims died, some of aplastic anemia and some of bone necrosis and osteosarcomas. Great care has been exercised since the occurrence of these tragedies to prevent inhalation or ingestion of radioactive substances.

The radioisotopes which naturally are deposited in the bone structure, such as isotopes of radium, barium, and strontium, are particularly dangerous. In general, alpha emitters have a higher specific poisoning effect because of the high ionization density which they produce. Although alpha particles have a short range, when they are emitted in tissues which produce the red blood cells, located in the bone marrow, severe cases of anemia result.

In laboratories where radioisotopes are produced, either for their own sake or as a by-product, stringent methods are used to prevent the radioactive contamination of work areas. When radioisotopes are released by accident prompt measures are taken to remove personnel from the area and to clean up the radioactive debris. In case of an accident, the investigator in charge should promptly inform the health physicist, who then has an opportunity to prevent many of the more serious consequences of the accident. In case of delay, the radioactive material may become spread over a considerable area, endangering many more individuals and increasing the cost of restoring the laboratory to a safe condition.

22.7. Instruments Used in Health Protection Measurements

The problem of protecting the worker from radioactive radiation is chiefly that of measuring the radiation exposure. Measurements must in general be continuous over the exposure period to take account of accumulating dosage. In general, two types of meters are needed. One type, a survey meter, is used to examine a work area in advance of occupancy to obtain an estimate of the probable exposure. Occupancy is permitted only

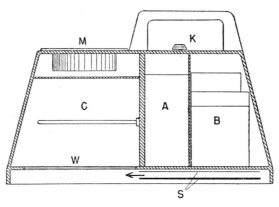

FIG. 22.1. *Portable survey meter for health protection measurements. M—indicating meter. C—collecting electrode of ion chamber. W—window for ion chamber. A—amplifier for ion current. B—batteries. K—control knobs. S—movable filters to screen out alpha and beta rays.*

when the radiation level is at or has been reduced to a satisfactorily low level. The other type is a continuously integrating device, carried at all times by the worker, which adds up the total dosage for the work period. Under certain conditions special instruments are needed as, for example, to survey regions suspected to be contaminated by radioactive materials and to aid in the removal of the contamination.

The most common form of survey meter is shown diagrammatically in Fig. 22.1. It is an ionization chamber with the ion current indicated on a conventional current meter through an electronic circuit. Operated by batteries, the survey meter is light in weight and completely portable. The indicating meter is usually calibrated to read in milliroentgens per hour. Frequently several ranges of sensitivity are provided from which selection can be made by a switch. The window of the ionization chamber is often closed by a film thin enough to permit alpha radiation to enter the chamber. Movable filters are then provided to screen out alpha particles alone and to screen out both alpha and beta particles. Survey meters are most useful where radiation levels change frequently, as when materials of unusual activity are to be handled from time to time. The indication of the meter permits an estimate of the limit of time, or the safe working distance from the active material, for personnel.

For the continuous monitoring of the exposure of each individual, two types of personnel meters are in common use. One is the pocket dosimeter, worn like a fountain pen. The dosimeter, shown in cross section in Fig. 22.2, is a miniature ionization chamber. The central insulated electrode is charged to a definite potential at the beginning of each day. The high quality of the insulation permits only negligible loss of potential in one day in the absence of radiation. When exposed to radiation, the ionization current between the central electrode and the case reduces the potential

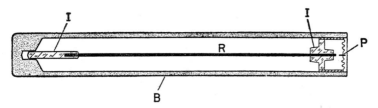

FIG. 22.2. *Pocket dosimeter. I—insulators. B—Bakelite case coated internally with graphite. R—graphite-coated collecting electrode. P—spring-mounted pin for charging R.*

of the central electrode with respect to the case. The relation between the residual voltage on the electrode and the amount of radiation in roentgens to produce this effect can be determined by calibration with known amounts of radiation. Pocket dosimeters are usually charged for use and read at the end of the day in a special electrometer circuit under the supervision of the health physicist. Under well-organized conditions, the dosimeter rarely records doses approaching the maximum permissible level. When such a reading appears, there is need for an immediate inquiry into the cause. A form of pocket dosimeter is also in use which has a miniature electrometer built into it. This device enables the investigator to read his own dosage at any time.

Supplementing the dosimeter and usually worn with it, is the photographic film badge, the other general type of continuous radiation monitor. Under controlled conditions, the amount of radiation exposure can be estimated from the degree of blackening of the developed film. The film badge, sketched in principle in Fig. 22.3, contains a sealed pocket of x-ray or similar film with various absorbers screening parts of the film. From the effect of the absorbers on the blackening, the energy of the gamma radiation may be estimated and the presence of beta radiation detected. When

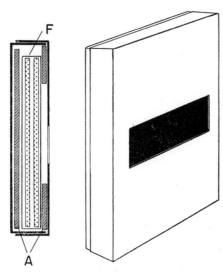

nuclear track emulsions are included in the film packet, the fast neutron exposure can also be estimated by counting the proton tracks with a microscope.

The levels of neutron intensity are most conveniently monitored with a BF_3 proportional counter. In the form of the long counter, where the BF_3 tube is covered with a layer of paraffin, the proportional counter can serve to measure fast neutrons. When used with and without a cadmium cover, the difference between the counting rates of the BF_3 counter indicates the slow-neutron intensity. Because in health-protection work high accuracy is not required, ± 15 percent usually being sufficient, proportional counters may be readily calibrated to measure neutron flux.

FIG. 22.3. *Diagram of a film badge.* *F—photographic film in light-tight inclosure. A—absorbers.*

Many other types of radiation-sensitive devices have been used in measurements to protect personnel from the effects of radiation, but the brief outline just given suffices to illustrate the principles involved. Obviously scintillation counters and Geiger counters have applications in this field, particularly in radioactive contamination surveys. Here qualitative indications are usually adequate and quite simple forms of equipment can be used.

23.1. Experimental Shielding for Neutrons

As was mentioned at the beginning of this chapter, the efficiency of the neutron shields often plays an important role in experiments with neutrons. A neutron shield for all energies of neutrons ordinarily combines the properties of a moderator for the fast neutrons and an absorber for slow neutrons.

The simplest shield is a tank of water thick enough (3 to 5 feet) to absorb practically all neutrons incident upon it. The required thicknesses of water are also effective shields for gamma radiation. More compact and convenient is the familiar layer of paraffin with a sheet of cadmium between the paraffin and the object to be shielded. The paraffin shield is usually molded to fit the equipment to be screened from neutrons. Cadmium, serving as a slow neutron absorber, is also a source of (n,γ) gamma rays and often demands additional lead shielding for the gamma rays. A gamma ray of 0.5 Mev also results from the reaction following neutron capture in boron. This gamma radiation is more readily absorbed in lead than the (n,γ) radiation from cadmium.

The most versatile shielding units are bricks, machined to a uniform size, which may be built into the form of shield required. They can often serve at the same time as stable supports for parts of the apparatus. Sintered boron carbide bricks are available commercially which have excellent shielding properties for slow neutrons.

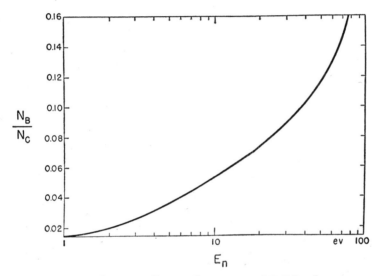

FIG. 23.1. *Curve showing relative effectiveness of* B_4C *bricks as a neutron sink by comparison of scattered counting rate with that of a carbon target of the same size.* N_B—*counting rate for the boron bricks.* N_C—*counting rate for graphite.* E_n—*neutron energy.*

Where cost must be considered, two substitutes for the commercial product have been suggested. Sheer and Tittman (2) describe compression-molded and baked boron carbide bricks which can be made in the laboratory. The 325-mesh B_4C is mixed with water until a plastic stage is reached. The moist material is put in a steel compression mold and subjected to pressures up to 8000 pounds per square inch. Finally the bricks are baked at temperatures ranging from 600° to 1000°C for periods up to 4 hours. Since a diamond wheel is required for cutting the baked bricks, it is more economical to mold the required shapes.

The effectiveness of these boron carbide bricks as a sink for slow neutrons is shown by the curve of Fig. 23.1. The arrangement in which the data for the curve were obtained is shown in Fig. 23.2. The curve shows the ratio of neutrons scattered from the boron carbide bricks to the number scattered from a block of graphite as a function of the neutron energy in electron volts.

The other substitute for commercial boron carbide bricks is described by Borst and Sailor (3). They prepared bricks with 300-mesh boron carbide to which a minimum of paraffin was added. The mixture was cast in brass boxes. After cooling and removal from the mold, the bricks could be machined accurately with carbide tools. These bricks held their original form indefinitely with moderate care in handling. The quality of the machined surfaces sufficed to permit the use of the bricks in collimation slits for slow neutrons.

It is also possible to use B_4C powder, either alone or mixed with paraffin, in metal-walled containers as blocks for neutron shielding. If mechanical strength is required, the walls of the container must be about one-half inch thick, and the blocks may be machined to accurate sizes. Canned shielding units of this type do not form a continuous shield but are satisfactory in a multi-tiered wall where joints may be staggered.

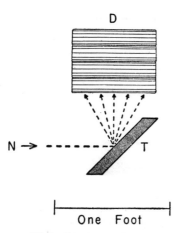

FIG. 23.2. *Diagram of arrangement in which data for curve of Fig. 23.1 were obtained. D— BF_3 counters. T—scattering target. N—neutron beam.*

In many experiments with neutron beams a simple absorber cannot be used to stop the beam after it has passed through the apparatus. Particularly with strong beams, the scattering of the neutrons from the absorbing material can make significant contributions to the neutron background and interfere with the measurements.

The usual device for obliterating a beam of neutrons with a minimum of scattering is the beam catcher. A typical example is shown in cross section in Fig. 23.3. The main neutron absorber is a mixture of paraffin and borax, covered externally with a layer of lead to reduce the gamma-ray intensity outside the catcher. Most neutrons scattered within the cavity of the catcher reenter the moderating and absorbing medium and are thus retained until absorbed. When beams of high intensity and energy are to be absorbed it is sometimes desirable to back up the beam catcher with a tank of water to capture stray neutrons and gamma rays which succeed in getting through the catcher. By lining the cavity of the beam catcher with a lithium compound, the intensity of the gamma rays escaping through

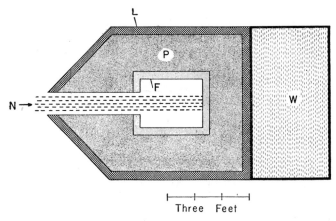

FIG. 23.3. *Cross section of a typical beam catcher. N—neutron beam. L—lead. P—borated paraffin. F—lining of lithium fluoride. W— water tank.*

the entrance to the cavity is reduced because no gamma rays are emitted following the capture of neutrons in lithium.

Most neutron experiments, fortunately, can be carried on in the presence of a considerable gamma-ray intensity. Foil detectors and BF$_3$ proportional counters are quite insensitive to gamma rays. Where experimental shielding from gamma rays is needed, the lead bricks now found in all nuclear laboratories make excellent temporary screens.

The gamma-ray intensity in neutron beams as they emerge from the reflector of a reactor is often reduced by the insertion of a thick bismuth plug in the beam channel, well within the shield of the reactor. The neutron absorption cross section of bismuth is very low, about 0.003 barn, but its coefficient of absorption for gamma rays is relatively high. Frequently the bismuth plug is permanently installed between the reflector and the thermal column of a reactor at the time the reactor is constructed.

We have mentioned water as a suitable material for screening off gamma rays. Absorption coefficients, as usually measured, are not suitable for the computation of the attenuation of gamma rays in thick layers of water by the direct application of the exponential law for absorption. Interactions of gamma rays in thick layers of matter do not always remove photon at each encounter with an atom. Scattering processes intervene to make the attenuation process more complex. Spencer and Fano (4) have developed a theory for the attenuation of gamma rays which takes into account the multiple scattering effects. The attenuation of 6-Mev gamma rays, as measured by Roys, Shure, and Taylor (5), is shown in Fig. 23.4. The circles represent the response of an anthracene detector at various

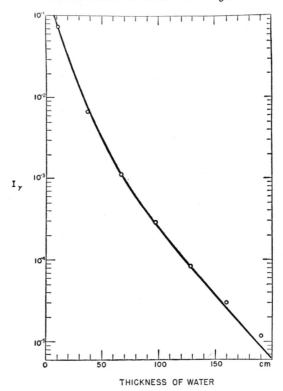

FIG. 23.4. *Relative gamma-ray intensity as a function of the thickness of the absorbing layer of water. The circles represent actual observations and the curve is that predicted by theory.*

distances in water from the source of gamma rays. The solid line represents the prediction of the theory of Spencer and Fano.

For other frequently used absorbers of gamma rays, iron and lead, Chappell (6) has designed nomographs giving the thicknesses of absorbers that produce various attenuations of gamma rays in the energy range from 0 to 3 Mev. These nomographs are also based on the theory of Spencer and Fano. Table 23.1 gives some approximate values of absorber thicknesses for 1-, 2-, and 3-Mev gamma rays and for attenuations in the range from 10^{-1} to 10^{-8}. These thicknesses were read from the nomographs by Chappell.

REFERENCES FOR CHAPTER VIII

1. R. D. Evans. *Science* **109**, 299 (1949).
2. C. Sheer and J. Tittman. *Rev. Sci. Inst.* **22**, 837 (1952).
3. L. B. Borst and V. L. Sailor. *Rev. Sci. Inst.* **24**, 141 (1953).

4. L. V. Spencer and U. Fano. *Phys. Rev.* **81,** 464 (1951).
5. P. A. Roys, K. Shure, and J. J. Taylor. *Phys. Rev.* **95,** 91 (1954).
6. D. G. Chappell. *Nucleonics* **15,** 52, Jan. (1957).

Table 23.1

ATTENUATIONS OF GAMMA RAYS FOR VARIOUS THICKNESSES
OF LEAD AND IRON ABSORBERS

Attenua-tion Factor	1-Mev Gamma Rays		2-Mev Gamma Rays		3-Mev Gamma Rays
	Lead (in.)	Iron (in.)	Lead (in.)	Iron (in.)	Lead (in.)
10^{-1}	1.4	3.5	2.3	4.3	2.6
10^{-2}	2.7	5.2	4.4	7.6	4.9
10^{-3}	4.0	7.9	6.3	11.2	7.0
10^{-4}	5.2	10.2	8.1	14.8	9.2
10^{-5}	6.4	13.0	9.9	18.2	11.2
10^{-6}	7.6	15.6	11.8		13.4
10^{-7}	8.8		13.7		15.6
10^{-8}	10.0		15.6		

Appendices

SOME FORMULAS OF NEUTRON PHYSICS

In Appendices I-VII, a few of the formulas offered in preceding pages without derivation will be derived to illustrate the methods used.

Appendix I—The Fermi Age Equation

The continuity equation for the slowing down density q of neutrons in a medium is

$$\text{div } j + \frac{\partial q}{\partial t} = 0 \tag{A.1}$$

where j is the neutron current. From the diffusion theory, $j = -D \text{ grad } q$ or $\text{div } j = -D\nabla^2 q$, where the diffusion coefficient $D = \lambda_{tr}v/3$, with λ_{tr} the transport mean free path and v the velocity of the neutrons. Eq. A.1 now becomes

$$\frac{\lambda_{tr}v}{3} \nabla^2 q = \frac{\partial q}{\partial t} \tag{A.2}$$

with the diffusion coefficient now dependent on the neutron velocity and therefore on the time. We now define a variable τ such that $d\tau/dt = D$, with $\tau = 0$ for $t = 0$, and multiply Eq. A.2 by $dt/d\tau$ to obtain

$$\nabla^2 q = \frac{\partial q}{\partial \tau} \tag{A.3}$$

Eq. A.3 is the usual form of the Fermi age equation for neutrons.

Appendix II—The Breit-Wigner One-Level Formula

Feshbach, Peaslee, and Weisskopf* have derived the Breit-Wigner one-level formulas for resonance scattering and absorption of neutrons by a method which avoids summations over levels distant from the resonance level. The cross sections are evaluated in terms of a function $f(E)$, defined as the derivative of the eigenfunction of the wave equation for the incoming neutron at the surface of the nucleus. The derivation proceeds from the consideration of an incident beam of slow neutrons. Outside the nucleus the neutrons have a wave number k. At the surface of the nucleus

---

* H. Feshbach, D. C. Peaselee, and V. F. Weisskopf, *Phys. Rev.* **71**, 145 (1947).

the exterior wave is joined continuously and smoothly by an interior wave of equal value and with the same derivative at the boundary as that of the exterior wave. A high kinetic energy is assumed for the neutron within the nucleus and a large wave number $K \gg k$. The problem then is to join, at the nuclear surface, a wave with wave number k to one with a wave number K. This can be done in general only if the amplitude A inside the nucleus is very much smaller than the amplitude outside, considered normalized to unity for convenience. Then A is of the order of k/K. In those exceptional cases, however, where the derivative of the inner wave function is near zero at the nuclear surface, the two waves can be joined at about equal amplitudes with A approximately unity. The particular narrow ranges of energies for which this unusual condition exists are the excitation energies of the compound nucleus at which the neutron can enter the nucleus. These energy ranges are the observed resonances, and the extent of each energy range is the resonance width Γ. Assuming that the phase of the inner wave function changes smoothly with the energy, the energy intervals in which the derivative of the eigenfunction is small enough to give rise to large A are proportional to the distance D, so that $\Gamma = \alpha D$ where α is a small number of the order of k/K. This assumption neglects absorption within the nucleus and applies only to neutrons.

For the case of neutrons with orbital angular momentum $l = 0$, the wave function ψ of the incident neutron outside the nucleus is a linear combination of an incoming and outgoing wave, as

$$\phi = r\psi = e^{-ikr} + \eta e^{ikr} \tag{A.4}$$

where η is a complex number giving the relative phase of the incoming and outgoing wave. With no absorption $|\eta|^2 = 1$ and with absorption $|\eta|^2 < 1$. The absorption cross section is given by

$$\sigma_a = \frac{\pi}{k^2}(1 - |\eta|^2) \tag{A.5}$$

as can be seen from the fact that π/k^2 is the maximum possible cross section when there is no outgoing wave e^{ikr}. The scattering cross section is

$$\sigma_s = \frac{\pi}{k^2}|1 + \eta|^2 \tag{A.6}$$

which follows from the case of a plane wave where the $l = 0$ part of the wave function has the form

$$r\psi = e^{-ikr} - e^{ikr} \tag{A.7}$$

Eq. A.7 differs from Eq. A.4 only by $(1 + \eta)e^{ikr}$ which, consequently, is the scattered wave.

The next step is to express the two cross sections in terms of the logarithmic derivative of ϕ at the nuclear radius a. For this purpose the function $f(E)$ is defined by

$$f(E) = a \left.\frac{d\phi/dr}{\phi}\right|_{r\,=\,a} \tag{A.8}$$

Then the relation between η and f is expressed by

$$\eta = e^{-2ix}\frac{x - if}{x + if} \tag{A.9}$$

with $x = ka$. The nuclear radius a may be defined for the present purpose as the smallest distance at which the incoming particle is still free of influence by nuclear forces. The cross sections now can be expressed as

$$\sigma_a = \frac{4\pi xh}{k^2}\left|\frac{1}{x + if}\right|^2 = \frac{4\pi}{k^2}\frac{xh}{(x + h)^2 + f_0{}^2} \tag{A.10}$$

$$\sigma_s = \frac{4\pi}{k^2}\left|\frac{x \cos x - f \sin x}{x + if}\right|^2 = \frac{4\pi}{k^2}\left|\frac{x}{i(x + h) - f_0} + e^{ix}\sin x\right|^2 \tag{A.11}$$

by putting Eq. A.9 into Eq. A.5 and Eq. A.6 and introducing $f = f_0 - ih$, where f_0 and h are real functions, with h always positive to insure that $|\eta|^2 \leq 1$. Eq. A.10 and Eq. A.11 show that resonances always occur at $f = 0$. The values of the energy at which $f_0(E) = 0$ are called resonance energies, E_r, of the nucleus. Near the resonances we can write

$$f_0(E) = (E - E_r)\left.\frac{df_0}{dE}\right|_{E\,=\,E_r} \tag{A.12}$$

and introduce the definitions

$$\Gamma_n{}^{(r)} = -\left.\frac{2x}{df_0/dE}\right|_{E\,=\,E_r} \tag{A.13}$$

$$\Gamma_a{}^{(r)} = -\left.\frac{2h}{df_0/dE}\right|_{E\,=\,E_r} \tag{A.14}$$

where $\Gamma_n{}^{(r)}$ is the neutron width corresponding to the reemission of the neutron with its original energy and $\Gamma_a{}^{(r)}$ is the absorption width containing the radiation width and also the width for any other process which does not lead to the elastic reemission of the incident particle, such as fission or inelastic scattering. The negative signs result from the fact the df_0/dE is negative. Then, for values of E near E_r, we have

$$\sigma_a = \frac{\pi}{k^2}\frac{\Gamma_n{}^{(r)}\Gamma_a{}^{(r)}}{(E - E_r) + \left(\dfrac{\Gamma_n{}^{(r)} + \Gamma_a{}^{(r)}}{2}\right)^2} \tag{A.15}$$

$$\sigma_s = \frac{4\pi}{k^2}\left|\frac{\frac{1}{2}\Gamma_n{}^{(r)}}{(i/2)(\Gamma_n{}^{(r)} + \Gamma_a{}^{(r)}) + E - E_r} + e^{ix}\sin x\right|^2 \tag{A.16}$$

Eq. A.15 and Eq. A.16 are in the form of the Breit-Wigner formulas although they contain contributions from only one level. They are valid as long as Eq. A.12 is a good approximation for $f_0(E)$. Eq. A.16 contains the characteristic potential scattering term which by itself gives

$$\sigma_s = \frac{4\pi}{k^2} \sin^2 ka \qquad (A.17)$$

which is the scattering cross section for an impenetrable sphere of radius a.

Appendix III—The Refractive Index for Neutrons

To derive the formula for the refractive index of neutrons we refer to Fig. A.1, representing a sheet of material of thickness t lying in the x,y plane and extending to infinity in both directions. We assume neutrons of

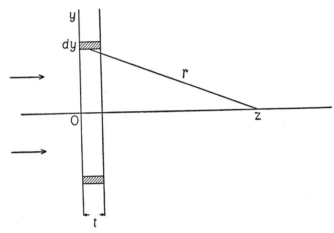

FIG. A.1. *Diagram for deriving the expression for the index of refraction of neutrons.*

wavelength λ_0 in a vacuum are incident in the direction of the arrows from the left. The thickness of the layer is much greater than λ_0 but thin enough to produce negligible attenuation of the neutrons. The layer is assumed to contain N nuclei, all of the same kind and with the same scattering amplitude a per cm³. If e^{ikz} represents the wave of the incident neutrons with the wave number $k = 2\pi/\lambda_0$, the wave number on entering the layer will be nk, with n the refractive index of the material in the layer. The transmitted wave will be

$$e^{i(nkt+k)(z-t)} \qquad (A.18)$$

Defining the waves in terms of the sum of the incident and scattered amplitudes we obtain

$$e^{ikz} - \int_0^\infty (a/r)e^{ikr}Nt2\pi y\,dy \qquad (A.19)$$

Putting Eq. A.18 equal to Eq. A.19 and replacing ydy by rdr, we have

$$e^{ikz}e^{ikt(n-1)} = e^{ikz} - 2\pi aNt \int_z^\infty e^{ikr}dr \qquad (A.20)$$

The integral, although indeterminate at $r = \infty$, following convention, can be assigned the value $(i/k)e^{ikz}$ giving for Eq. A.20

$$e^{ikt(n-1)} = 1 - i2\pi aNt/k \qquad (A.21)$$

Equating the imaginary parts of Eq. A.21 we have

$$\sin kt(n - 1) = -2\pi aNt/k \qquad (A.22)$$

When t is very small Eq. A.22 becomes $kt(n - 1) = -2\pi aNt/k$ from which

$$n = 1 - \frac{\lambda^2 Na}{2\pi} \qquad (A.23)$$

which is the usual form of the expression for the refractive index for neutrons.

Appendix IV—Radioactive Transformations in the Foil Activation Method

First we will deal with the formula for foils irradiated for times less than that required for saturation activation. When a target nuclide under irradiation in a constant neutron flux produces a radionuclide with a disintegration constant λ, the rate of production of radioactive atoms is the steady rate q from neutron capture minus the rate of radioactive decay, $-\lambda N$, where N is the number of radioactive atoms present at any time t. Therefore

$$\frac{dN}{dt} = q - \lambda N = -(\dot{N} - q/\lambda)\lambda dt \qquad (A.24)$$

We can now write

$$\frac{dN}{N - q/\lambda} = -\lambda dt \qquad (A.25)$$

Integrating we have

$$\log (N - q/\lambda) = -\lambda t + C \quad \text{or} \quad N - q/\lambda = Ce^{-\lambda t} \qquad (A.26)$$

When $t = 0$, $C = -q/\lambda$, which can be introduced into Eq. A.26 to give

$$N = (q/\lambda)(1 - e^{-\lambda t}) \qquad (A.27)$$

When $t = \infty$, $N = N_s$ the number of radioactive atoms at saturation. Also, $N = q/\lambda = N_s$. Therefore the number of radioactive atoms at any time t during irradiation is

$$N = N_s(1 - e^{-\lambda t}) \qquad (A.28)$$

Now to derive the formula for the saturated counting rate C_0 from the counts recorded in a selected time interval after removal of the target from the flux, we let t be the duration of the irradiation. Counting is started at a time t_1 subsequent to the removal from the flux and continues to time t_2. Let I represent the recorded counts in the interval $t_2 - t_1$. N_t is the number of radioactive atoms present in the target at the time of removal from the flux. The number present at time t_1, represented by N_{t_1} is $N_{t_1} = N_t e^{-t_1/\tau}$, where we have replaced λ by its equivalent $1/\tau$. The number of radioactive atoms present at time t_2, represented by N_{t_2}, is given by $N_{t_2} = N_t e^{-t_2/\tau}$. The number of radioactive atoms which have decayed in the counting interval is equal to I and is given

$$I = N_t(e^{-t_1/\tau} - e^{-t_2/\tau}) \tag{A.29}$$

From Eq. A.28 we see that $N_t = N_s(1 - e^{-t/\tau})$. Introducing this value for N_t into Eq. A.29 we have

$$I = N_s(1 - e^{-t/\tau})(e^{-t_1/\tau} - e^{-t_2/\tau}) \tag{A.30}$$

from which

$$N_s = \frac{I}{(1 - e^{-t/\tau})(e^{-t_1/\tau} - e^{-t_2/\tau})} \tag{A.31}$$

Now C_0, the saturated counting rate, is given by

$$C_0 = \lambda N_s = \frac{N_s}{\tau} = \frac{I}{\tau(1 - e^{-t/\tau})(e^{-t_1/\tau} - e^{-t_2/\tau})} \tag{A.32}$$

where τ is the mean life of the radioactive product.

Appendix V—Energy of Neutrons from a Photoneutron Source

The neutron energy from a (γ,n) reaction can be computed by applying the laws of conservation of energy and momentum to the collision of the photon with the target nucleus. Consider a gamma ray of energy E_γ incident on a target nucleus of mass number A. In the collision a neutron is released at an angle θ with respect to the direction of the incident gamma ray. The nucleus, now with mass number $A - 1$, recoils at an angle ϕ with respect to the direction of the gamma ray. Fig. A.2 is a diagram of the collision.

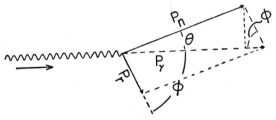

FIG. A.2. *Diagram of the collision of a photon with a target nucleus in a (γ,n) reaction.*

The momentum of the gamma ray P_γ is equal to E_γ/c, where c = velocity of light. If Q is the threshold energy for the reaction, the conservation of energy requires

$$E_\gamma - Q = E_n + E_r \tag{A.33}$$

where E_n is the kinetic energy of the neutron and E_r is the energy of the recoiling nucleus. We also note that

$$E_n = \frac{P_n{}^2}{2M_n} \tag{A.34}$$

where M_n is the mass of the neutron, and

$$E_r = \frac{P_r{}^2}{2(A-1)M_n} \tag{A.35}$$

Also from the geometry of Fig. A.2

$$P_n \sin \theta = P_r \sin \phi \tag{A.36}$$

The conservation of momentum is expressed by

$$\frac{E_\gamma}{c} = P_n \cos \theta + P_r \cos \phi \tag{A.37}$$

Squaring Eq. A.37, we obtain

$$\frac{E_\gamma{}^2}{c^2} - 2\frac{E_\gamma}{c} P_n \cos \theta + P_n{}^2 \cos^2 \theta = P_r{}^2 \sin^2 \phi \tag{A.38}$$

Squaring Eq. A.36 and adding the result to Eq. A.38 we have

$$\frac{E_\gamma{}^2}{c^2} - 2\frac{E_\gamma}{c} P_n \cos \theta + P_n{}^2 = P_r{}^2 \tag{A.39}$$

We now substitute this value of $P_r{}^2$ in Eq. A.35 and obtain

$$E_r = \frac{\dfrac{E_\gamma{}^2}{c^2} - 2\dfrac{E_\gamma}{c} P_n \cos \theta}{2(A-1)M_n} + \frac{P_n{}^2}{2(A-1)M_n} \tag{A.40}$$

Substituting this value of E_r in Eq. A.33 we have

$$E_\gamma - Q = E_n + \frac{E_n}{A-1} + \frac{E_\gamma{}^2}{c^2 2(A-1)M_n} - \frac{E_\gamma P_n \cos \theta}{(A-1)M_n c}$$

or

$$\frac{A}{A-1} E_n = E_\gamma - Q - \frac{E_\gamma{}^2}{(A-1)1862} + \frac{E_\gamma P_n \cos \theta}{(A-1)M_n c}$$

which can be written

$$E_n = \frac{A-1}{A}\left[E_\gamma - Q - \frac{E_\gamma{}^2}{(A-1)1862}\right] + \delta \tag{A.41}$$

where

$$\delta = \frac{E_\gamma P_n \cos \theta}{A M_n c} \tag{A.42}$$

To obtain an approximate value for δ, we note that

$$P_n = \sqrt{2M_n E_n} \tag{A.43}$$

We can make the approximation for E_n that

$$E_n \approx \frac{A-1}{A}(E_\gamma - Q)$$

Then Eq. A.43 becomes

$$P_n \approx \sqrt{2M_n \frac{A-1}{A}(E_\gamma - Q)}$$

Introducing this value for P_n in Eq. A.42, we have

$$\delta \approx \frac{E_\gamma}{AM_n c}\left[2M_n\frac{A-1}{A}(E_\gamma - Q)\right]^{1/2}\cos\theta$$
$$= E_\gamma \cos\theta\left[\frac{2(A-1)(E_\gamma - Q)}{(A^3)931}\right]^{1/2} \tag{A.44}$$

Appendix VI—The Bragg Law of Crystal Reflection

The relation between the angle θ of reflection of neutrons of wavelength λ from a crystal with a lattice spacing d can be deduced very simply from the geometry of Fig. A.3(a). In this figure, neutrons are represented as incident on a crystal at an angle θ to the crystal planes. We consider those collimated neutrons which strike the nuclei in the lattice of the crystal and are reflected with the angle of reflection equal to the angle of incidence. In the case of the two adjacent paths shown, one reflected in the surface layer of the crystal and the other in the next layer at a depth d in the crystal, we note that the difference in the lengths of the two paths is $2d\sin\theta$. This is more clearly shown in Fig. A.3(b) which is an enlargement of Fig. A.3(a) at the point of incidence. If the neutrons traversing these two paths are to be in phase and reinforce each other after reflection, the difference in the lengths of the two paths must be equal to an integral number of

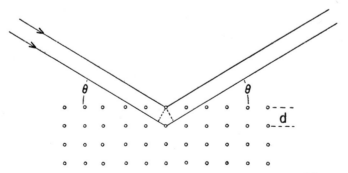

FIG. A.3(a). *Diagram of neutrons reflected from a crystal lattice.*

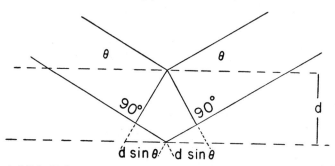

FIG. A.3(b). *Enlargement of the point of incidence of neutrons in Fig. A.3(a).*

wavelengths. At all other wavelengths destructive interference will obliterate observable effects of the neutrons. Therefore if n represents an integer, we have

$$n\lambda = 2d \sin \theta. \tag{A.45}$$

Appendix VII—Neutron Current Density

If there is a variation in the density of neutrons in a medium, we can expect a neutron current from regions of high density to regions of low density, described as a net flux of neutrons. When there is no gradient in the density of neutrons, the net flux in one direction is equal to the net flux in the opposite direction. The neutron current is then zero. To investigate the magnitude of the neutron current density, we will consider an element of area dS in the x,y-plane at the origin, as indicated in Fig. A.4. An element of volume dv is located as shown with respect to dS so that its spherical coordinates are r, θ, and ϕ. If nv is the neutron flux of a single velocity, the number of scattering collisions in dv is $(nv/\lambda_s)dv$, where λ_s is the mean free path for scattering. Assuming isotropic scattering in the laboratory system, we can say the probability that a neutron is scattered in dv in an appropriate direction to pass through dS is equal to the solid angle subtended by dS at a point in dv. This solid angle is $\cos \theta \, dS/4\pi r^2$. Since we are neglecting the absorption of neutrons, we can also say that the probability that a neutron originally scattered in the right direction will reach dS, without further scattering, is e^{-r/λ_s}. The number of neutrons scattered in dv which actually pass through dS per second will then be given by

$$\frac{nv}{\lambda_s} dv \frac{dS \cos \theta}{4\pi r^2} e^{-r/\lambda_s} \tag{A.46}$$

In spherical coordinates this number becomes

$$\frac{dS}{4\pi\lambda_s} nve^{-r/\lambda_s} \cos \theta \sin \theta \, dr \, d\phi \, d\theta \tag{A.47}$$

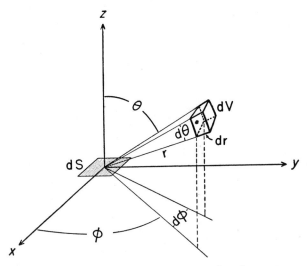

FIG. A.4. *Diagram for deriving the expression for the neutron current density.*

The total number of neutrons scattered into the area dS from above the x,y-plane will be obtained by integrating this number over the whole area above the x,y-plane. This triple integral will extend from $r = 0$ to $r = \infty$, from $\phi = 0$ to $\phi = 2\pi$, and from $\theta = 0$ to $\theta = \pi/2$. We define the neutron current density as the number of neutrons crossing a unit area of surface per second. The neutron current from above the x,y-plane is in the negative z-direction. We will designate it by J_-. We can now obtain $J_- dS$ by integrating Eq. A.47 as follows

$$J_- dS = \frac{dS}{4\pi\lambda_s} \int_0^\infty \int_0^{2\pi} \int_0^{\pi/2} nve^{-r/\lambda_s} \cos\theta \sin\theta \, d\theta \, d\phi \, dr \quad \text{(A.48)}$$

For the integration, it is convenient to express the neutron flux in rectangular coordinates by expansion in a MacLaurin's series. Limiting the expansion to terms of the second order, we have

$$nv(x,y,z) = nv_0 + x\left(\frac{\partial nv}{\partial x}\right)_0 + y\left(\frac{\partial nv}{\partial y}\right)_0 + z\left(\frac{\partial nv}{\partial z}\right)_0 + \frac{1}{2!}\left[x^2\left(\frac{\partial^2 nv}{\partial x^2}\right)_0\right.$$

$$\left. + y^2\left(\frac{\partial^2 nv}{\partial y^2}\right)_0 + z^2\left(\frac{\partial^2 nv}{\partial z^2}\right)_0 + 2xy\left(\frac{\partial^2 nv}{\partial x\partial y}\right)_0 + 2xz\left(\frac{\partial^2 nv}{\partial x\partial z}\right)_0 + 2yz\left(\frac{\partial^2 nv}{\partial y\partial z}\right)_0\right]$$

$$\text{(A.49)}$$

The subscript 0 refers to the requirement that the derivatives be evaluated at the origin. We can now return to spherical coordinates by the substitutions

$$x = r \sin \theta \cos \phi$$

$$y = r \sin \theta \sin \phi$$

$$z = r \cos \theta$$

Introducing the value of the flux from Eq. A.49 into Eq. A.48 and integrating, we obtain

$$J_- = \frac{nv_0}{4} - \frac{\lambda_s}{6}\left(\frac{\partial nv}{\partial z}\right)_0 + \frac{\lambda_s^2}{16}\left[\left(\frac{\partial^2 nv}{\partial x^2}\right)_0 + \left(\frac{\partial^2 nv}{\partial y^2}\right)_0 + 2\left(\frac{\partial^2 nv}{\partial z^2}\right)_0\right] \qquad \text{(A.50)}$$

We note that the terms in x, y, xy, xz, and yz do not contribute to the integral because the integral over ϕ of these terms is zero. Hence

$$J_- = \frac{nv_0}{4} - \frac{\lambda_s}{6}\left(\frac{\partial nv}{\partial z}\right)_0 \qquad \text{(A.51)}$$

Proceeding in a similar manner, we find for the current density in the positive z-direction

$$J_z = \frac{nv_0}{4} + \frac{\lambda_s}{6}\left(\frac{\partial nv}{\partial z}\right)_0 \qquad \text{(A.52)}$$

The net current density J_z will be the difference between Eq. A.51 and Eq. A.52, or

$$J_z = J_- - J_z = -\frac{\lambda_s}{3}\left(\frac{\partial nv}{\partial z}\right)_0 \qquad \text{(A.53)}$$

We can follow the same arguments to show that

$$J_x = -\frac{\lambda_s}{3}\left(\frac{\partial nv}{\partial x}\right)_0 \qquad \text{(A.54)}$$

and

$$J_y = -\frac{\lambda_s}{3}\left(\frac{\partial nv}{\partial y}\right)_0 \qquad \text{(A.55)}$$

We now consider the more general case where the element of area is not in one of the coordinate planes but is inclined at angles α, β, and γ with respect to the coordinate axes, respectively. The net current density through unit area will then be represented by the projection of the three components just calculated on the area. Therefore

$$J = -\frac{\lambda_s}{3}\left[\left(\frac{\partial nv}{\partial x}\right)_0 \cos \alpha + \left(\frac{\partial nv}{\partial y}\right)_0 \cos \beta + \left(\frac{\partial nv}{\partial z}\right)_0 \cos \gamma\right] \qquad \text{(A.56)}$$

Because the net flow of neutrons through the unit area depends on the orientation of the plane of the area, the neutron current density is a vector. It can be seen that Eq. A.56 is the scalar product of two vectors which may be represented by $\mathbf{N}$ and $\mathbf{J}$, where $\mathbf{N}$ is a unit vector given by

$$\mathbf{N} = \mathbf{i} \cos \alpha + \mathbf{j} \cos \beta + \mathbf{k} \cos \gamma \qquad \text{(A.57)}$$

with $\mathbf{J}$ now written as

$$\mathbf{J} = -\frac{\lambda_s}{3}\left[\left(\frac{\partial nv}{\partial x}\right)_0 \mathbf{i} + \left(\frac{\partial nv}{\partial y}\right)_0 \mathbf{k} + \left(\frac{\partial nv}{\partial z}\right)_0 \mathbf{k}\right] \qquad (A.58)$$

with $\mathbf{i}$, $\mathbf{j}$, and $\mathbf{k}$ the unit vectors along the x, y, and z axes. The result of the multiplication of vectors may now be written in the usual vector notation as

$$\mathbf{J} = -\frac{\lambda_s}{3}\operatorname{grad} nv = -\frac{\lambda_s}{3}\nabla nv \qquad (A.59)$$

where $\mathbf{J}$ is the net current density and ∇nv is the gradient of nv at the point where the neutron current density is measured.

Appendix VIII—Tables

Table A.1

COHERENT SCATTERING AMPLITUDES a_{coh}, COHERENT
SCATTERING CROSS SECTIONS σ_{coh}, AND BOUND SCATTERING
CROSS SECTIONS σ_s, FROM SHULL AND WOLLAN (2)

Z	Nuclide or Element	a_{coh} (10^{-12} cm)	σ_{coh} (barns)	σ_s (barns)
1	H^1	−0.40	2.0	80
	H^2	0.64	5.2	7.4
3	Li^6	0.7	∼6	
	Li^7	−0.25	0.8	∼2
4	Be^9	0.78	7.7	7.5
6	C^{12}	0.64	5.2	5.2
7	N^{14}	0.85	9.1	10
8	O^{16}	0.58	4.2	4.2
9	F^{19}	0.55	3.8	∼3.5
11	Na^{23}	0.35	1.5	3.5
12	Mg	0.44	2.4	4.2
13	Al^{27}	0.35	1.5	1.5
16	S	0.31	1.2	∼1.2
17	Cl	0.99	12.2	15
19	K	0.35	1.5	∼2
20	Ca^{40}	0.49	3.0	3.5
	Ca^{44}	0.18	0.4	
22	Ti	−0.38	1.8	∼6
23	V^{51}	<0.09	<0.1	5
24	Cr	0.37	1.7	3.8
25	Mn^{55}	−0.33	1.35	2.2
26	Fe^{54}	0.42	2.2	2.5
	Fe^{56}	1.00	12.6	13
	Fe^{57}	0.23	0.64	2
27	Co^{59}	0.28	1.0	∼5
28	Ni^{58}	1.47	27.0	27.0
	Ni^{60}	0.28	0.97	1

Table A.1 (continued)

Z	Nuclide or Element	a_{coh} (10^{-12} cm)	σ_{coh} (barns)	σ_s (barns)
	Ni^{62}	-0.85	9.1	9
29	Cu	0.76	7.3	7.8
30	Zn	0.59	4.3	4.2
32	Ge	0.84	8.8	8.5
33	As^{75}	0.63	5.0	~7
34	Se	0.89	10.0	~10
35	Br	0.67	5.7	6.0
37	Rb	0.55	3.8	5.5
38	Sr	0.57	4.1	9.5
40	Zr	0.62	4.9	~7
41	Cb^{93}	0.69	6.0	6.2
42	Mo	0.64	5.2	7.4
46	Pd	0.63	5.0	4.8
47	Ag^{107}	0.83	8.7	10
	Ag^{109}	0.43	2.3	6
50	Sn	0.61	4.6	4.9
51	Sb	0.54	3.7	4.2
53	I^{127}	0.52	3.4	3.8
55	Cs^{123}	0.49	3.0	~7
73	Ta^{181}	0.70	6.1	7.0
74	W	0.51	3.3	5.7
78	Pt	0.95	11.2	11.2
79	Au^{197}	0.77	7.5	~9
82	Pb	0.96	11.5	11.6
83	Bi^{209}	0.89	10.1	10
90	Th^{232}	1.01	12.8	12.8

Table A.2

TABLE OF ATOMIC MASSES FOR STABLE AND RADIOACTIVE NUCLIDES DERIVED ENTIRELY FROM NUCLEAR-REACTION DATA

Probable errors are given in 10^{-6} amu. The reference substandard used for many of the reactions is $Q = -1.6457 \pm 0.002$ Mev for $Li^7(p,n)Be^7$, corresponding to a threshold energy of 1.882 ± 0.002 Mev. By permission from *The Atomic Nucleus* by Robley D. Evans. Copyright, 1955, McGraw-Hill Book Company, Inc.

Mass number		Atomic mass	Mass number		Atomic mass
n	1	1.008 982 (± 3)	F	17	17.007 505 (± 5)
			F	18	18.006 651 (± 22)
H	1	1.008 142 (± 3)	F	19	19.004 456 (± 15)
H	2	2.014 735 (± 6)	F	20	20.006 350 (± 17)
H	3	3.016 997 (± 11)			
			Ne	19	19.007 952 (± 15)
He	3	3.016 977 (± 11)	Ne	20	19.998 777 (± 21)
He	4	4.003 873 (± 15)	Ne	21	21.000 504 (± 22)
He	6	6.020 833 (± 39)	Ne	22	21.998 358 (± 25)
			Ne	23	23.001 768 (± 26)
Li	6	6.017 021 (± 22)			
Li	7	7.018 223 (± 26)	Na	21	21.004 286 (± 39)
Li	8	8.025 018 (± 30)	Na	22	22.001 409 (± 25)
			Na	23	22.997 055 (± 25)
Be	7	7.019 150 (± 26)	Na	24	23.998 568 (± 26)
Be	8	8.007 850 (± 29)			
Be	9	9.015 043 (± 30)	Mg	23	23.001 453 (± 26)
Be	10	10.016 711 (± 28)	Mg	24	23.992 628 (± 26)
			Mg	25	24.993 745 (± 27)
B	9	9.016 190 (± 31)	Mg	26	25.990 802 (± 29)
B	10	10.016 114 (± 28)	Mg	27	26.992 876 (± 30)
B	11	11.012 789 (± 23)			
B	12	12.018 162 (± 22)	Al	27	26.990 071 (± 30)
			Al	28	27.990 760 (± 32)
C	11	11.014 916 (± 24)			
C	12	12.003 804 (± 17)	Si	28	27.985 767 (± 32)
C	13	13.007 473 (± 14)	Si	29	28.985 650 (± 34)
C	14	14.007 682 (± 11)	Si	30	29.983 237 (± 36)
			Si	31	30.985 140 (± 39)
N	13	13.009 858 (± 14)			
N	14	14.007 515 (± 11)	P	31	30.983 550 (± 39)
N	15	15.004 863 (± 12)	P	32	31.984 016 (± 41)
			P	33	32.982 166 (± 44)
O	15	15.007 768 (± 13)			
O	16	16.000 000 (std.)			
O	17	17.004 533 (± 7)	S	32	31.982 183 (± 42)
O	18	18.004 857 (± 23)	S	33	32.981 881 (± 44)

Table A.3

TABLE OF ATOMIC MASSES OF STABLE NUCLIDES DETERMINED BY MASS-SPECTROSCOPIC DOUBLETS

The substandards used are $H^1 = 1.008\ 146\ (\pm 0.3)$ and $C^{12} = 12.003\ 842$ (± 0.4). The probable errors are in 10^{-5} amu. By permission from *The Atomic Nucleus* by Robley D. Evans. Copyright, 1955, McGraw-Hill Book Company, Inc.

Mass number		Atomic mass	Mass number		Atomic mass
S	32	31.982 236 ($\pm$0.7)	Fe	57	56.953 59 ($\pm$10)
S	33	32.982 13 ($\pm$5)	Fe	58	57.952 0 ($\pm$40)
S	34	33.978 76 ($\pm$5)			
			Co	59	[58.951 3 ($\pm$30)]†
Cl	35	34.980 04 ($\pm$5)			
Cl	37	36.977 66 ($\pm$5)	Ni	58	57.953 45 ($\pm$10)
			Ni	60	59.949 01 ($\pm$29)
A	36	35.979 00 ($\pm$3)	Ni	61	60.949 07 ($\pm$23)
A	38	37.974 91 ($\pm$4)	Ni	62	61.946 81 ($\pm$9)
A	40	39.975 13 ($\pm$3)	Ni	64	63.947 55 ($\pm$7)
K	39	38.976 06 ($\pm$3)	Cu	63	62.949 26 ($\pm$6)
K	41	40.974 90 ($\pm$4)	Cu	65	64.948 35 ($\pm$6)
Ca	40	39.975 45 ($\pm$9)	Zn	64	63.949 55 ($\pm$2)
Ca	42	41.972 16 ($\pm$4)	Zn	66	65.947 22 ($\pm$6)
Ca	43	42.972 51 ($\pm$6)	Zn	67	66.948 15 ($\pm$6)
Ca	44	43.969 24 ($\pm$6)	Zn	68	67.946 86 ($\pm$7)
Ca	48	47.967 78 ($\pm$10)	Zn	70	69.947 79 ($\pm$6)
Sc	45	44.970 10 ($\pm$5)	Ga	69	68.947 78 ($\pm$6)
			Ga	71	70.947 52 ($\pm$9)
Ti	46	45.966 97 ($\pm$5)			
Ti	47	46.966 68 ($\pm$10)	Ge	70	69.946 37 ($\pm$7)
Ti	48	47.963 17 ($\pm$6)	Ge	72	71.944 62 ($\pm$7)
Ti	49	48.963 58 ($\pm$5)	Ge	73	72.946 69 ($\pm$4)
Ti	50	49.960 77 ($\pm$4)	Ge	74	73.944 66 ($\pm$6)
			Ge	76	75.945 59 ($\pm$5)
V	51	50.960 52 ($\pm$5)	As	75	74.945 70 ($\pm$5)
			Se	74	73.946 20 ($\pm$8)
Cr	50	49.962 10 ($\pm$7)	Se	76	75.943 57 ($\pm$5)
Cr	52	51.957 07 ($\pm$9)	Se	77	[76.944 59 ($\pm$5)]
Cr	53	52.957 72 ($\pm$8)	Se	78	[77.942 32 ($\pm$5)]
Cr	54	53.956 3 ($\pm$20)	Se	80	79.942 05 ($\pm$5)

Table A.3 (continued)

Mass number		Atomic mass	Mass number		Atomic mass
Mn	55	54.955 81 (±10)	Se	82	81.942 85 (±6)
Fe	54	53.957 04 (±5)	Br	79	78.943 65 (±6)
Fe	56	55.952 72 (±10)	Br	81	80.942 32 (±6)
Kr	78	77.945 13 (±9)	Cd	114	113.939 97 (±9)
Kr	80	[79.941 94 (±7)]	Cd	116	115.942 02 (±12)
Kr	82	81.939 67 (±7)			
Kr	83	82.940 59 (±7)	In	113	112.940 45 (±12)
Kr	84	83.938 36 (±7)	In	115	114.940 40 (±11)
Kr	86	85.938 28 (±8)			
			Sn	115	114.940 14 (±25)
Rb	85	84.939 20 (±8)	Sn	116	115.939 27 (±11)
Rb	87	86.937 09 (±17)	Sn	117	116.940 52 (±10)
			Sn	118	117.939 78 (±16)
Sr	84	83.940 11 (±15)	Sn	119	118.941 22 (±12)
Sr	86	85.936 84 (±11)	Sn	120	119.940 59 (±14)
Sr	87	86.936 77 (±8)	Sn	122	121.942 49 (±15)
Sr	88	87.934 08 (±11)	Sn	124	123.944 90 (±11)
Y	89	88.934 21 (±11)	Te	120	119.942 88 (±16)
			Te	122	121.941 93 (±8)
Zr	90	89.933 11 (±25)	Te	123	122.943 68 (±39)
			Te	124	123.942 78 (±11)
			Te	125	124.944 60 (±31)
Nb	93	92.935 40 (±9)	Te	126	125.944 20 (±7)
			Te	128	127.946 49 (±13)
Pd	102	101.937 50 (±9)	Te	130	129.948 53 (±10)
Pd	104	103.936 55 (±11)			
Pd	105	104.938 40 (±15)	I	127	126.945 28 (±13)
Pd	106	105.936 80 (±19)			
Pd	108	107.938 01 (±11)	Xe	124	123.945 78 (±7)
Pd	110	109.939 65 (±13)	Xe	126	125.944 76 (±14)
			Xe	128	127.944 46 (±9)
Cd	106	105.939 84 (±14)	Xe	129	128.946 01 (±15)
Cd	108	107.938 60 (±11)	Xe	130	129.945 01 (±10)
Cd	110	109.938 57 (±13)	Xe	131	130.946 73 (±42)
Cd	111	110.939 78 (±10)	Xe	132	131.946 15 (±10)
Cd	112	111.938 85 (±17)	Xe	134	133.948 03 (±12)
Cd	113	112.940 61 (±11)	Xe	136	135.950 46 (±11)

† Brackets designate masses of stable nuclides determined from mass-spectroscopic values for adjacent nuclides, combined with disintegration data.

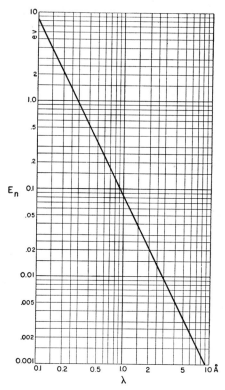

FIG. A.5. *Graph for converting neutron energy to wavelengths.*

Appendix IX—Some Useful Constants

Listed below are some of the constants used in neutron physics. The rounded figures are not intended to represent the most accurate values but will serve conveniently in usual calculations.

Atomic mass of the electron, M_e = 5.488×10^{-4}
Rest mass of the electron, m_e = 9.11×10^{-28} g
Atomic mass of the neutron, M_n = 1.00898
Rest mass of the neutron, m_n = 1.675×10^{-24} g
Atomic mass of the proton, M_p = 1.00759
Rest mass of the proton, m_p = 1.672×10^{-24} g
Atomic mass of the deuteron, M_d = 2.0147
Avagadro's number, N = 6.025×10^{23}
Planck's constant, h = 6.625×10^{-27} erg sec
$\hbar = h/2\pi$ = 1.054×10^{-27} erg sec
Ratio of proton mass to electron-
mass, M_p/M_e = 1836

Boltzmann's constant, k	$= 1.3804 \times 10^{-16}$ erg/degree
One nuclear magneton	$= 0.505 \times 10^{-23}$ erg/gauss
1 ev	$= 1.603 \times 10^{-12}$ erg
1 atomic mass unit, amu	$= 1.660 \times 10^{-24}$ g $= 931$ Mev

Appendix X—Bibliography

1. G. E. Bacon. *Neutron Diffraction*. Oxford (1955).
2. Robley D. Evans. *The Atomic Nucleus*. McGraw-Hill (1955).
3. Samuel Glasstone and Milton C. Edlund. *The Elements of Nuclear Reactor Theory*. Van Nostrand (1952).
4. D. J. Hughes. *Pile Neutron Physics*. Addison-Wesley (1953).
5. Raymond L. Murray. *Nuclear Reactor Physics*. Prentice-Hall (1957).
6. E. Segrè (Ed.). *The Neutron:* B. T. Feld. "Experimental Nuclear Physics." Wiley (1953).
7. H. Soodack and E. C. Campbell. *Elementary Pile Theory*. Wiley (1950).

AUTHOR INDEX

SUBJECT INDEX